Harry Clay Church

THE HERITAGE OF THE PRINTER

A Printer's Almanac

A Printer's Almanac

THE HERITAGE OF THE PRINTER

BY ALEXANDER S. LAWSON

VOLUME II

WITH ILLUSTRATIONS

North American Publishing Company
Philadelphia, 1966

Library of Congress Catalog Card Number 65-22399

PRINTED IN THE UNITED STATES OF AMERICA

Foreword

The basic idea for compiling an almanac for printers came about by indirection some years ago when I began preparations for a class in the development of printing types. After accumulating a file of about sixty dates encountered in my day-to-day reading, it occurred to me that it might be possible to assemble a short essay for each day of the year. Within two years I had collected almost two hundred dates, along with a drawer full of notes and the first draft of some three dozen essays.

The project was now advanced when in 1965 I was granted a six-month Professional Growth and Development Leave from the School of Printing of the Rochester Institute of Technology. During this leave it was possible for me to devote my full time to the search for historical data and to the writing of the balance of the essays.

I have made no conscious effort to limit the scope of the almanac to any particular specialty within the field of graphic arts, but—since I am a teacher of typography—that subject is perhaps better represented than any other. However, it is the craft of the printer, in all its aspects, which is here depicted. During a period when that craft is undergoing fundamental changes, it seems to me important that a long and honorable history be remembered, and that the contributions of so many of its practitioners be brought forth once again to demonstrate that it is to them that we owe a debt for the continuing progress of a fascinating calling.

I am indebted to many individuals and organizations for their help in obtaining source material for this volume and for permission to quote various passages. To Mr. Paul A. Bennett, guiding genius of the Typophiles, for quotes from several of the Typophile Chap Books, in the essays of February 7, March 7, March 20, September 14, November 8, and December 23; Mrs. Helen Macy of the Limited Editions Club for the quotation (July 6) from *Towards A Reform of the Paper Currency Particularly in Point of Its Design,* by William A. Dwiggins; Mr. Alfred A. Knopf for permission to quote from *Newspaper Days, 1899-1906,* by H. L. Mencken (September 12), and from *Some Random Recollections* by Alfred A. Knopf (October 21); Harvard College Library Department of Printing and Graphic Arts for permission to quote from *WAD to RR* (July 21); New York Public Library for the quote from *The Printer's Widow* (April 21); The World Publishing Company for the paragraph from *Pi, A Hodge-Podge of the Letters, Papers and Addresses Written During the Last Sixty Years,* by Bruce Rogers (October 24); and Harper & Row for the quote from *Disturber of the Peace* by William Manchester (March 20).

I also wish to thank the kind people in the library of the Rochester Institute of Technology, who were ever willing to be helpful during the long period of research in the preparation of my notes. Finally, the contributions of my wife, Evelyn T. Lawson, were vital to the successful completion of the project. Without the long hours of reading, typing, and checking of sources to which she unstintingly lent her enthusiasm, the work would indeed have languished.

ALEXANDER S. LAWSON

Pittsford, New York
1966

January

January 1

Upon a Monday morning on this date in 1787, was published the first issue of *The World, or Fashionable Advertiser,* a periodical which published the best current writers, including Richard Brinsley Sheridan. The proprietor of this immediately successful journal was John Bell—bookseller, printer, publisher, typefounder, journalist, &c, to use the title supplied by his 20th century biographer, Stanley Morison. A hundred years earlier Timperley had stated, "Few men have contributed more, by their industry and good taste, to the improvement of the graphic and typographic arts than Mr. Bell."

Bell's name lives for the present generation of printers through the medium of a roman type. The concept for this letter came about through Bell's desire to produce an edition of *The Way to Keep Him,* by Arthur Murphy. The first notice of this project was printed in *The World* on June 9, 1787:

"J. Bell flatters himself that he will be able to render this THE MOST PERFECT and in every respect the MOST BEAUTIFUL BOOK, that was ever printed in any country." The advertisement went on to describe a new type to be cast which was designed upon "improved principles." Bell thereupon established a firm which he called Bell's British Letter Foundry. He was most fortunate in obtaining for it the services as punchcutter of Richard Austin, a skilled copperplate engraver.

Austin's designs carried forward the improvements already made by John Baskerville but leaned more heavily on the precise letters introduced by Philip Grandjean for Louis XIV and called *romain du roi*. Morison has written that the Bell type is the first English example of "modern face."

Some of the Bell fonts were purchased by American printers, being used during the last decade of the 18th century. The more recent use of the type in America came about when Mr. Henry O. Houghton of the Riverside Press, Cambridge, Massachusetts purchased a quantity during a visit to England in 1864. The face was first shown in the Riverside specimen book in 1887, under the name of English Copperface. In 1895 Bruce Rogers, a young typographer employed by the Riverside Press, discovered the Bell type in the composing room and became interested in it. He learned that it had been used to print a series of books written by Martin Brimmer. At Rogers' suggestion the face was cast by American Type Founders from electrotyped matrices, and renamed Brimmer. It was used for many books printed at the Riverside Press until 1912.

In the meantime, the Boston printer, Daniel Berkeley Updike, "discovered" the type in England about 1903, and he also brought it to the United States, to become one of the stable fonts of the famed Merrymount Press, where it was known as Mountjoye.

January 2

According to Mr. P. J. Conkright, typographer to Princeton University, the first use, to his knowledge, of the type-cast dollar sign ($) occurred in the year 1802 on this date. The vehicle of this typographic innovation was William Duane's Philadelphia *Aurora,* in which appeared a Treasury Department report by Abraham Alphonse Albert Gallatin, the brilliant Swiss immigrant who was then Secretary of the Treasury in the cabinet of Thomas Jefferson.

The dollar mark used by Duane's sheet was cast by the Philadelphia typefounding firm of Binny & Ronaldson, but for a number of years its use was infrequent, primarily because most residents of the young United States continued to express their monetary demands in terms of pounds and shillings. Apparently Binny & Ronaldson, as canny Scotsmen, considered the new mark to have little marketable value, for they did not show it in their specimen book of 1812, a volume which is distinctive as the first American specimen book to show fonts of type. In the 1816 edition, however, ten sizes were listed, from nonpareil to seven-line pica.

After 1812 all American foundries offered the dollar sign. The Binny & Ronaldson design, which was originally cast in a single size, to be used with pica type, was drawn as a capital S, with two thin lines crossing the letter at a forty-five degree angle. This would seem to cast doubts upon a long-held opinion that the two lines were originally upright to form a U, supposedly expressing the initials of the United States. Another theory is that the sign derived from the Spanish piece of eight, the earliest currency of the conquistadors.

Thomas MacKellar, the great American typefounder and head of the firm of MacKellar, Smiths & Jordan, a successor of Binny & Ronaldson, wrote the history of his establishment in 1896 under the title, *1796-1896, One Hundred Years, MacKellar, Smiths & Jordan Foundry*. He stated here that Binny & Ronaldson first began to manufacture the dollar mark in 1797 and used it in their own ledgers during that year.

January 3

"Your suggestion that I write a note about the work of my friend W. A. Dwiggins falls happily with my mood." So began a letter written this day in 1939 by the President of the Society of Calligraphers, Dr. Hermann Püterschein. ". . . moreover," continued the good doctor, "there are one or two points about his association with me that need to be cleared up, and this will be a convenient opportunity for that also."

The mysterious relationship between William Addison Dwiggins, one of the great American graphic artists, and Hermann Püterschein was for many years a subject of controversy. The argument that Will Dwiggins was Püterschein was answered in rebuttal that really Püterschein was Dwiggins, and friends of both men were frequently called upon to untangle the riddle. Edmund G. Gress, editor of *The American Printer,* made a strong attempt to straighten the matter out in the columns of his periodical in 1927.

"Is there really a designer by the name of Will Dwiggins?" he asked. Through the agency of a Boston friend he secured the thumb prints of both men and printed them in the magazine, showing that they were identical. Shortly thereafter he received a letter from Dwiggins: "I am inclined to take a lenient view of your attempt to merge my identity with that of Dr. Püterschein, but his reaction to the affair obliges me to regard it more seriously. . . . I forward to you the imprint of Dr. Püterschein's thumb, also one of my own. I have taken the trouble to have a section of each of these enlarged." The enlargements show the whorls of Püterschein's print to be composed of Fraktur letters, while those of Dwiggins were joined fleurons in an engaging pattern.

"The thumb-prints and the enlargements taken together," continued Dwiggins, "should certainly prove (1) that the fingerprints exhibited by you in a late issue of *The American Printer* are forgeries, and that (2) Dr. Püterschein and I are disparate individuals."

Just about every person who has ever known of Will Dwiggins and his graphic art realizes that he was one of the great masters of our time in a variety of disciplines—calligraphy, type design, book design, and ornamentation. "I have known the artist for a long time," said Dr. Püterschein. "Probably I know more about the steps of his development than any other individual." And here is the hint that Dr. P. was indeed at one and the same person as WAD, an alter ego in residence, so to speak.

Adopted as a pen name for Dwiggins' many excursions into print, the apocryphal doctor almost became a noted figure in his own right, but the warmth of his personality and his whimsical viewpoint so akin to that of his master are perhaps the best clues to his real identity.

January 4

Henry George Bohn, English linguist, bookseller, publisher, and art connoisseur, was born upon this day in 1796. He achieved distinction in all of these endeavors until his death in his eighty-ninth year. Appearing before the Philobiblon Society in April, 1857, he gave a long and curious lecture concerning the history of printing. It was published in an edition of only thirty-seven copies.

Most of the speech, entitled *The Origin and Progress of Printing,* was a warming over of a variety of old saws about the craft. But when Bohn arrives at the "Progress" section of his talk, he becomes fascinating to modern students of the craft. Many of the processes which he discusses with some enthusiasm are now long since forgotten but remain of interest nevertheless, particularly when described in Bohn's quaint terminology.

The anastatic process was delineated as a method by which "exact facsimiles are produced from printed pages while they are recent, or at least before the oil is entirely exhausted by age." Bohn went on to describe it as "one of the branches of chemical printing, and like its congenitors, lithography and zincography, depends on affinities and antipathies. The printed page or engraving is prepared in such a way as to soften the ink and acidulate the paper. It is then laid on a polished zinc plate and submitted to great pressure, by which the black lines become transferred, and the intervening white parts etched away by the acid, while the original print is not perceptibly deteriorated, unless the operation is clumsily performed."

Photography is mentioned as a printing process, with a subtitle of sun-printing, "a new and valuable art by which external objects are delineated on chemically prepared plates or paper, by means of the camera obscura." Informing his audience that the subject was too well known for a detailed discussion, Bohn went on to mention a new phase of it called the dry collodion process, by which "The prepared plates are sold ready for use, occupy very little space in travelling, and will keep sensitive for an almost indefinite period. After the required number of views have been taken, the plates may remain in the portmanteau for months, till there is a convenient opportunity for developing them at home."

After dwelling upon chemitipy, nature printing, siderography, and compound printing, Bohn becomes the contemporary of present-day lecturers by describing the mathematical, or table printing of which "Mr. Babbage is the originator. By its self-acting changes, arranged to a great nicety, it calculates, according to any given formula, with more certainty than human power."

Some of our modern computer engineers should read Mr. Bohn, as the 19th century device he described was also capable of producing stereotypes!

January 5

"Eureka!" exclaimed a former compositor named Sam Clemens, at 12:20 p.m. on this day in 1889. The esteemed author and humorist, Mark Twain, then went on to say, "At this moment I have seen a line of movable type, *spaced and justified by machinery!* This is the first time in the history of the world that this amazing thing has ever been done."

The "dam typesetter" to which Clemens was referring was the machine known as the Paige Compositor, the brain-child of an eccentric Rochester, New York inventor named James W. Paige, called by Twain "a most extraordinary compound of business thrift and commercial insanity." Mark Twain overevaluated his own business acumen and for too many years was involved in a variety of ventures, all of which cost him money. While his ordinary enthusiasms generally relieved his pocketbook of only twenty to thirty thousand apiece, the Paige experiment cost him according to most accounts, close to a quarter of a million dollars and was the direct cause of the bankruptcy of his publishing business.

At a period when tremendous enthusiasm was being generated by the concept of automating the compositor, Paige's ideas seemed to Mark Twain to represent the highway to great wealth. A contemporary wrote that "he covered pages with figures that never ran short of millions, and frequently approached the billion mark."

In a letter to his brother, Orion Clemens, Mark dwelt upon the marvels of his new toy, saying, among other things, "This is indeed the first line of movable types that ever was perfectly spaced and perfectly justified on this earth. This was the last function that remained to be tested—and so by long odds the most important and extraordinary invention ever born of the brain of man stands completed and perfect. . . .

"But's a cunning devil, is that machine!— and knows more than any man that ever lived. You shall see. We made a test in this way. We set up a lot of random letters in a stick—three-fourths of a line; then filled out the line with quads representing 14 spaces, each space to be .035″ thick. Then we threw aside the quads and put letters into the machine and formed them into 15 two-letter words, leaving the words separated by two-inch vacancies. Then we started up the machine slowly, by hand, and fastened our eyes on the space-selecting pins.The first pinblock projected its third pin as the first word came traveling along the raceway; second block did the same; but the third block projected its second pin.

"Oh, hell! stop the machine—something wrong—it's going to set a .030″ space!" General consternation. 'A foreign substance has got into the spacing plates.' This from the head mathematician.

"Paige examined. 'No—look in, and you can see there's nothing of the kind.' Further examination. 'Now I know what it is—what it *must* be; one of those plates projects and binds. It's too bad—the first test is a failure.' A pause. 'Well, boys, no use to cry. Get to work—take the machine down.—No—Hold on! don't touch a thing! Go right ahead! We are fools, the machine isn't. The machine knows what it's about. There is a speck of dirt on one of these types and the machine is putting in a thinner space to *allow* for it!'

"All the other wonderful inventions of the human brain sink pretty nearly into commonplace contrasted with this awful mechanical miracle. Telephones, telegraphs, locomotives, cotton gins, sewing machines, Babbage calculators, Jacquard looms, perfecting presses, Arkwright's frames—all mere toys, simplicities! The Paige compositor marches alone and far in the lead of human inventions."

A footnote in the history of the manufacture of printing presses in the United States is taken from the *American Apollo,* published on this date in Boston in 1792, which stated that it had been printed on "the first complete Printing-Press ever made in this town—the wood-work was made by Mr. Berry, and the iron work by Mr. McClench."

There was at that time no press builder specializing in that activity in the United States. Printers were almost completely dependent upon European suppliers, although occasionally a local carpenter would manage to construct a press from a model already in existence.

In an advertisement appearing in the *New Jersey Journal,* of Elizabethtown, in June, 1796 a man named John Hamilton, calling himself a Printing Press Maker, mentioned that he had supplied a number of printers in his own state and in neighboring New York with presses of "good Quality," and that for the sum of seventy-five dollars he could supply others. However, Mr. Hamilton's influence was restricted to a limited geographical area, and no more is heard of his presses.

The first press manufacturer to make a reputation in America was Adam Ramage, who brought professional skills from his native Scotland to Philadelphia in 1795 and began the construction of the hand presses which during the next fifty years were to find their way to every part of the new nation.

Ramage improved the wooden presses of the period by enlarging the diameter of the screw from the commonly used 2½″ to 3″. The descent was reduced from 2½″ to 2″ in a revolution, thereby just about doubling the impression squeeze. C. S. Van Winkle, author of the first American printer's manual, *The Printer's Guide; or an Introduction to the Art of Printing,* published in 1818 mentioned but did not describe the Ramage press, telling his readers that the press was too well known to need description.

During the last half of the 19th century the Washington hand-press was the premier American hand press, but the Ramage machine was still widely available in the second-hand press market, being sold and resold until it had gained the reputation of being the "first" press in countless locations.

January 7

Born into the family of a French printer on this day in 1730 was François Ambroise Didot, who was destined to become the most influential member of one of the most distinguished families ever to practice the printer's craft. Along with his younger brother, Pierre François, F. A. Didot fully established the family reputation in the areas of printing, typefounding, publishing, and bookselling.

As a typefounder, François Ambroise made two outstanding contributions, the effects of both of which have lasted for almost two hundred years. In mid-18th century French typography, the types of Pierre Fournier—patterned upon the *roman du roi* which Grandjean had cut for Louis XIV in 1699—were widely admired. It was Didot who continued the development of this letter, which was so far removed from the earlier oldstyles. He increased the contrast between the heavy and light strokes and created serifs which were hairline and without brackets. The capitals of this design were considerably more condensed than the Italian styles of Aldus which had earlier been so influential in the development of the French types of Garamond.

This new letter, cut at Didot's direction about 1780 by the punchcutter Waflard, was no doubt also influenced by the types of the Englishman, John Baskerville. In turn, the Didot letter, which became the embodiment of the type classification now called modern, encouraged the Italian printer, Giambattista Bodoni, to rid himself of an earlier dependence upon the Fournier types. The new design of Didot was further developed by his successors in the family and dominated European typography for another sixty years. The Didot style prompted French printers to discard almost completely the oldstyle faces.

Didot's next great contribution was concerned with the mechanics of typefounding. As early as 1737 Fournier had introduced a method of type measurement in which he divided an inch into seventy-two divisions called points. The twenty type sizes established by Fournier were all given the names already applied to type sizes, but the fixed relationship between sizes, established by a standard, was the first important move in the direction of precise measurement in typecasting.

Didot improved upon the Fournier method by using as a standard the French *pied du roi* which contained 12 inches, equivalent to 12.7892 American inches. He further adhered strictly to type sizes described in points rather than in the indiscriminate names heretofore used. While there was opposition to such a system the wide reputation of the Didot family led to the general acceptance of the idea. As a result, the present European standard of measurement for type sizes remains that devised by Didot, and names are no longer assigned to sizes, although it took another century to accomplish this innovation.

January 8

On this day in 1775, John Baskerville died.

Born at Walverley, in Worcestershire, England, in 1706, Baskerville at an early age acquired such skill in penmanship that he was prompted to maintain a school in the subject in Birmingham. In 1735 he began a career in the japanning process which was then most popular for a variety of objects, such as snuff-boxes and carriage-sides. Becoming wealthy in this business he regained his attraction to letters, this time in the shape of printer's types.

Using the Caslon types as a model, he experimented with refinements of the form, seeking greater contrast of strokes and more graceful serifs. Not being satisfied merely with a new type, he decided to become a printer and had his own press constructed, featuring a platen and bed which were much more precise in manufacture than the usual presses of the period. He then insisted that the packing be hard and solid, a practice which was counter to the methods then common in printing offices.

He next formulated his own ink, producing a black glossier than any hitherto obtainable. His greatest innovation as a printer, however, was the insertion of the sheets from the press between heated copper cylinders immediately upon leaving the press, producing a very smooth sheet of paper in which the type appeared to be unusually crisp. This combination of new type style and smooth paper was not at all well received by his fellow English printers but on the Continent it was greeted with enthusiasm.

In his great *Manuel Typographique,* Pierre

Fournier wrote of the types: "He, Baskerville, has spared neither pains nor expense to bring them to the utmost pitch of perfection. The letters are cut with great daring and the italic is the best to be found in any English foundry, but the roman is a little too wide."

The English booksellers were nevertheless disenchanted with Baskerville's attempts to improve the quality of printing, and as a result he suffered heavy financial loss. His attempts to sell his punches and matrices were unsuccessful in his lifetime, his widow finally disposing of them in France, when they were purchased by Beaumarchais for an edition of Voltaire.

As recently as 1912 English opinion of Baskerville was still at a low ebb. The 1912 Printing Issue of *The Times* stated: "There is always the possibility that an enthusiast may be misguided; and the verdict of the connoisseurs of today is that this was the case with Baskerville." However, in the Printing Issue of the same newspaper published in 1929, the tide had turned. Baskerville's "great merit was that he relied on his types and his presswork to make fine books, instead of on ornaments, and thus revived the dignity of his craft."

Partial credit for this turnabout may be given to the American typographer, Bruce Rogers, who re-discovered the type in a French prospectus of 1917. He ordered fonts of the French casting, for use in a book published by Harvard University Press in 1921. Since that time the type has become immensely popular and is now considered to be one of the universal types.

January 9

Published upon this day in the year 1775 was the first great best-selling book on the American continent. Written by Thomas Paine, staymaker, pedagogue, customs officer, journalist, and toper, *Common Sense* was an instantaneous success, being hawked in almost every corner of the English Colonies within days of publication. It has been estimated that the tract had the most substantial sale of any single book in American history, taking into consideration the population of the Colonies in the 18th century. Within three months some 400,000 copies had been distributed to an audience of 3,000,000 colonists, many of whom could not even read. A comparative sale today would be over 24,000,000 copies.

Tom Paine arrived in Philadelphia in 1774 bearing a letter of introduction from Benjamin Franklin, addressed to his son-in-law, Richard Bache.

"The bearer, Mr. Thomas Paine, is very well recommended to me, as an ingenious, worthy young man. He goes to Pennsylvania with a view of settling there. I request you to give him your best advice and countenance, as he is quite a stranger there."

As an avocation Paine had long been interested in scientific ventures. It was through this association that he had won some influential friends, among whom was Franklin. Upon his arrival in Philadelphia he became a tutor and quickly entered the intellectual life of the city. One of his first friends was a printer, Robert Aitken, who was sufficiently impressed with Paine's attainments that he made Paine the editor of *The Pennsylvania Magazine,* presenting Paine with his first opportunity to reach an American audience.

It is through Aitken that we learn of Paine's methods of writing. Many years later Isaiah Thomas, the first historian of American printing, mentioned a letter which he had received from Aitken: "On one of the occasions, when Paine had neglected to supply the materials for the Magazine, within a short time of the day of publication, Aitken went to his lodgings and complained of Paine's neglecting to fill his contract. Paine heard him patiently, and answered, 'You shall have them in time.' Aitken expressed some doubts on the subject, and insisted upon Paine's accompanying him and proceeding immediately to business, as the workmen were waiting for copy. He accordingly went home with Aitken, and was soon seated at the table with the necessary apparatus, which always included a glass and a decanter of Brandy. Aitken observed, 'he would never write without *that*.' The first glass put him in a train of thinking; Aitken feared the second would disqualify him, or render him untractable; but it only illuminated his intellectual system; and when he had swallowed the third glass, he wrote with great rapidity, intelligence and precision; and his ideas appeared to flow faster than he could commit them to paper. What he penned from the inspiration of the brandy, was perfectly fit for the press without any alteration, or correction."

6

January 10

Pierre Simon Fournier, called *le juene,* applied upon this day in 1757 to be appointed a master printer, without the necessity of serving as an apprentice and journeyman. For Fournier this was no quick way to success, as he was then forty-four years of age and already a distinguished punchcutter and typefounder. He but wished to fill out what has been termed the trinity of the typographic art, by becoming a printer.

There were a number of legal obstacles to Fournier's request. The Bookselling and Printing code of France, promulgated in 1723, allowed only members of the Communauté des Imprimeurs to own and operate a press, and only a master printer's son could enter the Company without serving a four year apprenticeship, being unmarried, conversant in Latin and able to read Greek. Fournier was unable to qualify in any of these conditions.

Citing as a precedent the admittance in 1712 of a typefounder, Pierre Cot, by a special decree which permitted Cot to print a monumental work on typography, Fournier pointed out his own special circumstances. His types, he told the Communauté, were internationally recognized, and had been used as the basis for the establishment of royal foundries in Sweden and Sardinia. He also mentioned his system of type measurement, by units called points, and his many efforts to improve the quality of French types "to save French printing from disgrace at the hands of the Germans." He was also ready to publish his own typographical writings, covering both typefounding and printing.

In 1762 he received permission to print not only his own works but also music composition, for which he had designed new music types. This addition aroused the ire of Ballard, a music publisher who then enjoyed a monopoly in that specialty. Ballard opposed the order of the Communauté and induced them to ask the Chief of Police to suspend the new privilege granted to Fournier. This official visited the typefounder and later gave him permission to print his own writings in an edition to be called *Manuel Typographique.* The first volume of this book was issued in 1764. Fournier's ambition to write a complete printing manual was never realized. His first volume covered the art of typefounding, and the second volume—published in 1766—was a survey of the history of European typefounding.

At his death in 1768, the founder had done nothing on the volume of printing practices, but he had written a number of essays on the lives of the great typographers. The *Manuale* therefore does not live up to its name, but it is one of the great works on typefounding, containing much of the information upon which later scholarship has been based. To most printers the book is justly famous as the source of information concerning the Point System evolved by Fournier. This system was instrumental in bringing some order to the almost chaotic procedures of the world's typefounders, practices which had existed for over three hundred years.

January 11

"I wish you would resolve henceforth to write one such article per week," wrote publisher Horace Greeley to Bayard Taylor, born this day in 1825, "and sign your own initials or some distinctive mark at the bottom. I want everyone connected with the *Tribune* to become known to the public (in some unobtrusive way) as doing what he does, so that in case of my death or incapacity it may not be feared that the paper is to die or essentially suffer."

Bayard Taylor, born on a Pennsylvania farm, was another of those 19th century printers—such as Mark Twain and William Dean Howells—who distinguished themselves in the world of literature, although his fame had none of the enduring character of these printer-writers. Today, Taylor's poetry and novels are considered to be quite inferior, even though they were widely praised during his lifetime.

Taylor's great love for books and literature led him at the age of seventeen to become a teacher. However, he quickly found that such a profession was not to his liking and instead apprenticed himself in the office of a weekly newspaper in West Chester, Pa. During his apprenticeship he became infatuated with the idea of becoming a poet, publishing a book of verse when he was nineteen and in addition contributing to various periodicals. Following his four years of indenture Taylor decided to go to Europe. To help finance his venture, he contracted to write letters about his travels to newspapers and magazines. With one hundred and forty dollars, of which twenty-four was spent for passage on a sailing vessel, the youth left his home and spent two years in Europe, traveling mostly by foot, and writing of his experiences. Upon his return he published *Views Afoot, or Europe Seen With Knapsack and Staff,* which was an immediate best seller, establishing his reputation.

Taylor next attempted to publish a weekly newspaper. He found the experience tame indeed, as he was now corresponding with Longfellow and Emerson, and receiving many requests to lecture about his travels. Horace Greeley, publisher of the New York *Tribune,* hired him as a correspondent, and Taylor very quickly became that paper's crack travel reporter, entertaining the nation from a variety of exotic places.

In 1862-63 he was Secretary of Legation in St. Petersburg, Russia, and following the Civil War he continued his travels. In 1876 Taylor was selected to write the *National Ode* on the occasion of the Centennial Exposition. In 1871 he published his most important work, a translation of *Faust.* On the strength of this widely admired translation (which modern scholarship now considers to be second-rate verse) he was appointed Minister to Germany, in which office he died, shortly after arriving in Berlin in 1878.

January 12

The chronological account of the life of Jan van Krimpen states that he was born upon this day in 1892, that he died on October 20, 1958, and that between these dates he was a typographer specializing in the design of books and was, in addition, a type designer.

When typographers discuss among themselves the types designed in the present century which may be acknowledged to be first rate, two designs are placed at the top of the list, the position of the two being transposed, depending upon individual preference of the typographer. These types are the Centaur of Bruce Rogers and the Lutetia of Van Krimpen. The term most frequently used to describe both types is "noble."

Lutetia was the first type designed by Van Krimpen, in his thirty-second year. The designer had prepared for it since his graduation from the Academy of Art at the Hague in 1912, when he was twenty. He became interested in typography soon after his graduation through his reading of *The Imprint,* a short-lived English periodical which was attempting to improve the quality of English printing, and which contained articles by current authorities on the subject.

In 1923 Dr. Joh. Enschedé of the firm of Joh. Enschedé en Zonen at Haarlem, which had successfully combined typefounding with commercial printing since 1703, asked Van Krimpen to consider the design of a new type. Van Krimpen accepted the commission, and the type was completed for use in a book describing Dutch contributions to the International Exhibition of Modern Decorative and Industrial Arts held in Paris in 1925. The designer suggested Lutetia, the ancient name of Paris, for the new letter.

This first type of an unknown designer, in the words of the typographic historian, Stanley Morison, "created something of a sensation." Emerging at a time when the typefounders appeared to be interested only in display types, a classic roman of regal characteristics was very well received all over the world, particularly by the more traditional printers, who quickly accepted the face as an outstanding entry into the list of fine types. As an italic to complement his roman, Van Krimpen created a design patterned on the chancery letters of the early 16th century which has since become one of the most successful types of the genre.

In his other types, Romanée, Romulus, and Spectrum, the Dutch designer continued to investigate the standard roman letterforms, in all instances creating crisp, beautifully formed characters. As an italic for Romulus he experimented with a leaning roman rather than attempting either another chancery or an italic in the style of Robert Granjon. Whether the attempt was brought off successfully depends upon the reader's viewpoint concerning italic type. Many typographers are of the opinion that a sloped roman letter differs too little from the upright roman to provide the contrast so necessary in modern printing.

Van Krimpen was no exuberant extrovert, but approached type design from a cool intellectual viewpoint.

Felice Feliciano, calligrapher and antiquarian of Verona, Italy, wrote a dedicatory letter to Andrea Mantegna, the painter, on this day in 1464. This communication appeared in a book of epitaphs. Feliciano had earlier written *Alphabetum Romanum,* which is probably the earliest book concerning the geometric construction of roman capitals. A splendid new edition of this work was printed by the Officina Bodoni in 1960. The letter to Mantegna, embodying the idealism which nurtured the humanist expression of the period, says in part:

"See the young people of our time; some pursue wealth, cross the sea in ships, hasten through foreign lands, confront every danger, strive day and night after gain, and are ruined. Likewise we see others who love the life of soldiers, who despise all other things, are concerned with naught also and find pleasure only in horses and weapons. Or others who devote themselves only to pleasures and pursue them with passion.

"All this has no meaning for me. And when I had grown out of my youth and could lead a freer life, I directed my thoughts entirely to the study of many and praiseworthy things. Above all I turned my gaze upon the venerable ancient relics of our forefathers. Since it seemed to me easy to achieve my aim by a knowledge of inscriptions, I set to work diligently. Not only did I examine closely those inscriptions on stone which were accessible to all and set them erect, which is often necessary, but in many cases I turned them over, discovered them, as one says, from mother earth, dug them out and brought them to the light again. In this way I read many inscriptions, noted them and wrote them down correctly and truly, with praiseworthy zeal and in a form which even an adept could not question.

". . . And if this or that should seem to thee imperfect, do not ascribe this to my negligence or ignorance, but attribute rather the blame to too great age of the inscriptions, and to time, which obliterates everything; or even to the godlessness of those who have dared, with impious hands, to mar these things with iron, to overturn and destroy things once dedicated to the noble conception of immortality."

It was possible upon this date in 1920 for a fortunate bibliophile with an interest in printing to purchase at auction any of the more than two thousand books from the library of the great American printer, Theodore Low De Vinne, which were then being offered for sale. The sale realized just over twenty-four thousand dollars, and the printing historian Henry L. Bullen remarks that this was about forty percent more than De Vinne had paid for them, since he was a "careful buyer."

The Newberry Library of Chicago was the most notable purchaser at the auction, having fortunately received a short time before a bequest which was to be used for the acquisition of books about typography.

Another purchaser present at the auction, but with somewhat fewer cash reserves (a situation perhaps mitigated by a lively sense of humor), was the Printer to Yale University, Carl Purington Rollins.

While others who witnessed the sale spent a great deal of time lauding the great American printer whose library was being liquidated, Mr. Rollins went home to New Haven and composed a sonnet, which he entitled *"On Buying at Auction a Book Once in the Library of Theodore Low De Vinne."*

O scholar-printer! Ripe with all the lore
Which appertains to printing and to type,
And, as becomes a man with learning ripe,
A bookman with an ever growing store.
From out their teeming pages you distilled
The essence which you freely gave to us
Who followed in your footsteps, envious
To know it all, albeit far less skilled.

Your learning oft my ignorance has vexed,
But, Master, now you have me sore perplexed
(although *nil nisi bonum* one believes):
This book which so much pleases, also grieves,
For when I open it to read the text
I find that you had never cut the leaves.

"The Charles Whittinghams, Uncle and Nephew, were creditors of our age, or at least, of those among us who confess a liking for comely books. There is a real debt of thankfulness still owing them, and a considerable balance of it will be carried forward to the account of generations which are yet to come trooping along with Time." So stated the biographer of the Charles Whittinghams, printers, the elder of whom died on this day in 1840.

Charles Whittingham the elder, founder of the great Chiswick Press, which contributed almost a century of service to the printer's craft, was indentured at eleven years of age to Richard Bird of Coventry in 1779. At a very early age he must have succumbed to the love of books, as his name appears on the subscription lists of London booksellers before he had completed his apprenticeship. Just as soon as he had obtained his freedom at the age of nineteen, he journeyed to London.

Some three years later he had borrowed a sufficient sum of money to enable him to set up a press in a garret and to offer his services as a master printer. At first Whittingham was his own compositor, pressman, and all around workman, but within another three years he was printing specimen books for the great typefounding firm of William Caslon. No doubt upon the strength of being Caslon's printer, Whittingham soon had all the work he could handle for the various publishers and booksellers of the time. He expanded into a second shop, and then into a third. He decided also to do his own publishing, which of course brought the wrath of his customers down upon his head. Apparently this did not bother him. His own books were small at a time when most publishers requested large-size volumes. Whittingham began to issue standard authors in sets, an immensely successful undertaking.

As his business prospered, the printer kept abreast of all the technical developments of the trade. He bought the first improved press manufactured to Lord Stanhope's pattern. He became the outstanding printer of wood engravings, devising a system of makeready then unknown to his rival printers.

In 1828 Charles the younger made an arrangement with Charles Pickering, the publisher, to print one of his books. From 1830 the two men combined in a most notable achievement in English printing history, producing books at a consistently high level. The publication in 1844 of *The Diary of Lady Willoughby* revived the use of Caslon types after almost sixty years of decline following the introduction of the modern roman types by Bodoni and the Didots. Caslon has maintained its popularity since that time. The younger Charles Whittingham, as a printer, contributed in no small way to the great success of the Pickering imprints.

January 16

Suggesting a scheme for preparing correct texts, the Birmingham printer John Baskerville wrote to Robert Dodsley, the foremost 18th century London publisher of belles-lettre, on this day in 1754:

" 'Tis this. Two people must be concerned; the one must name every letter, capital, point reference, accent, etc., that is, in English, must spell every part of every word distinctly, and note down every difference in a book prefaced on purpose. Pray oblige me in making the experiment with Mr. James Dodsley in four or five lines of any two editions of an author, and you'll be convinced that it's scarcely possible for the least difference, even of a point, to escape notice. I would recommend and practice the same method in an English author, who most people imagine themselves capable of correcting. Here's another great advantage to me in this humble scheme: at the same time that a proof sheet is correcting, I shall find out the least imperfection in any of the types that has escaped the founder's notice. I have received great encomium on my Specimen from Scotland."

Good advice, and honored in the breach by too many printers who but casually route a job through production with scarcely a thought about proofreading, a non-chargeable item on the cost sheet. This, in spite of the great scholar printers of the past who built their reputations and that of the whole craft on the correctness of their texts.

Charles Dickens took the proofreader's task seriously, and at one time addressed a London meeting of the Correctors of the Press, saying, "I know from some slight practical experience, what the duties of the correctors of the press are, and how those duties are usually performed; and I can testify, and do testify here, that they are not mechanical, that they are not mere matters of manipulation and routine, but that they require from those who perform them much natural intelligence, much super-added cultivation, considerable readiness of reference, quickness of resource, an excellent memory, and a clear understanding."

January 17

If any printer doesn't know that his patron saint was born upon this day in 1706, he must be a hibernating mammal, as each year the printing industry uses Benjamin Franklin's birthday as an excuse to stand up and shout, "Look at me, I'm a printer, too!"

Possibly a hundred years ago this date was an occasion for quiet pride in an honest craft. Printers gathered to do honor to the greatest man of his era, who happened to be a printer, and who took real pride in that accomplishment, even after winning acclaim as a statesman, scientist, and philosopher. But that was a long time ago. Nowadays the celebration of Franklin's birth is used to put on a public relations pitch. It also affords an opportunity for printing executives to invite their customers to share in the festivities.

Over fifty years ago the original concept of the commemoration began to change. H. L. Bullen wrote in 1907: "Printers are associated together; we attend their national meetings and their dinners. Do we hear anything about the art? No, we are enthralled by eloquent statisticians, and excited by the contending schools of cost and profit finders. In a long course of annual dinners, ostensibly in honor of Doctor Franklin, a great printer, I have never heard one serious attempt to do anything else than get some fun out of the occasion; and the annual conventions of the undertakers are really much more funny."

Bullen should be around now. Had he heard just a few of the subjects treated by the principal speakers at Printing Week Dinners during the last few years, he would have been informed about the Dead Sea Scrolls, the Growing Appreciation of Capitalism in Russia, the Communist Menace in the Press, What the Government Should Do About the Schools, etc., etc.

And then, of course, January 17th is an excellent time to give a general a medal, or to honor a former member of the Cabinet, or perhaps an ambassador—even the mayor will do if a national figure cannot be persuaded to put in an attendance. At one recent banquet the speaker acknowledged his introduction, nervously fingered his notes, smiled knowingly, and said, "Ben Franklin! You know he was quite a guy with the gals!" When the laughs had subsided, he then said, "Now about these communists getting into the unions . . .".

For a number of years now, the International Association of Printing House Craftsmen, the National Graphic Arts Education Association, and similar organizations have been promoting Printing Week at the time of Franklin's birthday. This practice started with the commendable idea of introducing those young people who were attending printing classes to a group activity which included printers. Very quickly other organizations recognized the publicity value of the affair and took over, so that now the audience at a Printing Week banquet would actually feel cheated if someone were to get up and present a major address on the subject of printing.

Besides, there wouldn't be time, as the winner of the Miss Printing Week Award has to be introduced to the admiring wolf whistles of the males in attendance. So it's all rather confusing to a person who attends with the notion that Dr. Franklin is to be honored. Before he's settled in his chair, he'll undoubtedly entertain the uncomfortable notion that his secretary gave him the tickets to the wrong affair.

January 18

The Typothetae of the City of New York met on the evening of January 18 in 1886 to honor two printers, Benjamin Franklin and Mark Twain. The white-shirted audience who attended the affair, held at the grand old restaurant, Delmonico's, ostensibly to honor Dr. Franklin, was not above allowing the humorist to share the proceedings, particularly when he could indulge in his reputation as a raconteur.

The former Missouri swift did not disappoint his listeners as he regaled the group with nostalgic tales of his youth as a country comp.

"I wetted down the paper Saturdays," he remarked, "I turned it Sundays—for this was a country weekly; I washed the rollers, I washed the forms, I folded the papers, I carried them around at dawn Thursday mornings. The carrier was then an object of interest to all the dogs in town. If I had saved up all the bites I ever received I could keep M. Pasteur busy for a year."

Mark's reminiscences of his type-sticking days generally gave the impression that he had few equals as a compositor, although this ideal image was not born out by some of his contemporaries. One of these worthies, Anthony Kennedy, knew Sam Clemens as a young fellow remarkable only that he didn't drink whisky, a conspicuous oddity for any comp in the mid-fifties of the last century. Kennedy disclosed in 1903 that when the other compositors were making twelve dollars a week, at thirty cents per thousand ems, "it was all Sam Clemens could do to make eight or nine dollars. He always had so many errors marked in his proofs that it took most of his time correcting them. He could not have set up an advertisement in acceptable form to save his life."

Compositor Kennedy might have added, of course, that while Mark's fellow typos could have set circles around him, none of 'em could have written *Huckleberry Finn*.

Actually, in a letter written in 1853, and published by the *Hannibal Daily Journal* on September 10th, Mark deprecated his ability, but this was long before he was a famous man. He wrote, "The printers here in New York are badly organized and therefore have to work for various prices. These prices are 23, 25, 28, 30, 32, and 35 cents a 1,000 ems. The price I get is twenty-three cents; but I did very well to get a place at all, for there are thirty or forty—yes, fifty good printers in the city with no work at all; besides my situation is permanent and I shall keep it till I can get a better one."

The letter went on to describe the working conditions of the period. Twain noted the perplexing problems of a country printer trying to hold a job in the big town.

"The office I work in is John A. Grays, 97 Cliff St., and, next to Harper's is the most extensive in the city. In the room in which I work, I have forty compositors for company. Taking compositors, pressmen, stereotypers, and all, there are about 200 persons employed in the concern. . . . They are very particular about spacing, justification, proofs, etc., and even if I do not make much money, I will learn a great deal. I had thought Ustick was particular enough, but acknowledge now

that he was not old-maidish. Why, here you must put exactly the same space between every two words, and *every line must be spaced alike*. They think it dreadful to space one line with three-em spaces, and the next one with five ems."

January 19

"Amidst the darkness which surrounds the discovery of many of the arts, it has been ascertained that it is practicable to trace the *Introduction and Progress of Printing,* in the northern part of America, to the period of the revolution."

Thus a printer named Isaiah Thomas, who was born on this day in 1749, stated his case in the preface to *The History of Printing in America,* published in 1810 in Worcester, Massachusetts. This book is the first account we have of the development of the craft upon these shores. Subsequent scholarship has filled in a number of the gaps in the Thomas history, but the broad outline is that of the Worcester printer. It might have been of greater value had it included more details in the operation of the colonial printing offices, but as Thomas was concerned only with historical factors, we must be grateful for what we have been given.

Thomas had himself been a printer from his sixth year. He had advanced to the point where he was recognized as one of the important printers of his era. In addition he was one of the wealthiest. The last thirty years of his life were devoted to scholarship, the printing history being one product of this period. He was at work upon a second edition at the time of his death in 1831, having hoped to update much of the information contained in the original work. The second edition was finally published in 1874, by the Albany, New York printer and antiquarian, Joel Munsell. Munsell added a number of footnotes, including those left by Thomas in the possession of the American Antiquarian Society.

One of the valuable features of the history is the biographical information about the individual printers of the period. Although not complete in personal data, the book gives voluminous accounts of the printers' careers. In one of the biographies, that of Zechariah Fowle, Thomas slyly pays off an old debt. Having been indentured to Fowle for eleven years, during most of which time the master reneged on his contract with his apprentice, Thomas—recording for posterity—wrote, "Fowle was a singular man, very irritable and effeminate, and better skilled in the domestic work of females, than in the business of a printing office."

In addition to writing about the printing establishments in the American Colonies, Thomas included an account of the newspapers of the period which has become a most important source of information to modern students of journalism.

Thomas is honored as the first American scholar of the printer's craft. Upon his retirement from active participation in his scattered enterprises, he estimated his worth at over $150,000. At his death he was considered to be one of the richest men in the United States. In 1825 in an address before the Philadelphia Typographical Society, he said, "Could I live my life over again and choose my employment it would be that of a Printer."

January 20

The life of one of America's fine printers came to a premature end on this day in 1962. Peter Beilenson introduced countless book buyers to good printing at extremely reasonable prices through the medium of his Peter Pauper Press. He was a man who had early in life decided what he wanted to do and who had the good judgment to select two excellent tutors, Bruce Rogers and Frederic W. Goudy.

His apprenticeship in the Mount Vernon establishment of William Edwin Rudge during the period when Bruce Rogers was setting its typographic style was followed by typesetting for Goudy in the Deepdene workshop. Later a Golding treadle press was installed in the cellar of Beilenson's home in Larchmont, New York. It was from this location that the first Peter Pauper item came, in 1928, *Faithless Sally Brown and Faithless Nellie Gray,* written by Thomas Hood with decoration by Herb Roth. The second book produced that year was *With Petrarch: Twelve Sonnets,* which received the accolade of selection by the Fifty Books of the Year jury. Up to 1962 the Press turned out 304 ti-

tles, 46 of which appeared in the Fifty Books selections.

In addition to the Peter Pauper imprint, Beilenson produced in the same period 129 books bearing the name of the Walpole Printing Office. Of these, 16 were honored by selection for the Fifty. The majority of the Beilenson books were not of the rather precious limited edition variety but were designed to meet the approval of collectors of good taste and limited funds. For many purchasers, the Peter Pauper name was their first introduction to carefully planned and beautifully printed books. There has never, in fact, been so distinguished a list in the whole history of American publishing.

"Always with a pencil in hand," said Harry Behn, in a tribute to Beilenson published in 1962, "arranging words, type, color, meaning, in pleasing unpretentious proportion. Nothing stared-at, or glared-at, but seen, seen into."

Peter Beilenson never lost the early, amateur love he had for creating the printed word. Invited to discuss the pleasures and duties of the amateur printer at a Graphic Forms seminar conducted in Cambridge, Massachusetts in 1949, he said in part: "After you have set your author's type you must make up his pages, choose his decorations or illustrations, and set his headings. You must decide whether to stretch him to twenty-four pages or condense him to sixteen. You must buy his paper, lock up his pages in your chase, make him ready, curse your press which is printing him, apply your ink to his words, and impress him for posterity. Perhaps you will thereafter fold him, sew him, and encase him in boards.

"In so doing, you become, to the extent of sixteen or twenty-four pages, in an edition of one hundred or three hundred copies, God. You have created something which did not exist before, and which would not have existed save for your thinking brain and tired back and dirty hands. True, you have not created Heaven and Earth, and you have undoubtedly worked at your creation for more than the original quota of six days. But anyway you have given the world something which was at first only words you loved, and is now a whole, real book, which you love all the more because it is your book, your child, your embodiment of those words. That is the fun and satisfaction of being an amateur. In our printing world there is no other satisfaction equal to it."

January 21

"I have to apologize to my kind readers," wrote Editor James Gordon Bennett of the *New York Herald* on this date in 1836, "for the want of my usual life today." He went on to describe an attack upon his person in which he was severely caned by Col. James Watson, editor of the *Courier and Enquirer.* "The fellow, no doubt, wanted to let out the never-failing supply of good humor and wit which has created such a reputation for the *Herald,* and appropriate the contents to supply the emptiness of his own thick skull."

Bennett, a Scotsman who had come to the United States in 1820, had worked on the staffs of various newspapers before establishing the *Herald* in 1835 as a penny sheet which was both flippant and sensational and which aroused the ire of the editors of the other New York newspapers. Bennett was not at all put out by the attacks but wrote them up in his own paper. These accounts contributed to its popularity, as it reached a circulation of over fifty thousand copies by 1842.

Bennett could have served as the model for what the public conceived to be the typical newspaper editor. Colorful, controversial, energetic, he built the *Herald* into one of the finest newspapers of its time. "Shakespeare is the great genius of the drama," he wrote, "Scott of the novel, Milton and Byron of the poem—and I mean to be the genius of the newspaper press."

One of his peculiarities was his inability to dismiss an employee. At one time he mistakenly did fire a reporter for a supposed blunder. When asked to rescind the order by several of his editors, he listened to their arguments and finally stated, in the broad Scots tongue which he never lost:

"The mon has been discharged, do ye mind, and that ends the matter. But this office is a large one, and ye ken I dinna know all my men, and if I dinna see him about the place I canna find fault."

The editors took the hint and the reporter was sent off on a roving mission. On his return to the *Herald* a year or two later, the first person he met was Bennett, who greeted him kindly, asking:

"Weel, young mon, and how are ye getting on? What paper are ye with now?"

"Why, I'm still on the *Herald,* Mr. Bennett," said the correspondent.

"Eh, young mon, there are some things it's weel not to know, and that's one of them," and Bennett passed on without a smile. The reporter remained with the paper for the rest of his life.

One of the important news features in the New York papers of the time was the arrival of steamships with European newspapers. There was great rivalry in getting out in the street first with the information contained in them. Bennett's editor had a fondness for setting some of the "clip" news items in italic type for emphasis. One day Bennett found that the *Tribune* and the *Times* had extras out but the *Herald* was still on the press. Demanding to know the reason for the delay, he was informed that there were not enough italic cases in the office to set the news fast enough.

"Dom the italic!" Bennett shouted. "Now, Mr. Putnam, I'd have ye to know that the readers of the *Herald* are not all fools. They can see what is important in the news without having it disfigured with yer dommed italic. Stop it, mon!"

January 22

In a bull dated January 22, 1587, Pope Sixtus V issued a mandate officially recognizing the press which he had ordered established the previous year in the Vatican Library. Called at first the Typographia Vaticana, this press has survived under a variety of names and is presently known as the Vatican Printing Office.

Sixtus V, the Pope of Catholic Reform and considered to be one of the greatest statesmen to occupy the Chair of St. Peter, had originally decreed the press to be set up in order to print a Vulgate Bible. He brought from Venice a printer named Dominicus Basa to take charge of the production of this work, which was finally completed as a three-volume folio in 1590, the year during which Sixtus died. The title of this work was *Biblia sacra vulgate editions, tribus tomis distincta jussu Six. V. pontificus maximi edita; Romae, ex typographia apostolia vaticana.* In a further bull affixed to the first volume of this edition, Sixtus V warned of excommunication for all printers, editors, etc. "who in reprinting this work shall make any alterations in the text."

No corrector of the press was His Holiness, however. In spite of the fact that he personally examined every sheet as it was pulled from the press, this Vulgate was, as described by one source, "without a rival, to the amazement of the world—swarming with errata." To the great joy of 16th century heretics, the erroneous words were covered over with pasted corrections, and papal infallibility in the art of proofreading became a thing of the past.

Gregory XIV, successor to Sixtus V, ordered the Vulgate suppressed. Clement VIII, who succeeded Gregory, decreed that it be revised, and having made alterations in the text thus ran the risk of excommunication. The corrected edition became the official text of the Vulgate as prescribed by the Council of Trent.

Aldus Manutius the younger was appointed to the directorship of the Typographia Vaticana in 1590. Grandson of the celebrated Aldus, he had published his first work at the age of eleven. He was a professor of eloquence at several universities, attesting to his greater interest in literature than in printing, although he had inherited the great printing office which had begun in Venice a century before.

January 23

"Mr. Caslon is an Artist, to whom the Republic of Learning has great obligations; his ingenuity has left a fairer copy for my emulation, than any other master." So wrote John Baskerville about the most famous of all English typefounders, William Caslon, who died January 23, 1766.

It is curious that the various accounts of how Caslon became a typefounder are in disagreement. Talbot Baines Reed mentions the conflicting stories in his *History of the Old English Letter Foundries,* published in 1887. The typefounder, born in 1692, became apprenticed to an engraver of gun-locks and barrels in London. In addition Caslon did silver-chasing and upon occasion designed tools for bookbinding. Some punches which he prepared for a bookbinder attracted the attention of a famous printer of London, John Watts, who has had some subsequent

reputation as the employer of Benjamin Franklin when the American printer worked in London in 1725.

Watts, encouraging Caslon to continue his studies in letter-cutting, introduced him to other London printers. About the same time, another well-known printer, William Bowyer the elder, also saw some lettering on the binding of a book designed by Caslon. Seeking out the young man, Bowyer took him to visit the typefoundry operated by Thomas James in Bartholomew Close. Bowyer then asked him whether he could cut types. As he had never been to a typefoundry before, Caslon requested one day to think about the matter. Later he agreed to set up his own foundry with loans from Bowyer, John Watts, and another printer named James Bettenham.

Thus established, Caslon quickly justified the faith of his printer friends. After a short period of dependence upon their custom, he was on his own. The foundry he began about 1720 is still in existence under the name of Stephenson Blake, the Caslon Letter Foundry. The reliance of English printers upon Dutch sources was thus halted. Caslon began a school of English type design which continued through the work of Baskerville, Martin, Austin, and the 19th century founders.

In 1734 Caslon published his famous broadside specimen sheet, showing his great roman with its fine italic, an excellent English blackletter, and a number of "exotic" letters such as Coptic, Armenian, Hebrew, Greek, etc. A copy of this specimen was bound into the second edition of Chambers's *Cyclopaedia* in 1738, with the notice: "The above were all cast in the foundry of Mr. W. Caslon, a person who, though not bred to the art of letter-founding, has by dint of genius, arrived at an excellency in it unknown hitherto in England, and which even surpasses anything of the kind done in Holland or elsewhere."

D. B. Updike has attempted in his *Printing Types* to explain the popularity of the Caslon types. Except for a short period from about 1800 to the 1840's, these types have never been out of fashion: "Why are William Caslon's types so excellent and so famous? To explain this and make it really clear, is difficult. While he modelled his letters on Dutch types, they were much better; for he introduced into his fonts a quality of interest, a variety of design, and a delicacy of modelling which few Dutch types possessed.

. . . His letters, when analyzed, especially in the smaller sizes, are not perfect individually; but in mass their effect is agreeable. That is, I think, their secret—a perfection of the whole, derived from harmonious but not necessarily perfect individual letterforms."

January 24

The United States Patent Office on January 24, 1854, granted to William Overend of Cincinnati a patent for a machine "intended to give to paper the proper dampness, in order to prepare it for the press. A given quantity of paper is placed upon the table, and is fed into the machine by nippers, when it is carried forward between wetted blankets, passing between rollers, and is finally deposited on a pile beneath the machine, having received the required amount of moisture in its passage."

Luther Ringwalt, in his *American Encyclopedia of Printing,* listed three other patents granted in the mid-19th century for wetting machines. But the rapidly advancing technology of the printing press was already making such devices obsolete. For four hundred years it had been necessary to wet paper to obtain the best results in printing, but the demands of the industrial revolution for the high-speed production of print were soon to change radically the manufacture of paper to meet the more precise characteristics of power-driven rotary and flat-bed presses. The so-called "slick" machine-finished and coated papers are no longer adaptable to the dampening process, which is now practiced only by those printers who wish to emulate the old craftsmen, printing uncoated paper at slow speeds on a power press or a sheet at a time on a hand press.

January 25

Apprentice contracts are still required between employer and employee, but the language in which they are composed is quite mild compared to that used during the last century, if we can accept as normal a contract made this day in 1852, in Ontario, Canada. It is probably quite typical for the period.

"This indenture, made the Twenty-fifth day of January, one thousand eight hundred and fifty-two, between John Fessant Eby, of the age of twelve years, the son of Jonas Eby, of Elora, in the County of Wellington, cabinet maker, of the first part; the said Jonas Eby, of the second part, and the Elora Newspaper, Job Printing and Bookbinding Company, of the third part, witnesseth, that the said John Fessant Eby, by and with the consent of his father, the said Jonas Eby (testified by his being a party to and executing these presents), doth put himself apprentice to the Elora Newspaper, Job Printing and Bookbinding Company, to learn the art and mystery of a printer, in the printing-office of the said company, and with the said company, after the manner of an apprentice, to serve from the day of the date of these presents, unto the full end and term of three years, from thence next following (determinable, nevertheless, upon the dissolution of determination of the said company) during which term the said apprentice shall faithfully serve the said company and obey the lawful demands of the officers thereof.

"He shall not waste the goods of the said company nor lend them unlawfully to any; he shall not contract matrimony during the said term; he shall not buy or sell himself from the service of the said company unlawfully; but in all things during the said term as a faithful apprentice he shall demean himself toward the said company and the officers thereof. And the said Elora Newspaper, Job Printing and Bookbinding Company, in consideration of the faithful services of the said apprentice, shall and will instruct or cause to be instructed, the said apprentice in the art and mystery of a printer, and shall and will pay to the said apprentice or to his father on his behalf the sums or wages hereinafter mentioned (that is to say) during the first year of the said term five shillings ($1.25) weekly; during the second year of the said term seven shillings and six pence ($1.87) weekly; and during the third year of the said term ten shillings ($2.50) weekly.

"And the said Jonas Eby for himself, his executors and administrators doth hereby covenant with the said Elora Newspaper, Job Printing and Bookbinding Company, that the said apprentice during the said term shall faithfully serve the said company in the manner aforesaid; and that he, the said Jonas

Eby, during the said term, shall and will find and provide for the said apprentice good and sufficient board, lodging, clothing, washing and other necessaries. In witness whereof, the said John Fessant Eby and Jonas Eby, and the said company by Charles Allen, Esquire, the president thereof, have hereunto set their hands and seals the day and year first aforesaid. Signed, sealed and delivered in the presence of John F. Eby, Jonas Eby, Charles Allen, President."

January 26

"The old pre-Revolutionary mill at Marlborough, in which Frederic W. Goudy, famous type designer, had his studio and workshop since 1923, burned to the ground early Thursday morning [January 26, 1939], with everything it contained. The loss is tentatively estimated at $50,000 at least; the money value of many of the things destroyed is beyond estimate. Between $35,000 and $40,000 in type matrices was lost."

The *Marlborough Record* gave over its front page banner to this catastrophic event in the life of the town's most illustrious citizen and America's most famous type designer. Goudy gave the newspaper a list, itemizing his loss in some detail. The list included the matrices for twenty-five of his types and patterns for over one hundred designs, in addition to five tons of type which had been cast and packed in boxes for shipment. Also destroyed were all of the accoutrements of The Village Letter Foundery — casters, engraving machines, milling machines, microscopes, etc.

Naturally enough, when the word of Goudy's misfortune was circulated, Deepdene bcame a magnet which drew scores of curious spectators. In a letter to his friend Howard Coggeshall of Utica, New York a short time later, Goudy wrote with some asperity, "What with the influx of visitors, well-meaning but inopportune, the avalanche of letters, telegrams, requests for materials for articles, making inventories for insurance, and visits to town to get rid of some of the asinine suggestions and plans being made for me without my consent or knowledge, and lately a bit of physical and mental let-down —the past three weeks have not made it easy to write."

Goudy's workshop was covered by an $8,000 insurance policy. But the seventy-four year old type designer lost little time in mourning his loss, immediately setting to work to continue his career. A number of projects which were hopefully suggested in the weeks following the fire never did come to fruition. The American Type Founders Company negotiated for thirty-two of the Goudy designs, suggesting that Goudy secure from his customers sufficient type to enable them to manufacture electrotype matrices. The same firm also requested information on the cost of a new type, as did the University of Chicago. None of these offers were fulfilled, the ATF gesture apparently foundering, as Goudy later stated, by "quibbling over a few hundred dollars."

However, Goudy was optimistic about his future and began to plan a new workshop for his home. He concluded his letter to Coggeshall with some nostalgic comments on his past.

"I do not anticipate any salvage," he wrote, "but there may be some *souvenirs*. I feel like the gink Browning writes about who intimated that at his death the word 'Calais' would be found written on his heart—I know d—d well 'Village Press' is on mine; and yet I seem entirely detached from it all—the ruins stun me because of the happy hours spent in the old shop—but I'm still here and kicking. . . ."

January 27

On January 27, George Phineas Gordon died, leaving a will which was so well hidden that it was not found for twelve years, and about one million dollars for his heirs to squabble over—all of which had been acquired in the manufacture of printing presses. Gordon, born in Salem, New Hampshire in 1810, had been on the stage for a period after leaving school. Apparently finding the thespian career unproductive, he learned the printer's trade in New York. He opened his own shop about 1835. Of mechanical bent, Gordon spent a great deal of his time planning the automation of the hand press for job printing.

His efforts resulted in a patent being granted to him on March 26, 1850. His invention was a press which resembled in some ways the machine introduced by Stephen P. Ruggles ten years earlier. Ruggles' press was called the Engine Press by its manufacturer but printers called it the upside down press, as the form was mounted in position over the platen, both of which were in the horizontal position. Gordon's patent covered a procedure for gripping the sheet of paper and inking mechanism. Although the press was not successful, Gordon was already at work on another principle, resulting in a device which he called the Alligator Press. In this unit, the bed and the platen were placed in a vertical position, the former being stationary at a forty-five degree angle. A cam moved the bed of the press forward to the same angle, making the impression. The late Ralph Green, chronicler of the history of job presses, says of the Alligator, "probably a more dangerous piece of apparatus was never built. The feeder had no warning device to signal him the necessity of withdrawing his hands."

Although a few Alligators were built, they were not successful. Perhaps the only surviving model is now in the State Capitol Museum in Lincoln, Nebraska. Gordon's next press was really the result of inspired thought by the inventor. He followed the Spiritualist persuasion, at that time being popularized by the Fox sisters of upstate New York. Evidently Gordon's poltergeist was Benjamin Franklin, as the worthy approached him in a dream for the single purpose of describing the next press which Gordon was to produce. This machine, called the Turnover, was patented but nowhere does the name of the distinguished printer-statesman appear as the inventor, as Gordon himself claimed all the credit. But he did call the machine the Franklin Press.

From this point Gordon became truly successful. The Franklin jobber with modifications became the typical Gordon press, the most widely used job press of its time. During the life of the inventor none of his presses were power driven, being operated by a foot treadle, although some printers attached a crank to the flywheel to actuate the mechanism.

During the last thirty years of the 19th century there were eighteen different firms building old style Gordons. In 1901, Chandler & Price bought the Gordon Press Works, thus securing the right to call their presses Gordons, although they had been manufac-turing the old style press since 1886. In country printing offices scattered throughout the land there are still Gordons operating and turning out job printing just as efficiently as they did seventy-five years ago.

January 28

On this day in 1706 John Baskerville was baptized. He thus began life with a blessing, although he ended as a Free Thinker and—in the opinion of many of his contemporaries—an atheist. Honored now for his reputation as a great printer and as the designer of one of the universal typefaces, Baskerville's personal life is not much remembered. In actuality, he was probably not an atheist but merely rebellious against some of the practices of the established church. He had, after all, printed a notable bible, an edition of the Book of Common Prayer, and editions of the Psalms. His eccentricities, however, were legion, and they were continued in the writing of his will.

When friends asked him how he wished to be buried, Baskerville is reputed to have answered that they could "bury him sitting, standing, or lying, but he did not think they could bury him flying." Upon his death he was buried in a vault in a conical building on his own property of Easy Hill. He wrote his own epitaph, as follows:

> Stranger—
> Beneath this cone in unconscrated
> [sic] ground
> A friend to the liberties of mankind
> Directed his body to be inhum'd
> May the example contribute to
> emancipate thy mind
> From the idle fears of superstition
> And the wicked arts of priesthood.

In the short, informative biography written in 1914 by Josiah Henry Benton, the author describes the macabre events which followed:

"When Baskerville House was sold to a Mr. Reyland in 1789, the owner did not disturb the body and it remained for nearly fifty years in comparative peace. During the Birmingham riots of 1791, Baskerville House was stormed, sacked, gutted, and burned. It was not, however, until alterations were made on the property that Baskerville's coffin was removed, and taken to a warehouse, where it remained for some time subject to visits from the curious, and even to scientific observations on the condition of the body. Mr. Ryland, ascertaining that a show was made of the remains, insisted that they should be suitably interred, and Mr. Marston, in whose shop the coffin had been placed, applied to the rector of St. Philip's for permission to bury the body there. This was refused on account of Baskerville's atheism, when Mr. Knott, the bookseller, said that he had a vault in Christ's Church, and should consider it an honor to have Baskerville's remains rest there, and they were there placed about 1829.

"Even here Baskerville's body did not rest permanently, for the necessary extension of Birmingham caused Christ's Church to be demolished, and his remains, which should have been placed in St. Philip's Church by the side of his wife, being again refused interment there by the rector, were placed in one of the catacombs of the Church of England Cemetery at Warnstone Lane. And so, finally, after being turned out of the garden at Easy Hill for a canal wharf, exposed to neglect and ignominy in a plumber's warehouse, interred by stealth in the vault of Christ's Church, and then again removed by the march of business, Baskerville's bones at last found permanent rest in a quiet cemetery of the Church of England."

January 29

At 10:00 o'clock on this Monday morning in 1951, three men drove a station wagon to Idlewild Airport in New York City. One of these men was a Customs broker. He was equipped with a set of pre-entry forms by which he expected to appease the Customs officials sufficiently to bring about the release of a suitcase which had been locked in a cargo shed of British Overseas Airways Corporation the previous Saturday. In the suitcase were the two volumes of a bible, composed in two columns of forty-two lines each and consequently known to bibliophiles as the 42-line bible, although perhaps more widely known as the Gutenberg Bible.

The story of how a Gutenberg Bible happened to be in such lowly surroundings began in December, 1950 when a hitherto unlocated copy of the book had been discovered in a private library in England. This copy

had been acquired by Sir George Shuckburgh, Bt., during the 18th century, and had last been mentioned by Thomas Frognal Dibdin, the well-known bibliophile, in 1824. It had come down through various female lines until the knowledge of its existence became known to the booksellers, Quaritch's of London. By a coincidence, just three months prior to this discovery, an American lady had commissioned Scribner's in New York to find a Gutenberg Bible. This was a rather difficult order to fill, since there were then but forty-seven known copies.

Mr. John Carter, Scribner's representative in England, concluded an agreement with the book's owner and on January 20th he brought it to the Quaritch shop in Grafton Street. There upon examination it was determined to be a fine copy, lacking but five of the 643 leaves of a complete copy. It was taken to the British Museum to compare it with the Grenville and George III copies there. The examination was halted at five o'clock when the Museum closed and resumed again on Monday morning, the 22nd. At three o'clock in the afternoon the comparisons were completed and Scribner's office in New York notified. Carter received orders the following day to bring the bible to New York in the utmost secrecy.

On the 26th at 4:30 p.m., Carter packed the two volumes into an old suitcase, and presented himself to the B.O.A.C. office at the London airport, where airline officials took a dim view of considering the thirty-six pound bag to be personal luggage to accompany the passenger. When it was stated firmly that no bag, no passenger, the matter was resolved satisfactorily. At 6:00 p.m., the first airplane to be honored by the passage of a Gutenberg Bible took off for New York via Iceland. At Idlewild, in spite of the remonstrances of a Scribner representative, the bible was refused entry to these United States under the rule that any commercial object valued at over $500 requires a "pre-entry form."

A few minutes later the bible was locked in a cargo shed, and bookman Carter was imbibing a double Bourbon. On the 27th, armed with the proper papers, Scribner's again attempted to retrieve its most valuable property. There was a slight delay when Carter insisted upon quoting a passage from a letter in 1870 by the London bookseller, Henry Stevens, to George Brinley, the purchaser of the second Gutenberg Bible ever to cross the Atlantic:

"Pray, Sir, ponder for a moment and appreciate the rarity and importance of this precious consignment from the old world to the new. Not only is it the first Bible, but it is the first book ever printed. It was read in Europe half a century before America was discovered. Please suggest to your deputy that he uncover his head while in the presence of this great book. Let no Custom Official, or other man in or out of authority, see it without first reverently raising his hat. It is not possible for many men ever to touch or even look upon a page of a Gutenberg Bible."

Quite naturally, the Customs' staff was impressed, but at the same time somewhat confused. By four o'clock the book had been cleared through Customs and was on its way to the Scribner safe. The lady for whom all this effort had been made, now politely declined to purchase the bible. Charles Scribner authorized its purchase from Quaritch's and placed it "in stock" in his Rare Book Department.

The bible, known as the Shuckburgh copy, was later purchased by George A. Poole of Chicago. Upon his death his entire library, including the Gutenberg Bible, was purchased by the Lilly Library of Indiana University.

January 30

Henry Barth died on January 30, 1907. A printer, engineer, and typefounder, in 1888 he invented the typecasting machine which bears his name and upon which all the present-day typecasting machines used by the world's typefounders are modelled.

Barth was born in Leipzig, Germany in 1823. He first worked for the typefounder Schelter & Giesecke as a machinist, and then spent several years in the Navy. His first job in the United States was as an engineer on an Ohio River steamboat, working out of Cincinnati. He then took a position with the Cincinnati Type Foundry. For that firm in 1855 he constructed the first cylinder press built in the West.

Six years later he was president of the foundry. In 1870 he designed the double casting machine, which cast two types at a time. Then he developed a lead-shaving ma-

chine for the precision production of strip leads. Many other foundries adopted this machine. Barth also designed a number of machines for the printing of playing cards, for which Cincinnati later became a world center.

The typecasting machine which was patented in 1888 was an improvement of the Bruce machine for the making of single types. The earlier typecasters were hand operated and the types required several finishing operations, such as breaking off the jets at the bottom of the letters, and hand-planing the grooves, in addition to rubbing the flash or burrs from each character. But the Barth machine automatically ejected the type in a finished state. Four sizes were manufactured, to encompass all sizes of type from 5-point to 144-point. The Barth machine speeded up typecasting about fifty percent over the machines then in use.

Barth also designed a height-to-paper gauge, which was most useful for printers who had the type of various foundries in their cases. To modern printers, such lack of precise manufacture on the part of typefounders now seems incredible. As late as 1885, the following type heights were listed by typefounders in this country: Boston Type Foundry, .9200″; Cincinnati Type Foundry, .9170″; Marder, Luse & Company, .9180″ (three other foundries, Johnson; Farmer, Little & Company, and James Connor's Sons also maintained a .9180″); George Bruce's Sons & Company, .9190″; Benton, Waldo & Company, .9200″; Barnhart Brothers & Spindler, .9200″; Phelps, Dalton & Company, .9200″.

Such chaotic conditions were of course put to rights just a few years later when most of the nation's foundries amalgamated into the American Type Founders Company.

January 31

British Standard 2961:1958 titled *Typeface Nomenclature* was published on January 31, 1958. It represents an attempt to systematize the terminology of a craft which had heretofore resisted such endeavors for over five hundred years. While there is a reasonable amount of agreement on some printing trade terms and it wouldn't take very long for any aggregation of printers representing a number of nationalities to be able to communicate with one another on the point, the pica, x-height, italic, font, series, family, etc., a smoky haze might interfere with rapid comprehension when the conversation turned to such matters as gothic, sans serif, antique, roman, Latin, Egyptian, etc. The British Standards Institution—aided and abetted, no doubt, by various printers' organizations—leaped into the breach and valiantly attempted to define the weight and the width of printer's typefaces. They importuned printers everywhere to come to an understanding on the matter.

In the relatively unsophisticated days of the 15th century, a printer had a type in his shop. If he wanted to use a little emphasis, he printed words or lines in a different color. Later on, different sizes of type came into use for such a purpose and then different styles of type. With the 20th century came variations of stroke thickness.

British Standards defined weight reasonably by stating that it is the degree of blackness of a typeface. The relative weights of a family of type are recommended to be known as: extra-light, light, semi-light, medium, semi-bold, extra-bold, and ultra-bold. Then, having taken the bull by the horns, British Standards bravely faced the morass of type width.

A type style which is correct for a specific measure, or length of line, might possibly be too wide to incorporate into a narrow space or too narrow for a wider one. The idea was developed that a type should be made available in a width narrower than normal and wider than normal. As in the business of weight, typefounders were delighted with the opportunity to sell type in a number of widths. The trouble arrived when they attempted to name the widths. This is one of the problems which received the attention of the compilers of the British Standard on *Typeface Nomenclature*.

Their suggestion for meeting this enigma was to dictate that the relative widths of typefaces should be ultra-condensed, extra-condensed, condensed, semi-condensed, medium, semi-expanded, expanded, extra-expanded, and ultra-expanded. And there the matter stands, the committee apparently having gone off on holiday, leaving the poor printers to try to ascertain the differences between semi-expanded and expanded.

The Bureau rates a B for effort, though, as present nomenclature is certainly just as cloudy. Take as an example the name of a current type, Record Gothic Heavy Medium Extended. To the making of types there will be no end.

February

February 1

"Abel Buell, of Killingworth in Connecticut, Jeweller and Lapidary, begs leave to acquaint the Public, and the Printers of the Several Colonies, that he hath already entered upon the Business of founding Types, which as Soon as he can furnish himself with Stock, will sell for the same price at which they are purchased in LONDON, in which Business he hopes for the Encouragement of the Printers, and all American Patriots."

So reads the first proof ever struck from American types, representing the work of Abel Buell, born this day in 1742. A typical American entrepreneur, Buell was active in a dozen fields of endeavor—typefounder, engraver, cartographer, auctioneer, privateersman, mint master, packet boat proprietor, etc. In none of these activities did he ever acquire either wealth or affluence.

Born in Killingworth, Connecticut, Buell had completed his apprenticeship as a goldsmith in that town by the time he was twenty years of age. In addition he possessed himself of the first of his four wives. Very quickly once he was on his own, he proceeded to cast off any ideas about settling down to small-town family life. According to his biographer, Lawrence C. Wroth, "Applying his skill in the use of delicate tools to the paper currency of the colony, he succeeded only too well in altering a number of two shillings six pence bills to the more comfortable denomination of thirty shillings."

After two years in prison for this attempt to improve the currency, Buell was released in 1764. Within another two years he was in Boston specializing in the cutting and polishing of precious stones. At this time he also began to experiment with the manufacture of printer's types. We next hear of him back home in Connecticut where the Assembly voted him a loan, in 1769, to continue his work in this field. There was at the time no typefounding in the colonies, which had to depend upon European sources for type.

For the next fifteen years he was most active as an auctioneer, combining this work with his numerous other business enterprises. In 1885 he was master of a mint established by the Connecticut Assembly for the purpose of coining and manufacturing coppers. Eight years following this appointment Buell was in New York as the owner of a cotton mill. The last years of his life were uneventful. He established himself in Stockbridge, Massachusetts, where he died in an alms house, destitute, at 81 years of age.

While Buell's types were the first to be cast in America (1769), they were not successful. After the failure of his first foundry, he again made type in 1781. The *Connecticut Journal* gradually replaced its worn-out English type with those of Buell's casting. As pure letterforms, the Buell designs were lacking style and crispness and from all indications were not very well cast. Perhaps Buell's constant searching for excitement, coupled with rather poor business judgment, insured against the first American type being a success. Of course the period of the Revolutionary War was not conducive to the establishment of a typefoundry, particularly when the product was inferior to the types available from overseas.

22

February 2

On this day in 1952 the writer received from William A. Dwiggins of Hingham, Massachusetts a limited edition printing of an excerpt from the pen of Hokusai, the remarkable 19th century Japanese draughtsman, book illustrator, painter, and wood engraver. The philosophy expressed in this fragment from the introduction to Hokusai's *Hundred Views of Fuji* unquestionably conveys WAD's own dispassionate approach to a lifetime in the field of graphic arts, during which he achieved the first rank in as many specialties as the Japanese artist himself. Certainly everyone who knew Dwiggins and recognized the notable contribution he made to American design will perceive his affinity to the viewpoint of the Japanese.

"From the age of six," wrote Hokusai, "I had a mania for drawing the forms of things. By the time I was fifty I had published an infinity of designs; but all I have produced before the age of seventy is not worth taking into account. At seventy-three I have learned a little about the real structure of nature, of animals, plants, trees, birds, fishes and insects. In consequence, when I am eighty, I shall have made still more progress; at ninety I shall penetrate the mystery of things; at a hundred I shall certainly have reached a marvelous stage, and when I am a hundred and ten everything I do, be it a dot or a line, will be alive.

"I beg those who live as long as I do to see if I do not keep my word.

"Written at the age of seventy-five by me, once Hokusai, today Gwakio Rojin, the old man mad about drawing."

Hokusai died in his eighty-ninth year, just short of penetrating the mystery of things, while Dwiggins died at seventy-six just after having learned a little about the real structure of nature, of animals, plants, trees, birds, fishes and insects.

February 3

Born on this day in Troy, Ohio, in 1844 was the American inventive genius, Tolbert Lanston, the producer of the successful typesetting machine, the monotype.

Leaving school at fifteen years of age, Lanston worked in Ohio and Iowa before volunteering for service with the Union Army during the Civil War. After this term he was appointed to the Pension Office in Washington, where he served for twenty-two years as chief of four different divisions within the Bureau. During this time he also studied law, receiving admittance to the bar and actually practicing this profession on a part-time basis. In addition to all this activity he was tinkering with machinery and exercising his bent for invention.

Such items as adjustable horseshoes, a mail bag lock, an adjustable hydraulic dumb waiter, and an adding machine were all successfully developed and were patented before Lanston began to experiment with a typesetting machine. His interest in printing sprang from his friendship with an army officer whose father was a newspaper publisher and who helped finance the development of Lanston's machine.

In 1885 Lanston applied for a patent on a typesetter. It was granted in 1887. This machine embodied a unique approach which is now considered to be an integral part of present-day electronic typesetting equipment; that is, the separation of the keyboarding operation from that of typecasting. Lanston's keyboard delivered two perforated tapes which contained the necessary information for justification of a line of type in addition to the selection of the characters to be cast. In his original machine, however, type was not cast but was impressed into pieces cut from type-high metal strips. One of the punched paper ribbons set this strip in motion and controlled its movement in accordance with the width of the character to be made. The single type was then cut from the strip automatically and impressed with a female die or matrice containing the desired character. The second punched tape positioned the die-case, which contained 196 matrices.

Following a great deal of work on the machine, Lanston became convinced that it was impractical and that the device should actually cast the type from molten metal. This idea he patented in 1897. He then perfected the keyboard to permit the use of just one punched ribbon, which positioned the matrices in the casting machine and delivered justified lines of type. His final patents, granted in 1897, represent the foundation of the present machine.

From this point, most of the development of the monotype machine was in the hands of an engineer, J. Sellers Bancroft, who reduced its size and increased its speed while simplifying its operation. One hundred machines were produced from Bancroft's model, the first being installed in the plant of Gibson Brothers in Washington, D. C. in 1898.

In 1899, the machine was manufactured in basically the same form in which its exists today, except for refinements. A few years later Lanston suffered a stroke which incapacitated him until his death in 1913.

February 4

Probably the earliest known use of a printer's mark which pictured the printer himself occurred in a book, *Heures à l'Usaige de Rome,* published on this day in Paris in 1489 by Jean du Pré. The device was apparently cut in relief on metal, a method quite common in French books of the period. This particular mark did not show any of the tools of the printing craft. That innovation came into use about twenty years later and has been of value in the attempts to trace the development of printing.

While the first printer's trade mark depicting a printing press was used in 1507 by Jodocus Badius Ascensius of Lyons and Paris, the implements of the printing office were shown in a somber illustration in an edition of *Danse Macabre,* printed in Lyons in 1499. This wood cut vividly renders a scene in which death, represented by three skeleons, interferes with a seated compositor at his case. Two pressmen are shown at their machine, and another section shows a clerk in a bookshop.

The most notable of all printer's devices is the crossed shields used by Johann Fust and Peter Schoeffer in the magnificent *Psalter* of 1457. There have been a number of attempts to decipher the cryptic symbolism delineated in the shields. H. W. Davies, the authority on printer's marks, believed them to be ancient German house marks, although admitting the possibility that they are merely printer's rules.

Most of the early marks—particularly those of northern European printers—are badly designed, being overly decorated and much too large for their purpose, which was merely to indicate the printer of the book in which they appeared. Notable exceptions to this trend were the marks of the great Venetians, Nicolas Jenson and Aldus Manutius.

Jenson's device was from the hand of a partner, Johannes de Colonia, and is the beautifully simple orb and cross, printed in reverse. Variations of this mark have been so widely used that it undoubtedly represents the most commonly encountered of all press devices. As in the crossed shields of Fust and Schoeffer, there is some controversy concerning the origin of the orb and cross. It is probable that it derives from pagan origins, although the religious symbolism is most frequently mentioned as inspiration. In many instances its use may be attributed merely to imitation, from one printer to the next. The same device has survived into our own time in the beautiful setting of it designed by Frederic W. Goudy for his Village Press and outside of the industry, in the more prosaic trademark of the National Biscuit Company.

The Aldine press mark, first used in 1502, is the dolphin and anchor representing quickness (dolphin) and firmness (anchor). Aldus adopted the device from a medal of the Emperor Vespasian given to him by the humanist Pietro Bembo. Owing to the popularity of its originator, the dolphin and anchor quickly became the most widely pirated printer's mark. Its modern counterpart is the trademark of the publishing firm of Doubleday.

February 5

"The generosity of your invitation to me to speak on this important occasion leaves me a trifle bewildered. I am so accustomed to being told to keep my opinions to myself that being thus unexpectedly encouraged to express them gives me some cause to wonder if I have, or ever had, any opinions upon the graphic arts worth expressing. . . . So if I accept it as wholeheartedly as I believe it was given—if I take you at your word and say things that I have long wanted to hear somebody say—I hope it will not be thought an abuse of this kindly tendered privilege."

So began one of the most forthright statements ever made before an audience gathered to celebrate the opening of a Fifty Books of the Year Exhibition. The speaker was Thomas Maitland Cleland, one of America's most distinguished typographers. The date was February 5, 1940. Cleland's address, described by one listener as "refreshing as a cool, fresh breeze," was thereafter entitled *Harsh Words,* and was so received by many of the younger designers who were present that evening.

T. M. Cleland had long since earned the right to either praise or damn the graphic art of his times. From 1900 he had been a first-rate book designer, advertising typographer, type designer, and artist. While he was perhaps most at home in the production of traditional typography, he had nevertheless been "contemporary" for most of his professional life. During the thirties many designers had not come to terms with any particular school. As a result much shoddy work was being produced that was merely imitative of a number of conflicting artistic creeds. It was this approach which prompted Cleland's contempt when he said:

"Much as I am filled with admiration and respect for many individual talents and accomplishments that still contrive to exist, they seem to me to stand unhappily isolated in what I can't help viewing as artistic bankruptcy and cultural chaos. . . . To paraphrase a remark in the concluding chapter of Updike's classic work on printing types, it has taken printers and publishers five hundred years to find out how wretchedly books and other things can be made and still sell.

". . . The idea that originality is essential to the successful practice of the graphic arts is more prevalent today than it ever was in the days when the graphic arts were practiced at their best. The current belief that everyone must now be an inventor is too often interpreted to mean that no one need any longer be a workman. Hand in hand with this premeditated individualism goes, more often than not, a curious irritation with standards of any kind. The conscious cultivator of his own individuality will go to extravagant lengths to escape the pains imposed by a standard. . . .

"It seems to me that *all* art was *modern* when it was made, and still is if it is suitable to life as we now live it; and I look in vain for any applied art worth the name that was not also, in some sense functional. From the buttresses of a gothic cathedral to the gayest Chippendale chair one finds, upon analysis, a perfect work of engineering perfectly adapted to its purpose. If this were not so,

these things would hardly have endured for so long a time. . . . As students and beginners in search of truth, we are today being pushed and pulled about by no end of such bogus preachments—familiar faces with false whiskers—old and common principles dolled up with new names and often used to account for incompetence and laziness."

February 6

On February 6, 1868, the English printing periodical, *The Printers' Register,* published the "Reflections of an American Country Printer on Printing Considered as a Fine Art." The country printer evidently chose to remain anonymous but his meditations have the universality of all printers in love with their craft.

"The great intelligence of printers," he wrote, "is a proverb, and popular belief, always blundering, attributes this as a cause, rather than as a result, of their connection with the profession. Granted that it requires a higher intelligence in a boy to fit him for apprenticeship to printing than to making horse-shoes; the truth still remains, that the effects of the art upon him are to produce a higher form of culture than any common trade could furnish him.

"What further conditions can be required to establish the rank of Typography? I can think but of one: it is that printers should in all honorable ways *claim* the social rank they are entitled to. . . . We need to crush out of ourselves that cringing hypocrisy which causes many to say, 'I am a Printer' in a tone and with a manner that convey the impression that the avowal is made by one who regrets that he is not a blacksmith or a bricklayer. There should be something of the proud *Civis Romanus Sum* air accompanying the declaration; for he who worthily fills a printer's place in this busy age is fit companion for poets and painters—yea, a nobler art is his, for he not only furnishes the inspiration and the form of beauty, but creates the capacity to comprehend it. He is the high-priest of intellect, teaching it the very alphabet, and spreading before it the grandest of heroic epics! . . . Who shall measure the bounds of his influence, or compute the reach of his importance? He uncloses the iron doors of despotism and tyranny, and Liberty comes forth radiant among men. Oh! the manacles that must still have corroded and borne down the limbs and the aspirations of all races, but for the followers of Fust! Oh! the grand bonfire of royal pomps, vanities, and atrocities that these four centuries of printing have already set ablaze: and the grander crashing of worn-out superstitions, the banishment of leprosies of kingly folly, the tearing down of all hoary structures of Wrong, soon to come, when, through the apostleship of the Press, the peoples are educated to know their rights,—'and knowing, dare maintain them!'

"And shall the humblest neophyte in the exalted Art blush to his own connection with it? Shall he not rather exalt that he wears a dignity greater than prince or potentate can confer, in that he serves at the altar of civilization, progress, freedom? How can such a one degrade his profession by calling it a trade and speak of its temple as the shop?"

February 7

On this day in 1941, Daniel Berkeley Updike acceded to a request from the Typophiles to write a short introduction to the collection of war-time letters which Beatrice Warde wrote from London to her mother in New York. This compilation was published as one of the Typophile Chap Books under the title, *Bombed But Unbeaten.*

"Since Mr. Paul Bennett suggested, in behalf of the Typophiles, that I should contribute to this book a brief appreciation of Mrs. Warde's services to Typography, I have been thinking how best to fulfill my promise to do so; and the more I considered the matter, the less I felt that Mrs. Warde's contribution to the history and practice of typography were any more important than the spirit she had brought to her investigations. In so saying, I do not underrate the value of her admirable work in the important tractate on Jean Jannon of Sedan—published over the pseudonym of Paul Beaujon in 1926—in which she cleared away the mists which long obscured the provenance of types attributed to Garamond; the excellent occasional addresses appearing in *The Fleuron* and *Signature,* and elsewhere on various aspects of typography, and the ingenious and thoughtful promotional papers, that since 1927 have

appeared in the *Monotype Recorder.* Yet I feel that the qualities of patience, resourcefulness, courage, and imagination that have marked these investigations and conclusions are but part of a much larger achievement."

Beatrice Warde, or BW as she is known to her friends in every part of the world, is the author of the famous inscription, *This Is a Printing Office.* Written in 1932, it has been translated into a score of languages and may be seen in thousands of printing establishments throughout the world, including the door of the United States Government Printing Office where it is cast in bronze.

This is a Printing Office
*
Crossroads of Civilization
Refuge of all the Arts against
the Ravages of Time
Armory of Fearless Truth Against
Whispering Rumor
Incessant Trumpet of Trade
*
From This Place Words May Fly Abroad
Not to Perish on Waves of Sound
Not to Vary with the Writer's Hand
But Fixed in Time, Having Been
Verified by Proof
Friend, You Stand on Sacred Ground
This is a Printing Office

February 8

"It was born of compromise and courage, but grew and prospered through the faith of men who believed in its destiny." These were not the resounding words of one of the founding fathers of our nation, but instead represent the opinion of a president of the American Type Founders Company, which was incorporated this day in 1892, to the tune of a concerted babel of voices raised in both praise and protest by most of the nation's printers.

From the establishment in 1796 of the earliest American typefoundry to be fully successful, that of Binny & Ronaldson in Philadelphia, competition among typefounders had grown to such a point that by the middle of the 19th century there were some two dozen firms, all striving for the printer's business. Price cutting, especially in the period immediately following the Civil War, became ruinous. Since these founders were also in the printer's supply trade, anxious to sell everything from em quads to shooting sticks, the competition for business was fierce, resulting in costly and unbusinesslike practices.

The price war reached its peak in the late eighties. Middlemen, or jobbers, who sold directly to the printer were increasing in number and were in a position to pressure the typefoundries individually to such an extent that production standards deteriorated and the foundries themselves were placed in an unstable financial position. Another factor which had frightening aspects to the harassed founders was the development of the Mergenthaler Linotype machine at about the same period. There had been many other devices constructed for the composition of printer's types, all of which had employed foundry type, but the linotype actually cast its own type from self-contained matrices. Since this machine was immediately successful in newspaper offices, the principal source of income to the foundries was irretrievably lost. It became obvious that in order to survive, the typefounders would have to cooperate with one another.

The first overture in this direction was made by John Marder of the Chicago Type Foundry, in company with Arthur Brower of the Union Type Foundry, also of Chicago. Marder and Brower first sought to persuade the most reknowned of American typefounders, Thomas B. MacKellar, head of the Philadelphia firm of MacKellar, Smiths & Jordan, to join with them in the formation of a combined firm. When MacKellar was won over to the idea, its success was almost assured. For the first year or so, however, many of the twenty-three foundries which joined the association could not rid themselves of their old competitive urges and insisted on keeping their original names. In 1894 the dynamic new general manager of American Type Founders, Robert W. Nelson, convinced them of the effectiveness of the new title, and as a result the old signboards came down one by one.

The four large foundries which did not join ATF attempted to rally printers to their own cause, representing the new firm as a combine and as a trust, words which had distinct red-flag potentialities in the nineties. But that they were fighting in a lost cause became even more evident in 1896 when the Lanston Monotype machine was introduced, enabling printers to cast their own single types and freeing them from dependence upon the foundries.

February 9

This day in 1777 Samuel Johnson nominated for membership in the exclusive Literary Club of London, Richard Brinsley Sheridan, whose play, *The Rivals,* had so captivated audiences two years previously. Perhaps Dr. Johnson was attempting to placate the playwright's father, with whom he was constantly embroiled, but he did enjoy the comedy and may indeed have found uproarious the satire on popular literature in this scene:

Lucy. Indeed, ma'am, I traversed half the town in search of it. I don't believe there's a circulating library in Bath I ha'n't been at.

Lydia Languish. And could not you get *The Reward of Constancy?*

Lucy. No, indeed, ma'am.

Lydia. Nor *The Fatal Connexion?*

Lucy. No, indeed, ma'am.

Lydia. Nor *The Mistakes of the Heart?*

Lucy. Ma'am, as ill luck would have it, Mr. Bull said Miss Sukey Saunter had just fetched it away.

Lydia. Heigh-ho!—Did you inquire for *The Delicate Distress?*

Lucy.—Or, *The Memoirs of Lady Woodford?* Yes, indeed, ma'am. I asked everywhere for it; and I might have brought it from Mr. Frederick's, but Lady Slattern Lounger, who had just sent it home, had so soiled and dog-eared it, it wasn't fit for a Christian to read.

Lydia. Heigh-ho!—Yes, I always know when Lady Slattern has been before me. She has a most observing thumb; and I believe cherishes her nails for the convenience of making marginal notes.

* * *

. . . O Lud! ma'am, they are both coming upstairs. . . .

Lydia. Here, my dear Lucy, hide these books. Quick, quick. Fling *Peregrine Pickle* under the toilet—throw *Roderick Random* into the closet—put *The Innocent Adultery* into *The Whole Duty of Man*—thrust *Lord Aimworth* under the sofa—cram *Ovid* behind the bolster—there—put *The Man of Feeling* into your pocket—so, so, now lay *Mrs. Chapone* in sight, and leave *Fordyce's Sermons* open on the table.

Lucy. Oh, burn it, ma'am, the hairdresser has torn away as far as *Proper Pride*.

Lydia. Never mind—open at *Sobriety*. Fling me *Lord Chesterfield's Letters*.—Now for 'em.

(Mrs. Malaprop and Sir Anthony Absolute enter after Lydia has been ordered to her room—)

Mrs. Malaprop. There's a little intricate hussy for you!

Sir Anthony. It is not to be wondered at, ma'am—all this is the natural consequence of teaching girls to read. Had I a thousand daughters, by Heaven! I'd as soon have them taught the black art as their alphabet!

Mrs. Malaprop. Nay, Sir Anthony, you are an absolute misanthropy.

Sir Anthony. In my way hither, Mrs. Malaprop, I observed your niece's maid coming forth from a circulating library! She had a book in each hand—they were half-bound volumes, with marble covers! From that moment I guessed how full of duty I should see her mistress!

Mrs. Malaprop. Those are vile places, indeed!

Sir Anthony. Madam, a circulating library in a town is as an evergreen tree of diabolical knowledge! It blossoms through the year! And depend on it, Mrs. Malaprop, that they who are so fond of handling the leaves, will long for the fruit at last.

February 10

The compositor who composed on this day in 1734 the even lines of Latin prose which made up William Caslon's first specimen sheet no doubt considered the task quite ordinary, such was the level of literacy of most of the printers of that period. His employer, the typefounder William Caslon, had started something however which was to plague type specimens for well over a century.

"Quosque tandem abutere, Catalina, patientia nostra?" The Ciceronian quotation might have been a standard element in the education of generations of youths, but eventually printers became disenchanted with it, even after it had appeared in the specimen books of all the great typefounders from Caslon to Bodoni, all of whom slyly took advantage of the rich curves prevalent in Latin prose, the better to show off their wares.

Here in the United States the first specimen book to appear—that of Binny & Ronaldson dated 1812—followed the leadership of their transatlantic brethren.

The famed bibliographer, Dr. Dibdin, took issue with the practice, citing it as a deception:

"The Latin language, either written or printed, presents to the eye a great uniformity or evenness of effect. The m and n, like the solid sirloin upon our table, have a substantial appearance; no garnishing with useless herbs, or casing in coat of mail, as it were, to disguise its real character. Now, in our own tongue, by the side of this m or n, at no great distance from it, comes a crooked, long-tailed g, or a th, or some gawkishly ascending or descending letter of meagre form, which are the very flanking herbs, or dressings of the aforesaid typographical dish, m or n. In short, the number of ascending or descending letters in our own language, the p's, l's, th's and sundry others of perpetual recurrence, render the effect of printing much less uniform and beautiful than in the Latin language. Caslon, therefore, and Messrs. Fry & Co., after him, should have presented their 'Specimens of Printing Types' in the *English* language, and then, as no disappointment could have ensued, so no imputation of deception would have attached."

It may be remarked that the garrulous Doctor, a great admirer of Giambattista Bodoni, refrained from mentioning the equal guilt of the Parma typographer in this "deception."

American typefounders, when they discarded Cicero, resorted to the phraseology of the marketplace. Instead of depending upon resounding Latin prose, they became cute, although it must be admitted that many of the 19th century specimen books remain a monument to the skills of the advertising copywriter in his embryo stage.

The simple alphabetical sentence, "The quick brown fox jumps over the lazy dog's back," became in a specimen book of the Keystone Type Foundry, "Dalmatian greyhounds leaping over the fence and field reynard," a phrase which was preceded by "Frolicksome Maltese kitten frisking recklessly through blooming flower beds."

Realizing, perhaps, that even the Latin quick brown fox is superior to such variegated prose, the modern typefounders are primarily content to show simple alphabets.

February 11

The first person ever to print on a train was born on February 11, 1847. As he was to become the greatest inventive genius of his time, it is unfortunate that his interest in printing was of short duration. The present electronic upheaval in the craft might have come a half century earlier had Thomas A. Edison actively continued his printing career.

As a boy, Thomas Edison received virtually no formal schooling. He was sent to a one-room school at the age of eight, but owing to his years of running free, he could not mold himself to the classroom. After three months the schoolmaster told the boy's parents that he was "addled," and his mother forthwith removed him from the school, undertaking on the strength of her one year of teaching in a small country school the task of educating her son. The limitations of such education plagued Edison for a good part of his life, as he never learned to spell and his grammar was below even the limited standards of the day. However, his mother was intelligent enough to realize that the boy needed guidance rather than the restrictions of disciplined study. In later years the inventor stated that she allowed him to follow his own bent and was thus responsible for the "making of me."

In 1859 when the railroad was extended from Detroit to Edison's home town of Port Huron, he applied for the non-paying job of "candy butcher" on the cars. His job involved the concession of selling sweets and newspapers to the passengers, Although only twelve years of age, Edison had to be on the train prior to its 7:00 a.m. departure for the three hour trip to Detroit, and then had to wait until it left that city for the return trip, which was completed at 9:30 p.m. The boy developed considerable ingenuity in this job, taking aboard such items as fruit, vegetables, and butter which he sold at retail along the way.

During the long lay-over in Detroit, Edison at first wandered about the city, but when the Detroit Free Library was opened in 1862 he became one of its earliest card-owners. He later wrote, "I started with the first book on the bottom shelf and went through the lot, one by one. I didn't read a few books. I read the library." At this time he also developed a strong interest in the craft of printing. He had made some extra money selling at a premium price the newspapers which carried the account of the battle of Shiloh. This sum he invested in a small hand-press with some three hundred pounds of type which he purchased in Detroit. He then taught himself how to set type and operate the press, editing a small local newspaper which he produced in its entirety in the baggage car of the train. This sheet, *The Weekly Herald,* was sold for eight cents a copy and reached a circulation of four hundred copies.

Edison's atrocious spelling didn't seem to faze his readers, as the paper was lively and informative. The boy editor, with a friend, enlarged the scope of the weekly and renamed it the *Paul Pry*. One of the items in the new paper, however, discussed the vicissitudes of a local personage and so enraged that individual that he sought out the editor. Although not equipped with the traditional horsewhip, he satisfied his ire by throwing Edison into the St. Clair River. From that point the boy's interest in a career in journalism abruptly declined, and the paper went out of business.

Shortly after this incident, a railroad telegrapher excited Edison by offering to teach him the skills of that trade. Thus the printing craft lost an outstanding recruit.

February 12

Residents of 1600 Pennsylvania Avenue in the City of Washington, D. C. have from time to time been prevailed upon to say a few words about printing, generally about the time of Benjamin Franklin's birthday. It is rare indeed that any President of the United States has mentioned the art prior to his elevation to the first office of the land. The man born on this date in 1809 was an exception in this, as in many another quality. On the eve of his fiftieth birthday, Abraham Lincoln addressed the Phi Alpha Society of Illinois College at Jacksonville in a dissertation called the Second Lecture on Discoveries and Inventions. It was so titled because it was a revised version of an earlier talk on the same subject presented at Bloomington, Illinois the previous April. Printers may recall that it was in Bloomington that Frederic W. Goudy was born just a few years later.

Discussing the effects of a written language on science and invention, Mr. Lincoln pointed out its limitations and went on to say:

"At length printing came. It gave ten thousand copies of any written matter, quite as cheaply as ten were given before; and consequently a thousand minds were brought into the field where there was but one before. This was a great *gain;* and history shows a great *change* corresponding to it, in point of time. I will venture to consider *it,* the true termination of that period called 'the dark ages.' Discoveries, inventions, and improvements followed rapidly, and have been increasing their rapidity ever since. The effects could not come all at once. It required time to bring them out; and they are still coming. The *capacity* to read, could not be multiplied as fast as the *means* of reading. Spelling-books just began to go into the hands of the children; but the teachers were not very numerous, or very competent; so that it was safe to infer they did not advance so speedily as they do now-a-days. It is very probable—almost certain—that the great mass of men, at that time, were utterly unconscious, that their *conditions,* or their *minds* were capable of improvement. They not only looked upon the educated few as superior beings, but they supposed themselves to be naturally incapable of rising to equality. To emancipate the mind from this false and under estimate of itself, is the great task which printing came into the world to perform. It is difficult for us, *now* and *here* to conceive how strong this slavery of the mind was; and how long it did, of necessity, take to break its shackles, and to get a habit of freedom of thought established. It is, in this connection, a curious fact that a new country is most favorable—almost necessary—to the emancipation of thought, and the consequent advancement of civilization and the arts."

February 13

On this day in 1890 the *Pall Mall Gazette* of London carried an account of an interview with a pair of ladies who had possessed the temerity to invade the province of the Victorian Male by founding a Journalists' Training Home for Women, in which were to be trained compositors, readers, shorthand writers, reporters, and journalists. Furthermore, the pupils were to be drawn only from the homes of such middle class persons as military officers and clergymen.

Answering an interrogation by an amused and supercilious reporter, one of the proprietors of the Home stated: "Female labor is slowly, but nevertheless surely, finding a footing in the printing world, a footing that is well-nigh impossible to eradicate; therefore, the men had better look to their laurels, for in the event of an eight-hour system being introduced, women will prove a very formidable obstacle in the field of labor." To further emphasize her point, she added, "In France, Eugenie Noboyet says, 'It is we who make man, why should we not have a voice in his counsels?' "

At about the same time there was a journal being published in Boston, entitled *Elle,* devoted primarily to women compositors. According to the London account, "this sheet is a veritable manhater; not the slightest mention of man in any shape or form is to be found in its columns, neither is *genus homo* allowed to hawk it!"

In the United States, the printing journals frequently carried snide accounts of female typos. One of these, appearing in 1889, stated: "Were one to visit the printing offices in Chicago or any other city where female compositors are employed, a pale, worn-out set would be seen. Many there are, 'tis true, who have their usual robust appearance; but many, and a majority, wear that peculiarly pale, determined expression which follows a term at the case. The average time a young woman can endure continuous work at the case is considerably less than five years. Some go over that time, but when they leave the case at five years, headaches, backaches, and other aches have played sad havoc with their constitutions, unfitting them for other employment."

This intemperate attack on lady comps did not go unanswered. A reply, written by an anonymous editor taking protection behind the pseudonym of Pica Antique, asked of the predominantly masculine readers: "And who will have the unblushing effrontery to deny that women compositors are doing as good, clean and tasty work as those of the opposite sex? Aye, more, that their presence purifies, elevates, and is a strong incentive to nobler lives and a higher manhood; that every printing office where women are employed is blessed with more decorum than formerly; is more free from vulgarity, profanity, drunkenness; that work is done in a more quiet and orderly manner; that the moral atmosphere is far more fit for man to live in and the day a red-letter one when woman devoted herself to the temple of the art wherein Benjamin Franklin sits a crowned king."

February 14

In the light of the contemporary relationship between printers and their employers, there is a certain aura of respect evident in a document prepared by the Compositors of London on February 14, 1793 for delivery to the Master Printers. Under the heading of *The Address of the Compositors of London to the Master Printers,* the comps stated their grievances—but most politely—as follows:

"Seven years have now elapsed since we addressed the Master Printers on the Subject of an Advance of Prices; with Gratitude we call to our Remembrance that they then deemed our Application worthy Their Attention, and that they thought fit to redress, in Part, the Grievances we complained of. As we disclaim all Proceedings militating against Justice, or that are subversive of decent and respectful Behaviour, we presume that any Communication, which the present Situation of the Business renders necessary to be opened with our Employers, will be received in a Manner suitable to its Importance, and with Candour coinciding with its Equity. Impressed with this Idea, we respectfully submit the Two following Propositions for your Sanction:

"I. That all works be cast up with Heads and Directions inclusive.

"II. That *Em* or *En* Quadrats, or whatever is used at the Beginnings and Ends of Lines, be considered each as a Letter, and be included as in the above Article.

"The Reason we beg to offer that Heads and Directions should be included in the future Estimation of Works, is, that they are to all Intents and Purposes a Part of the Page; and that the former are often attended with peculiar Trouble, especially when composed in a Type different from that employed on the Body of the Work, sometimes consisting of Capital and Small Capital Letters united, and frequently of Italic Capitals, which

require the utmost Skill of the Compositor to space with Neatness and Propriety; insomuch, that the Time employed in this Part of the Business would be fully sufficient (in many Instances) for the Composition of Four Lines of ordinary Matter; this Trouble, when it is extended to the supplying running Titles for two or three Sheets of Letter, occasions a considerable Drawback from the Earnings of the Compositor, and is a Hardship which we hope our Employers can have no objection to remove."

The compositors then reminded their employers that the cost of living had increased considerably since 1785 and closed with this paragraph:

"The communication of your sentiments to the Compositors in your Office or in any Manner agreeable to the Masters in general, to the Committee of Compositors at the Hole-in-the-Wall, Fleet Street, on or before the first of March, will be gratefully received by your Humble Servants."

Some 539 journeymen comps signed the address, and the Master Printers agreed to but one of the requests.

February 15

A newspaper clipping had been inserted in a copy of the original journal maintained by Horace Walpole in which he recorded his experiences with the "Press at Strawberry Hill." It described an event taking place on this day in 1731.

"A Printing Press, and Cases for Composing, were on Monday put up at St. James's House, for their Majesties to see the Manner of the Noble Art of Printing. His Royal Highness the Duke wrought at one of the Printing Cases, to compose for the Press a little Book of his own Writing, call'd, *The Laws of Dodge Hare,* one of his Recreations, which is to be printed off for his Royal Highness's Amusement. And the two youngest Princesses composed their own Names, &c. under the Direction of Mr. Samuel Palmer, a Printer of the City."

The newspaper then proceeded to editorialize upon this event.

"We are extremely pleased to hear the Press hath met with so gracious a Reception at Court; and it must be the greatest Mortification to Those, whose Guilt makes Them Enemies to this useful Invention, to see it encouraged by their Majesties, in such a Manner, and even to behold some of the Royal Family initiating Themselves in the noble Arts of Writing and Printing.—We could wish that our Nobility and Gentry would follow this Royal Example, and set up a Printing-Press in their Houses; which, we apprehend, would be a much more polite, as well as a more instructive Amusement for Themselves and their Heirs, than the modern fashionable Diversions of Billiard-Tables and Fox-hunting."

The plea fell upon deaf ears, since the history of the private press movement records no awakening of interest in the craft among the wealthy residents of country homes or of even a deepening sense of respect on the part of royal personages. However, the product of the more distinguished private presses, a century and a half later, became most desirable to the affluent collectors, with the result that such presses as Kelmscott, Doves, and Ashendene lacked no opportunity to excite buyers. Of course the rarer these items have become, the more desirable they are to those collectors who consider a library to be a "modern fashionable Diversion."

February 16

On February 16, 1914, died the most honored printer in the United States—Theodore Low De Vinne.

With no formal education, De Vinne was the recipient of the degree of Master of Arts from both Yale and Columbia Universities. The citation at the Columbia convocation was read by President Low: "As you are thus the master of the art preservative of all arts, and because you have shown yourself a scholar in everything related to it, I admit you to the degree of Master of Arts of this University."

From the time of his apprenticeship as a compositor in Newburgh, New York at the age of 14, De Vinne had loved the printer's craft, and in a period when the industry was completely involved in the problems of mechanization brought about by the industrial revolution, he brought to it the idealism which it so badly needed. He became a master craftsman in the production of printing, a most valuable attribute in his later attempts to improve the status of printers by raising

their philosophical standards. His fellow printers were impressed by his great success as a master printer and by his technological accomplishments, even though many of these men could not quite understand his continuing motivation to interest them in the more aesthetic values of printing.

De Vinne's first books were on the subject of costs in the printing plant. His system of pricing profitably was adopted by many other plants. His technical innovations included the introduction of hard packing and more rigid impression of his cylinder presses. He began experiments with ink and paper which resulted in the formulation of inks for high speed printing and in the first coated paper to be used for magazine printing. He was one of the first printers to print with half-tone engravings. The *Century* magazine, for which he was the printer, was considered to be the best printed periodical in the world.

As a founder of the United Typothetae of America, now the Printing Industries of America, he was active in promoting better relationships among the owners of plants and in bringing about the cooperation of printers with their suppliers—such as equipment manufacturers, paper mills, engravers, etc. For this act alone De Vinne should be honored, but in addition his contributions as a scholar are of the first rank.

At this time the only literature of printing generally available was the printer's manual, essentially practical in nature. De Vinne became a student of typography through reading, finding it necessary to study several languages in order to understand source material, which was then almost exclusively of European origin. His great work, *The Invention of Printing*, published in 1876, was followed by a four volume manual, *The Practice of Typography*, 1901-04; *Title Pages as Seen by a Printer*, 1901; and finally *Notable Printers of Italy in the Fifteenth Century*, 1910. The last two volumes were printed by De Vinne for the Grolier Club, of which he was a founding member. They represent De Vinne at his best both as a printer and as an exponent of the history of his craft.

February 17

"A. D. 1801, February 17th—No. 2481. Mathias Koops of James Street, Westminster, gentleman, for a method of manufacturing paper from straw, hay, thistles, waste, and refuse of hemp and flax, and different kinds of wood and bark, fit for printing and other useful purposes."

So stated the Great Seal Patent Office of London, upon the granting of a patent to Koops from which emerged The Straw Paper Manufactory at Mill Bank underneath the Bridge at Westminster. Although this mill, set up in 1801, began business with great expectations, it was bankrupt within two years. However, the venture was, according to Dard Hunter, the noted historian of paper, the "paper manufactury upon which is based the greater part of our modern paper industry." Hunter credits the Koops mill with being the first in Europe to manufacture paper from other than linen and cotton rags.

While a number of documents concerning the short life of this undertaking were discovered in 1941, there is no available account of the methods used by Koops in his manufacturing process, although the mill was the largest of its kind constructed in England up to that time.

Improvements in printing presses during the 18th century had placed pressure on the paper manufacturers to increase their production, as it took considerably longer to make a sheet of paper than to print upon it. The hand methods were notoriously slow, and the industry was completely dependent upon the supply of rags. In 1700 English papermakers used 700 tons of linen a year, but by the time of the experiments of Mathias Koops, they required almost 9,000 tons.

The tremendous expansion which took place in the textile industry during the early decades of the 19th century due to the impact of the industrial revolution significantly reduced the price of the raw materials of paper manufacture, but by the 1850's the bulk of papermaking was being produced by machines utilizing wood pulp as a source in place of rags. While such paper was inferior to that manufactured from rags, this was a minor factor in a period when the vociferous demand for economic printing production seriously interfered with the search for greater quality.

February 18

In a Dedicatory Epistle addressed to Matthieu de Longue-Joue, Bishop of Scissons, the punchcutter Claude Garamond thanked the ecclesiastic for the use of a theological work printed in his new type. Dated February 18, 1545, the dedication read:

"That I, an unknown and private individual, should offer and dedicate the first fruits of my work as a publisher to you, Reverend Father, with one whom I am unacquainted, may rightly be a matter of surprise to you and to anyone not fully cognizant of my purposes. I have been advised and persuaded to this course by Jean Gagny, first almoner of the Most Christian king, a man who has deserved well of the literary world by the commentaries which he has issued on sacred literature and by promoting the publications of the labours of learned and pious men. . . . Since he considered me capable of advancing the glory of the craft of printing by the art of engraving and letter-founding which I had studied from boyhood and with little profit to my personal purse, with the goodwill which he manifests to all the industrious, he advised, that I, who had been accustomed hitherto to engrave and cast types for the publishers, should enjoy my own labours and enter the publishing trade; for those, he said, who merely engrave types and go no further, are only making honey for the publishers. . . . He declared that the best way of starting would be to cut as soon as possible new types after the italic of Aldus Manutius, adding in his liberality a considerable gift in order that I might be better able to advance the work. . . . So I engraved italic types after the model of the Aldine, with what success others will judge, though certainly they have satisfied the taste of Danés, of Vatable and of others. And not content with these I applied my mind to designing minute types of the same proportion and form (men of our trade call the fount 'glossa'). As these too seemed neat and elegant to Master Jean Gagny, he told me that he had received from you a learned and devout work of David Chambellin, formerly your father-in-law, who in earlier days had been the most distinguished of advocates and counsel in the Parlement. . . . Master Gagny thought this work worthy of being in the hands of all Christians, especially in this time of Lent. . . .

"I have heard Gagny say that your Chambellin in sacred literature has such charm and facility that he may be compared with the learned men of bygone days, and that in his writings his very soul inspired by the Holy Spirit seems to be speaking. Therefore in order that the devout and religious labours of such a man may not be lost to the men of our age and in order that those who are entirely devoted to public affairs may learn by his example not to plead without intermission but to turn to God in the inner sanctuary of the soul, Gagny handed me the work to be printed in my new types. I at once thought that these first fruits should be dedicated to you alone, the author's son-in-law and one who boasts and thanks the gods who gave you children by the daughter of so learned and devout a man. Accept then this offering, which we have desired to go forth in your name in gratitude for the loan of the manuscript and for your generosity towards us. . . . May God be with you. Paris, A.D. 1545, 18 Feb."

February 19

In the Old Bailey, on this day in 1663, one John Twynn, printer, was condemned to death for high treason for the printing of a "seditious, poisonous, and scandalous book, entitled *A Treatise on the execution of Justice is as well the people's as the magistrate's duty, and if the magistrates prevent judgment, then the people are bound by the law of God to execute judgment without them, and upon them.*"

The sentence upon Printer Twynn was, "That he be led back to the place from whence he came, and from thence to be drawn upon an hurdle to the place of execution; and there to be hanged by the neck, and being alive, to be cut down, and his privy members to be cut off, his entrails to be taken out of his body, and he living, the same to be burnt before his eyes; his head to be cut off, his body to be divided into four quarters, and his head and quarters to be disposed of at the pleasure of the king's majesty."

It is to be wondered just what poor Twynn put into his long-titled book, as on the same day, a printer and two booksellers were indicted by the same court for the production of two books which caused his majesty an equal amount of displeasure. After disposing of Twynn, Lord Chief Justice Hyde meted out a rather mild punishment to the others, with the following remarks: "You three have been severally indicted for a heinous and great offence: Brewster, you have been indicted for two several books, as full of villainy, and slander, and reproach to the king and government, as possibly can be: And I will tell you all three, it is the king's great mercy you have not been indicted capitally; for every one of those books are filled with treason, and you for publishing of them, by strictness of law, have forfeited your lives and all to the king: It is his clemency towards you. You may see the king's purposes; he desires to reform, not to ruin his subjects. The press is grown so common, and men take the boldness to print whatever is brought to them, let it concern who it will, it is high time examples be made. I must let you and all men know, by the course of the common law, before this new act was made, for a printer, or any other under the pretence of printing, to publish that which is a reproach to the king, to the state, to his government, to the church, nay to a particular person, it is punishable as a misdemeanor. He must not say he knew not what was in it; that is no answer in law."

The prisoners were then condemned to stand in the pillory for two hours on two different days and then were committed to the next gaol-delivery, without bail, and were to remain prisoners during the king's pleasure, following which they were to be fined £600 each.

February 20

On this day, in 1947, James T. Babb, librarian of Yale University, journeyed to New York City with a check in his pocket made out in the sum of $151,000 to Dr. A. S. W. Rosenbach, America's great rare book dealer. In return for this slip of paper he received a copy of what appeared to be a rather insignificant little book containing 294 pages and bearing upon its title page the words, "The Whole Booke of Psalmes Faithfully Translated into English Metre." At the foot of the page was the simple inscription "Imprinted 1640."

This, then, was the *Bay Psalm Book* as printed by Stephen Day in the Bay Colony of Massachusetts—the first book to be printed in the American Colonies. Yale University now owned this most desirable American book to display alongside its copy of the Gutenberg Bible. But the astute **Dr. Rosenbach** was hit for a $50,000 loss where it hurt the most—to his own pocketbook.

Late in 1946 it was reported that the Crowninshield-Stevens-Brinley-Vanderbilt-Whitney copy of the famous book was to be auctioned for the benefit of a Long Island hospital early in 1947. Since this volume was one of just three perfect copies out of the eleven known, there was a great deal of excitement in the book world. The last time that a perfect *Bay Psalm Book* had come up for sale was in 1879 when the very same copy had been sold for $1200.

Dr. Rosenbach, who had been instrumental in obtaining the Gutenberg Bible for the Yale Library, immediately began to work upon a similar plan. He hoped to interest wealthy Yale alumni in contributing toward the purchase of the book, on which Rosenbach would receive his usual commission. The idea bore fruit. Within a week $85,000 had been pledged for such a purpose. Yale officials promptly expressed their desire to acquire the book. Rosenbach's agent, John F. Fleming, was thereby authorized to bid up to $90,000 at the auction.

The actual sale was an event of historical importance in the book world. Everything would undoubtedly have gone according to plan, but Cornelius Vanderbilt Whitney, acting upon a whim, decided to bid for the book. Fleming's bids were matched by those of Scribner's, from $55,000 up to $91,000. At this point the Scribner man dropped out and Fleming was sure that the book was his. Whereupon Mr. Whitney bid $95,000 and the battle was on. Every time that Fleming bid an extra thousand dollars, Whitney raised it to an even five thousand, until finally at $151,000 the little volume was knocked down to Fleming.

Now Rosenbach had his book, but the pledges toward its eventual purchase by Yale were short some $60,000. The price he had paid was the highest ever given for a printed book at a public auction. He was sure that this fact alone would generate sufficient interest to raise the extra cash. However such was not to be the case. Yale ruefully imagined that it had lost its *Bay Psalm Book*. Dr. Rosenbach, figuring that perhaps the actual possession of the book would help the University raise the balance, wrote to the school suggesting that he send the book—along with his check for $49,900—receiving in return a Yale check for $151,000. In his letter Rosenbach mentioned that he was "not asking for any remuneration whatsoever," meaning only, of course, that he would not charge his usual commission.

After Yale had its book, letters began to pour into the good Doctor's office praising him for his magnificent "gift" to the college. It soon became evident that the balance was not going to be made up. From that point on, bitterness reigned, along with threats of law suits. Rosenbach never received his balance, and on the record he does stand as a benefactor of the University, albeit a reluctant one.

February 21

"I thank God," wrote Sir William Berkeley, royal governor of Virginia, in 1671, "*there are no free schools,* nor *printing* and I hope we shall not have, these hundred years; for learning has brought disobedience, and heresy and sects into the world, and *printing* has divulged them. . . . God keep us from both!"

In such a climate, the First Colony necessarily had to do without a press long after Massachusetts had introduced the art in 1639. In 1682, when Lord Culpeper had replaced Berkeley, a merchant named John Buckner, bringing a printer—William Nuthead—and a press to Jamestown, proceeded to prepare an edition of session laws. The Virginia Council took umbrage at this act, meeting on February 21 to upbraid both Buckner and Nuthead. The record of that meeting follows:

"At a Councell held att James Citty February 21: 1682/3. . . . Mr. John Buckner being by his Excellency Thomas Lord Culpeper ordered to appear this day before him & the Councell to answer for his presumption, in printing the acts of Assembly made in James Citty in November, 1682, and several other papers, without lycence, acquainted this board, that he several times commanded the Printer not to let anything whatever passe his presse, before he had obtained his Excellencies lycence, and that noe acts of assembly are yet printed, only two sheetes, wch were designed to be presented to his Excellency for his approbation of the print: This board having seriously considered, what the said Mr. John Buckner has said, in his defence, are well satisfied therewith, but for prevention of all troubles and inconveniences, that may be occasioned thorow the liberty of a presse, doe hereby order that Mr. John Buckner and William

Nulhead [sic] the Printer enter into bond of one hundred pounds sterling with good security, that from and after the date thereof, nothing be printed by either of them, or any others for them of what nature soever, in the aforesaid presse or any other in this Colony, until the signification of his Maj'ties pleasure shall be known therein, which his Excellency hath promised to acquaint his Majesty with."

The following September the Virginia Council order was transmitted to the Lords of Trade in England, who decided that printing be prohibited in the Colony.

Such stringent requirements effectively halted the establishment of a press in Virginia until 1730 when Williams Parks set up a printing office in Williamsburg after leaving Annapolis in the neighboring colony of Maryland. Printer Nuthead removed his press from Jamestown and began printing in St. Mary's City, Maryland, in 1685, being the first printer in that colony.

that the time is not far distant, when the *employer* and the *employed* will vie with each other, the one in *allowing* a competent salary, the other in *deserving* it. Under these impressions we submit the following prices to your decision:

COMPOSITION

Per week, not less than	$8.00
Every 1000 m's, from Brevier to English, inclusive	25
Common Rule or Figure Work	50

PRESSWORK

Per week, not less than	$8.00
All paper below medium, per token . .	30
Ditto above medium	37½
Broadsides, per token	75
Cards, per pack	12½
A single pack of cards	30
All small jobs	30

George White, President
John Childs, Vice-President
William Little, Secretary"

February 22

On this day in 1802 the Philadelphia Typographical Society presented a list of rates which printers expected to receive from their employers for the various classes of work. The Society had been formed that year as a benevolent and trade group. It exists in that capacity at the present time and is the oldest of the craft associations. The list of prices stated:

"Sir: 'Philadelphia Typographical Society,' takes the liberty to furnish you with their *List of Prices.* We hope that we shall be indulged with at least a candid examination of our demands. . . . We presume you are not unacquainted with many of them. We would wish to be placed on a footing, at least, with mechanics . . . our wages have, in no instance, kept pace with them. We have the merit of not being the most dissatisfied, and in no one instance of demanding anything unjust. We have, in the following statement, confined ourselves to what a majority of the employers in this city give. Our object is, to have one uniform price established. In doing this, we shall act as men towards men. . . . No person will leave his employ until he has given a reasonable notice. . . . In return, we expect that your conduct towards us will be equally candid. Indeed, we cherish a hope,

February 23

"John Howard Benson died on February 23, 1956, in Newport, Rhode Island, where he had spent all the fifty-four and a half years of his life. Artist, calligrapher, sculptor, scholar, and humanist, he was unquestionably America's leading designer of incised letters."

Thus begins the short biography of Benson, written by his friend Philip Hofer, and published by the Typophiles in 1957. In an age when classic craftsmanship, in any field, is on the ebb, it is most unfortunate that such a person as John Howard Benson should be so quickly forgotten. His name appears on the title page of but two books and one pamphlet. *The Elements of Lettering,* written in 1940 with Arthur G. Carey was first printed by Daniel B. Updike's Merrymount Press and is one of the finest books on lettering to be written in this country.

In his second book, Benson performed a service which had been waiting for over four hundred years, the first translation into English of *The First Writing Book* written in 1527 by Ludovico degli Arrighi. It is curious that the original of this little book, known and admired for so long a period, had never before been translated, even in the revival of interest in calligraphy which followed the contributions made by Edward Johnston, in England, in the early years of the century.

Benson's translation, which occupied the last three years of his life, was a great deal more than a simple copying job. It was his desire to make an exact reproduction of the original, and further, to make it available in an inexpensive edition which would serve to enlarge the influence of such a splendid work. "The aim of this book," he wrote in his introduction, "is to help those who wish to reform their handwriting." Benson's translation follows the exact page for page structure of the original, an extremely difficult, as well as laborious, task, making it necessary to rewrite certain pages as frequently as twenty times in order to capture the feeling of the Italian writing master.

February 24

In the city of Providence, Rhode Island, Daniel Berkeley Updike was born upon this day in 1860. With no practical background as a printer, he was destined to become one of the great American printers, and with no formal education as such, to become an outstanding scholar of printing, responsible for the revival of interest in the history of typography which took place forty years ago.

"Printing became the occupation of my life by pure accident," Updike wrote as the opening statement in *Notes on the Merrymount Press and Its Work,* published by Harvard University Press in 1934. When he was twenty, a friend of his family secured a job for him as errand boy with the Boston publishing firm, Houghton, Mifflin & Company. After a few months he went on a short vacation, determining not to return, as he liked nothing about the job. He was, however, asked to come back. He was then given slightly more responsibility, working with the advertising manager in the writing and designing of the firm's advertisements.

For a period of twelve years Updike held this position. He took time out for two European trips with his mother, one of which was of a year's duration. During this period he acquired an intimate knowledge of the publishing field, meeting such literary luminaries as Longfellow, Howells, and Dr. Holmes. He was beginning to have ideas of his own, however, and wished to have some measure of independence. He was also becoming deeply involved in the affairs of the Episcopal Church of America, an enthusiasm which was later to mean, according to his biographer, George Parker Winship, "more to him personally than even his world-wide reputation."

In 1893 Updike left Houghton, Mifflin & Company, and set himself up as a typographic adviser, or middleman between the customer and the printer. Naturally enough, he found that there were many frustrations in such a position. The solution was to perform his own printing. For this purpose the Merrymount Press was born, becoming one of the truly great printing offices on the American continent.

February 25

In a letter to the editor of the *Press News* on this date in 1893, William Morris, proprietor of the Kelmscott Press, substantiated what he had said to a representative of the London *Daily Chronicle* when pressed for his views upon printing and the current state of the art in England and across the Atlantic in America. In reply to a question Morris stated, "Taking the worst view of English printing, we are far ahead of other countries. Here and there in France nice type may be in use, but not often, and now there are one or two good fonts in Germany. Italy has the worst printing in Europe, and as for American printing, it is quite abominable."

Apparently believing that Morris had been incorrectly quoted, the editor had written for further confirmation. The reply follows: "Dear Sir,—I *do* think the American printing the worst from the point of view of good taste. Of course I am aware that there are technical matters in which the American printers excel; but what is the use of that, if the result is ugly books very trying to the eyes? I am, dear sir, yours very truly, William Morris."

The Inland Printer editorialized with some acerbity, that "it ain't so!" "Mr. William Morris is a man of taste, so far as books are concerned," wrote the editor of IP. "The productions of his fad, the Kelmscott Press, evidence this. Yet we are at a loss to know what has induced this condemnation of American printing—insular prejudice, to which Mr. Morris should be superior, or ignorance of the subject—which is to say, Mr. William Morris is not well enough acquainted with American work to pass an opinion. It may be quite true that we do not subscribe so generously as the British public for the superb publications in which Mr. Morris and other book connoisseurs delight, but this class of book-lovers is increasing in America, and the quality of some of the work produced in this country to gratify this growing taste will not take a lower rank than the best. . . .

"First class work is far more general in America than in any country in the world. Specimens received from every country in the globe convince us of this. In simplicity and effectiveness the work of the American printer cannot be surpassed, and the taste of the American public demands that all periodicals and newspapers sustain a degree of typographical beauty which our British cousins generally are ignorant of. In thus writing we are dealing with facts of which we have positive knowledge. Indeed, it requires but a moment's reflection to stamp the assertion of Mr. Morris as in every way ridiculous, though it is charitable to assume that he intended to characterize only as 'abominable' the American printing that *he* had *seen*."

February 26

In the city of Munich, Germany on February 26, 1834 there died in moderate circumstances in his sixty-third year, a former actor-dramatist named Alois Senefelder, the inventor of the printing process called lithography.

The son of an actor of the Theatre Royal in Munich, Senefelder was sent to the university of Ingolstadt to study jurisprudence, but the death of his father left him with insufficient capital to complete his studies. The young man thereupon became an actor himself and also began the production of several plays, one of which was honored with a performance and was issued in printed form. After an unsuccessful attempt to establish himself as a dramatist, he decided instead to become an author.

He soon learned that he would have to publish his books himself, so he secured the services of a printer for this purpose. This individual was so high-priced that Senefelder quickly found himself in financial straits and decided to do his own printing. Lack of funds prompted him to make his own type.

When he found that this was impractical he experimented with copperplate engraving. Again he was discouraged by the high cost of the copper plates. Not to be daunted, he next tried to letter on a slab of stone which he had bought as a surface for mixing ink, with the basic idea of utilizing it merely to practice his lettering. He quickly learned that the limestone was easier to work with than copper. There then occurred the historic accident which led directly to the discovery of lithography. Senefelder later described it:

"I had just succeeded in my little laboratory in polishing a stone plate, which I intended to cover with etching ground, in order to continue my exercises in writing backwards, when my mother entered the room, and desired me to write her a bill for the washerwoman, who was waiting for the linen. I happened not to have the smallest slip of paper at hand; nor was there a drop of ink in the inkstand. As the matter would not admit delay, and we had nobody in the house to send for a supply of the deficient materials, I resolved to write the list with my ink, prepared with wax, soap, and lamp black, on the stone which I had just polished, and from which I could copy it at leisure. Some time after this I was just going to wipe this writing from the stone, when the idea all at once struck me to try what would be the effect of such writing with my prepared ink, if I were to bite in the stone with aquafortis and whether, perhaps, it might not be possible to apply printing ink to it the same way as wood engravings, and so take impressions from it. I hastened to put this idea in execution, surrounded the stone with a border of wax, and covered the surface of the stone to a height of two inches, with a mixture of one part of aquafortis and ten parts of water, which I left standing five minutes on it; and on examining the effect of this experiment, I found the writing elevated about the tenth part of a line, or a hundred and twentieth part of an inch. . . ."

Thus, in the year 1796, was a new printing craft born.

February 27

Johann Fust, a money-lender of Mainz who had been a partner of Johann Gutenberg in the establishment of the world's finest printing office, died in Paris on this day in 1466, whence he had gone to sell printed bibles. He was probably the victim of a plague which swept that city during that year. Fust has never been dealt with sympathetically by printing historians, and there appears to be some justification for such treatment. Inventors have traditionally been troubled by a lack of finances. Of course the bankers who have loaned them money have suffered in public opinion whenever they have attempted to protect their investments when endangered by impractical innovators.

The original agreement between Fust and Gutenberg, signed in 1450, stated that the partnership was to be for a period of five years, during which period the work projected by the inventor should be completed. Fust advanced 800 guilders at 6 per cent interest with Gutenberg's tools and materials to be mortgaged as security for this sum. When these tools should be made and the materials (undoubtedly the types) manufactured, the banker was to furnish an additional 300 guilders every year to pay for the paper, vellum, ink, wages, and other supplies which would be required for the execution of the work. For all of this, Fust was to have one-half of the profits ensuing from the sale of the products of the partnership and was to be exempt from the performance of any work or service connected with the partnership. In addition he was not to be held responsible for any of its debts.

But, like most inventors, Gutenberg was delighted only to be free of financial worries so that he could devote his entire energies to the problems at hand. He was confident that his project would be so highly successful that the revenues would completely satisfy the money-lender. He had already cast the types to produce a bible, each page of which was to contain 36 lines. Fust insisted, however, that such a book would be too costly to produce and it became necessary for Gutenberg to cut a new font of type, which allowed for a more economic job of production. Thus the final fruition of his hopes was delayed. The situation was not at all helped when Fust told him that the 800 guilders could not be paid at once. In fact, he waited for two years before making the payment.

With costs mounting, Gutenberg was soon in trouble. He readily agreed when Fust rewrote the contract to commute the 300 guilders for the three successive years and to pay 800 guilders immediately. Meanwhile production problems delayed the completion of the bible. Fust brought suit, in November of 1455, for the recovery of his money. It would seem that Fust had planned to embarrass the inventor, as he gave no previous warning of his resort to a legal proceeding. His future son-in-law, Peter Schoeffer, was already employed in the printing office and fully competent to continue the work on the bible without the inventor.

The money-lender won his suit and was awarded all the materials made by Gutenberg for the common profit. Apparently this was all that he desired, as there is no record of his asking for the return of the money loaned, which he could very well have done, as was his legal right. There is of course little likelihood that any additional details of the Fust-Gutenberg partnership will come to light, so depending upon the viewpoint of the contemporary reader, one or the other of the two men was a contemptible villain.

February 28

The colophon of a private press book which was completed in Pittsburgh on this date in 1926 reads:

"Here endeth (paradoxically) 'That Endeth Never,' written by Hildegarde Flanner as a gift for Porter Garnett and now embellished and put into type by him, at the Laboratory Press, for her and a few of their common and uncommon friends. Printed on a hand press, with prayer & song, by his faithful students, Joseph Arnold Foster & George Earl Sheer. Finished on the twenty-eighth day of February MDCCCCXXVI."

The manuscript of this book was a gift, and the printed copies were to be gifts. For these reasons and also because it was completed in the fifty-fifth year of his life and was the first to be set in type completely by his own hand, Porter Garnett expressed the wish that "no copy of this book shall ever be bought, sold or bartered."

The volume thus epitomizes the pure private press tradition along with the ideals of its printer. While it is surprising that after three years of teaching the course in fine printing at the Carnegie Institute of Technology, Porter Garnett had previously set no type, he most certainly inspired his students to do so. Their work at the Laboratory Press represents a definite contribution to the history of fine printing in the United States. While some of the student projects reproduced were examples of a preciosity beyond the years and experience of student printers, they represented in all instances first-rate craftsmanship in their execution.

Garnett's idealism in the teaching of the craft of printing was under constant attack by elements of the printing industry during his tenure in Pittsburgh. Nevertheless he continued along the path he had set for himself in 1922 when his course had first been projected. In the *Documentary Account of the Beginnings of the Laboratory Press,* published in 1927 "as an exercise in the technique of book printing," Garnett presented what he considered to be the reason for being of the press. In his introduction to the book, Garnett asked, "Will the students wish most to give or to get; to serve mankind or to exploit it?"

February 29

"The Printer to the Reader, Philadelphia, February 29, 1743/4." So began the colophon to *M. T. Cicero's Cato Major, or His Discourse on Old Age,* printed and published by Benjamin Franklin, and considered to be Franklin's finest effort as a printer. The colophon continued:

"This version of CICERO's Tract *de Senectute,* was made Ten Years since, by the Honourable and Learned Mr. LOGAN, of this City; undertaken partly for his own amusement, (being then in his 60th year, which is said to be nearly the Age of the Author when he wrote it) but principally for the Entertainment of a Neighbour then in his grand Climacteric; and the Notes were drawn up solely on that Neighbour's Account, who was not so well acquainted as himself with the Roman History and Language: Some other

Friends, however, (among whom I had the Honour to be ranked) obtained Copies of it in M.s. And, as I believed it to be in itself equal at least, if not far preferable to any other Translation of the same Piece Extant in our Language, besides the Advantage it has of so many valuable Notes, which at the same time they clear up the Text, are highly instructive and entertaining; I resolved to give it an Impression, being confident that the Publick would not unfavourably receive it.

"A certain Freed-man of Cicero's is reported to have said of a medicinal Well, discovered in his Time, wonderful for the Virtue of its Waters in restoring Sight to the Aged, *That it was a Gift of the bountiful Gods to Men, to the end that all might have the pleasure of reading his Master's Works.* As that Well, if still in being, is at too great a Distance for our Use, I have, *Gentle Reader,* as thou seest, printed this Piece of Cicero's in a large and fair Character, that those who begin to think upon the Subject of OLD-AGE, (which seldom happens till their Sight is somewhat impair'd by its Approaches) may not, in Reading, by the *Pain* small Letters give the Eyes, feel the *Pleasure* of the Mind in the least allayed."

Franklin's "large and fair Character" was truly just that. The introduction was set in 24-point type, and the text in 18-point, with footnotes in 12-point. Such a book represented a distinct departure from the editions of the classics then available, in which 10-point or even 8-point was not at all unusual for text composition.

Cato Major is recognized as one of the handsomest books produced in the American Colonies. Franklin's experiences as a compositor in one of the best London printing offices gave him an insight into fine bookmaking which was denied to most colonial printers. As a prosperous printer he also was in a position to do a prestige item, which might not necessarily be profitable.

March

March 1

On this day in 1837 was born a man who became one of the great literary critics of his time—William Dean Howells. Beginning as a compositor in his father's country printing office in Ohio, Howells received very little schooling. He is an outstanding example of the self-educated man. He served as U. S. Consul in Venice, became editor of the *Atlantic Monthly* 1871-81, and produced novels, plays, and books of criticism, his great book being *The Rise of Silas Lapham*. He received honorary degrees from many universities, and served as the first president of the American Academy of Arts and Letters.

Howells never quite forgot his early career as a country printer. In several essays of reminiscence, he wrote of such a life. His essay, *The Country Printer*, is one of the best accounts ever to be written of the life of such a printer in mid-19th century America.

Included in the essay is an amusing episode concerning the purchase of a steam press, with which to replace the hand press which had seen long years of service.

"We were very vain of that press, which replaced the hand press hitherto employed in printing the paper. This was of the style and make of the hand press which superseded the Ramage press of Franklin's time [actually the first Ramage Press was built after Franklin's death]; but it had been decided to signalize our new departure by the purchase of a power press of modern contrivance and of a speed fitted to meet the demands of a subscription list which might be indefinitely extended. A deputation of the leading politicians accompanied the editor to New York, where he went to choose the machine, and where he bought a second-hand Adams press of the earliest pattern and patent. I do not know, or at this date I would not undertake to say, just what principle governed his selection of this superannuated veteran; it seems not to have been very cheap; but possibly he had a prescience of the disabilities which were to task his ingenuity to the very last days of the press.

"Certainly no man of less gift and skill could have coped with its infirmities, and I am sure that he thoroughly enjoyed nursing it into such activity as carried it hysterically through those far-off publication days. It had obscure functional disorders of various kinds, so that it would from time to time cease to act, and would have to be doctored by the poor pressman before it would go on. There was probably some organic trouble, too, for, though it did not really fall to pieces on our hands, it showed itself incapable of profiting by several improvements which he invented, and could, no doubt, have successfully applied to the press if its constitution had not been undermined.

"It went with a crank set in a prodigious fly-wheel which revolved at a great rate, till it came to the moment of making an impression, when the whole mechanism was seized with such a reluctance as nothing but an heroic effort at the crank could overcome. It finally made so great a draught upon our forces that it was decided to substitute steam for muscles in its operation, and we got a small engine which could fully sympathize with the press in having seen better days. . . . What is certain is that, somehow, the engine and the press did always get us through publication day, and not only with safety, but often with credit; so that not long ago, when I was at home, and my brother and I were looking over an old file of his paper, we found it much better printed than either of us expected; as well printed, in fact, as if it had been done on an old hand press, instead of the steam-power press which it vaunted the use of."

March 2

The first United States patent for a power printing press was awarded on this date in 1826 to a silversmith turned inventor named Daniel Treadwell. This press, a bed-and-platen machine, was first produced about 1822 and was an improvement over the hand presses of the period, supplying as it did, power to make the impression in the place of the pressman's muscle. Both bed and platen were horizontal, making contact for the impression by the turning crank or by the use of horse power, or even as the inventor himself did, by water power.

Treadwell had earlier automated the hand press of the period by supplying a treadle to bring the platen down upon the form of type. He had built, in England, a number of such machines, one of which was owned by T. C. Hansard, who enthusiastically endorsed the press in his famous work, *Typographia*, published in London in 1825.

When the inventor found that printers in the United States were not receptive to his power machine, he established his own printing firm to put his presses to work. A short time later, the plant burned down, an act of sabotage, according to Ringwalt in his *Encyclopedia of Printing*, by "hand-pressmen, who were intensely hostile to his invention."

Probably Treadwell's most important contribution to printing was the invention of the revolving ink-disc, without which the later development of the platen press would have been delayed. This disc was included in the inking mechanism for his power press. The revolving principle was responsible for the higher speed and efficiency of the Gordon

platen press over the earlier platens with a fixed ink plate. It was Gordon who added the additional feature of the disc within a disc which is still an important part of the inking mechanism of the standard platen presses.

Treadwell's inventive genius, however, soon removed him from most contacts with printers. The rest of his long and productive life was devoted to other industries. He patented a hemp-spinning machine which was used all over the world; later he developed a procedure for manufacturing that important 19th century instrument, the military cannon. Internationally honored as a man of science, he died in Cambridge, Massachusetts in 1872.

March 3

The Library of Congress was assured of continous growth by an enactment of the Congress on March 3, 1865 which required that one copy of each work copyrighted in the United States was to be deposited in the library within one month of the date of publication. The same act extended protection to photographs and negatives. A few years later the Act of 1870 included works of art and further stipulated that the Librarian of Congress be appointed Copyright Officer, in which office he was to receive a printed title page of every single book prior to its publication, and two copies of the complete book within ten days of publication. By 1964 the Copyright Office employed 254 people, who handled as many as 279,000 copyright registrations in a year. The Library of Congress had grown to be a repository which contained almost forty-four million items.

While American authors were protected by law and were quite well satisfied with the provisions of the Copyright Act, the situation was a great deal different for European writers, particularly those who wrote in English. These people suffered the widespread pirating of their works in this country during most of the 19th century. Continuous denunciation of American practices in the reprinting of literature came from outraged English authors and the literate segment of the population in the United States who argued for the freedom of ideas on an international scale. But Congress could not be persuaded to pass necessary legislation to extend the copyright privilege.

During the early years of the American nation there was a continuing dependence upon European sources for books. American printers were eager to reprint everything which came their way, especially if there was any possibility of a profit. When the publishing industry was making a tentative start, it, too, began to show no reluctance to place an imprint on the product of any European writer who was popular in America. One group of Philadelphia publishers when asked to present their case, claimed that "Thought, when given to the world, is as light, free for all."

The publishers were in great measure aided by the attitude of the printing crafts, the printers, the papermakers, typefounders, stereotypers, bookbinders, etc., all of whom felt that American copyright of the work of foreigners would flood the American market with books printed overseas. Such an attitude delayed until 1891 the enactment of an international copyright law. The Chance Act of that year provided that a foreign book had to be printed in the United States in order to be protected by the copyright. In 1955 American membership in the Universal Copyright Convention was finally ratified, but an amendment provided that only fifteen hundred copies of an original work of an American citizen could be imported without loss of copyright.

March 4

On March 4, 1921, Warren Gamaliel Harding was inaugurated as the twenty-ninth President of the United States. Upon his nomination the previous summer, he was referred to in the trade press as "Our Printer President," the first presidential nominee to be so honored.

"Senator Harding is practical in every department of the newspaper game," said George H. Van Fleet, Managing Editor of the Marion (Ohio) Star, which was owned by Harding. "He is an easy editorial writer, a strikingly good reporter; he knows the business of the mechanical department, is a cracker-jack publicity seller and a fine ad writer; and thoroughly at home in any place you may put him, either in the business,

news, editorial or mechanical departments of a plant."

To which The American Printer, in which this panegyric appeared, practically said "Amen," stating editorially, "A man who does all these things cannot but be a great President."

As a boy, Harding had learned to set type during a summer job. After deciding that the study of law was beyond his intellectual resources, he and a friend purchased for a few hundred dollars the Star, a weekly newspaper. At nineteen years of age the young editor was started upon a career which led to the White House. After marrying the daughter of the richest man in town, Harding made the Star a daily. Its editor became the most important person in Marion. While Harding enjoyed newspaper work more than anything else, he allowed his friends to promote him for the state Senate. Of this predilection to be easily swayed, his father had once said to him, "It's a good thing you wasn't born a girl, because you'd be in the family way all the time. You can't say no."

From the state Senate, Harding was elected Lieutenant Governor of Ohio and then United States Senator. Even with these responsibilities he "kept his hand in" on the paper. A friend had occasion to call upon him in Marion during his tenure in the Senate. He was amazed to find the Senator in the composing room, helping to make up the paper because the shop was short-handed. His fellow comps told the visitor that the Senator could "lift twice as much metal as the average stone man."

While in Indiana on a speaking engagement, Harding went into a printing office and asked for a job as a linotype operator. After the Senator had set a galley of type, the foreman offered to recommend him to the proprietor, whereupon Harding presented him with a calling card listing himself as a United States Senator from Ohio.

After Harding's nomination to the presidency, the printing organizations were quick to "honor" him. The Richmond (Va.) Club of Printing House Craftsmen inducted him as an honorary member. On January 10, 1921, he became an honorary member of Marion Typographical Union No. 675. In his acceptance speech upon the latter occasion, Harding told the members that labor must weed out the slackers in its ranks if the present scale of wages was to be maintained.

43

He also mentioned that during the campaign it had been erroneously reported that he was a member of the printer's union. "And I never denied it," he said.

March 5

In a letter written to the editor of *The American Printer* on this day in 1921, a printer from Pittsburgh tried to express his attitude toward his work. Undoubtedly the personal philosophy of James E. Creech has been matched by countless other printers who remain completely anonymous, particularly in the days when men accepted simpler standards and were given to expressing themselves in less prosaic terms than at present.

"These are the words of a printer," the letter began. "These are the thoughts of one who, being incapable of adding to the wealth of worthwhile literature, has found pleasure in reproducing for the benefit of the readers and thinkers of the world the gems of thought which have been expressed by the inspired masters of the universe.

"Where there has been one masterpiece of art it has been my privilege, my pleasure and my ambition to reproduce thousands of copies. It has been a duty as well as an interesting pleasure to attempt in every case a reproduction as near the warmth and beauty of the original as the pigments, oils and varnishes of today would permit. How well I have succeeded in my ambitions and my efforts is of little concern to those who will read these words. I must say, however, that I have not had time to get tired of work. It has been interesting and I have not had time to acquire a store of worldly goods, nor have I had time to hate or let jealousy become part of my makeup. . . .

"I suppose the reader is beginning to wonder what am I driving at—what is the object of this discussion. As explained in the beginning, I am not capable of adding to the wealth of the world's literature. This is not intended as a treatise on printing. It is not intended as a word picture to be hung before the eyes of men for the inspiration of their minds; it is the simple expression of the thoughts of a printer. . . .

"The true printer—the one who is a printer at heart—is so wrapped up in his work, he is so contented and so busy creating master-pieces of his art and reproducing master-pieces of others' art that he is seldom bothered by a craving for worldly goods. I know I will be accused of being a dreamer. Are not all printers dreamers? Where is the person who can go to the case or the press and create a masterpiece of typography or a work of real art unless he has previously gazed into vacancy and perceived in all its glory the beauty he aspires to match in his product? Have not all men in the past, locked in prisons, gazed through solid walls and seen the rarest beauty of open fields and rich meadows?

"Yes, you must be a dreamer to be a real printer, but don't confuse the terms 'dreamer' and 'sleeper.' Dreams of real worth come only to those who are wide awake. Dream on, ye printers, and may all your dreams result in work of real value to the Art Preservative—but as you dream don't fall asleep."

March 6

The British periodical, *The Printer's Register,* dated on this day in 1868, contained the following item: "The Typos and Artemus Ward—*The Chicago Evening Journal* says that the National Typographical Union at its session in Washington, adopted a resolution directing that the funds now in the hands of the late secretary and treasurer, collected for the Artemus Ward fund, be transferred to the secretary and treasurer of the National Typographical Union, and by them invested in United States bonds. They also favorably considered the proposition of the Milwaukee Union, that the monument, when erected, be built of type metal, but took no action thereupon."

Charles F. Browne, who had a short but spectacular career as an American humorist in the years just prior to and during the Civil War under the name of Artemus Ward, would have been happy indeed to know that he was to be immortalized in type metal. Probably, too, had he lived in the present time he would not have changed a name like Charley Browne to anything else. As Charley Browne, aged thirteen, he apprenticed himself to the compositor's case in the office of the *Weekly Democrat* in the White Mountain town of Lancaster, New Hampshire. In addition to setting type, he learned to write news items and to perform every other responsibility pertinent to a country weekly. After working with several such publications, Browne spent three years in Boston at the printing trade. At the age of eighteen, he published his first real literary production in the Boston *Carpet Bag.* He then wandered westward in the tradition of his craft, "hoping," he said, "to get as far as China."

Browne's Asiatic adventure ended in Cleveland, where he received his chance to write humorous articles for the *Plain Dealer* at ten dollars a week. It was then that he adopted the name of Artemus Ward. He was an immediate success as a newspaper columnist and was soon in great demand on the lecture circuit. Here he hit his stride, becoming one of the most sought after comics of his time. Since in appearance he resembled—in fact was almost a caricature of—the typical New England Yankee, his satirical sketches were the rage in every part of the country. Constance Rourke, in her work on American humor, says of Ward, "His long countenance was always dull and impassive as he talked. Everything he said seemed unstudied; his best lines were uttered with hesitation as if they were afterthoughts of which he was hardly sure. Yet his lectures and newspaper squibs had the outline, close and unobtrusive, which belonged to the best of the Yankee tradition."

Abraham Lincoln admired Ward's brand of humor. At his cabinet meeting of September 22, 1862, the President read aloud the humorist's "High Outrage in Utica," laughing uproariously "amid the anxious silence of his advisers, and then, with a sigh, opened and read the draft of the Emancipation Proclamation."

After lecturing in every part of the country, Ward went to England in June, 1866, becoming even more popular there than he had been at home, appearing on the platform and writing for *Punch.* Early in 1867 he developed tuberculosis and died in Southampton in March of that year in his thirty-third year.

March 7

"This book has been a conspiracy. Building it has been an adventure, an experience, a headache and a pleasure . . . mixed up day by day." So wrote Paul A. Bennett in the introduction of a book put together for a single purpose, presentation to Frederic W. Goudy on this day in 1935, the eve of his seventieth birthday.

The book, called *Spinach From Many Gardens,* was the first publishing effort of the Typophiles, a group described by the late Paul McPharlin as "Paul Bennett surrounded by a body of printing enthusiasts." Since the early Thirties this group—held together by Bennett's personality—has met for lunch on Wednesdays in a variety of different locations. This happy company is composed of printers and others who are especially fond of matters typographical and as such it has represented a haven for visiting firemen of that persuasion who find themselves in New York upon a Wednesday.

The idea of producing this first Typophile volume was first presented at a luncheon meeting on February 6th. Just one month later some twenty-two signatures had been written, printed by the same number of presses, and bound into a book, together with a title page by Bruce Rogers. None of the subsequent books produced by the group have been completed with such dispatch, but all have represented the same labor of love approach.

Upon the completion of *Spinach,* three additional books and two portfolios were turned out before it was decided to adopt a standard size of 4½ x 7 inches and to number each volume. Through 1966, this program has resulted in the publication of forty-three Chap Books, as they are called, in addition to numerous Monographs contributed by individual members. There is no regular publication date, which makes the arrival of a Typophile "package" an event to be remembered by most of the fortunate members.

The subject matter of the series is as varied as the specialties of the members. Many of the titles are books which are just not commercially practicable, no matter how worthwhile they may be individually. Included are books about early American currency, calligraphy, type design, etc., in addition to collected essays of such well-known writers as W. A. Dwiggins, Carl P. Rollins, and Lawrence C. Wroth. Biography has been covered with accounts of Baskerville, Bruce Rogers, John Howard Benson, W. A. Dwiggins, Elmer Adler, and others. The famous autobiography of Frederic W. Goudy appeared as a two-volume work, *A Half Century of Type Design and Typography, 1895-1945,* published in 1946.

Paul Bennett wrote a lively account of the Typophile publishing program for *The Penrose Annual, 1960,* to which, without his knowledge, a footnote was added, written by Joseph Blumenthal: ". . . and Paul Bennett failed to mention the name of the one person who made the whole project start, continue, and thrive. That person conceives the books, he wet-nurses them, he nourishes and worries and licks them into form (like the bears in the old Bestiaries), he humors the printer, the papermaker and the binder into begging to do these books, he wraps them up and carries them to the post office, collects a pittance from subscribers, and so on and so on into the long hours of the night."

March 8

Born on this day in 1865 in Bloomington, Illinois, Frederic W. Goudy lived to be the best known American printer of his times. He achieved international renown as a letterer, a type designer, and a typographer. He was also the operator of a most distinguished private press, the Village Press.

Fred Goudy came late to his great career. He was thirty-three years of age before he decided that the printer's art was the one he most desired to follow. In 1899 he had already designed his first type, Camelot, for the Dickinson Type Foundry of Boston. He had also dabbled in lettering and advertising design, at the same time becoming more and more disillusioned with his vocation of bookkeeper.

When he established himself in Chicago as a free-lance designer, he knew merely that he was drawn toward the practice of typography. From that time on, nothing occurred to make him change his mind. He obtained a post as instructor in lettering at the Frank Holme School of Illustration and provided inspiration to such future greats as Bill Dwiggins, Oz Cooper and Will Ransom. With Will Ransom in 1903 he set up the Village Press in Park Ridge, Illinois. For the next forty years it was to be a motivating factor in his life in such locations as Hingham, Massachusetts, New York City, and Marlborough-on-Hudson.

In 1897 he married Bertha Sprinks. She was to stand at his side in all of his endeavors, particularly the Village Press, until her death in 1935. Goudy's career as a type designer began in earnest in 1910 when he designed a type for the setting of a book by H. G. Wells, *The Door in the Wall,* published by Mitchell Kennerley, for whom the type was named. Kennerley was followed by an inscriptional roman font called Forum. Both of these types were widely admired in the United States and in Europe.

In 1915 he designed for the American Type Founders Company a face which was called Goudy Old Style. It became an immediate commercial success. There was so much demand for this letter that the foundry issued such variants as a bold face and an extra-bold, in addition to an inline version called hand-tooled; in none of these, however, did Goudy have a hand. And of course he received no royalties, even though the series carried his name. Until 1944 scarcely a year was to pass without the introduction of a new Goudy type, many of which were produced by Lanston Monotype Company.

Goudy was completely individualistic as a type designer. He drew all of his letters freehand. From time to time Lanston found it necessary to change some of the characteristics of his letters to conform to the mechanics of matrix manufacture. In order to be completely free of such interference, Goudy set up his own Village Letter Foundery, in which he could control every step of manufacture. Thus, he suffered a complete disaster when in 1939 his workshop burned, destroying everything which he had created during the preceding fifteen years — drawings, matrices, type, and equipment. The types which he himself sold had had a relatively narrow distribution. Now they were gone forever. At the age of seventy-four he found it necessary to begin all over again. This he almost immediately proceeded to do.

Goudy was an inspired drawer of roman letters. His inspiration was the Italian 15th century letterform. He was constantly attempting to execute the most perfect roman type based on the classic examples. In his search, he was not at all commercial, as he refused to take the time to cut a variety of sizes in each type which he designed. As soon as a design was completed, his mind was visualizing improvements, and he was off on a new search for his ideal.

Throughout his long career he designed 123 types, most of which are in the category of "lost Goudy types." He never designed a letter for the manufacturers of line-casting machines, although his Goudy O.S. has been adapted for that use. His book types were all cut for use with the monotype machine. Fortunately a number of these are still available, such as Garamont, Deepdene, Italian Old Style, Kennerley, Goudy Modern, Californian, Village No. 2, etc.

Goudy was in the tradition of the great type designers of history. He spent a great deal of his time writing and lecturing about typography, providing further inspiration for knowledge and understanding of the craft of the printer. His death in 1947 at the age of eighty-two brought to an end his personal involvement, but many of his types will undoubtedly speak in his name for generations to come.

March 9

A slyly inserted item appeared in the *New York Tribune* under this date in 1868, concerning its rival, the *World:* "On Wednesday night the compositors of the *World* quarrelled over a 'fat take,' and during the row accidentally pied a 'saving galley,' containing the following words:—146 Grants, 122 drunken louts, 40 Greeleys, 6,000 Tribunes, 1 Hiram Sidney, 22 trooly loils, 60 niggers, 38 Beast Butlers, 970 Hiram Ulysseses, 40 Uncle Simpsons, 10 Violated Constitutions, 6 Howling Radicals, 38 Freedmen's Bureaus, 70 Hang the *Heralds* (small caps), 1,000 Carpet-baggers, 52 Seymour, the patriot's; and several similar terms, all of which account for the unexampled decency of the *World* on Thursday morning."

Aside from the almost gleeful description of some of the more popular newspaper clichés of the period, the *Tribune's* account did uncover one of the practices of newspaper composing rooms in the days when all of the typesetting was done by hand; hence the attempt to save a few moments in the composition of a late "take" by saving the more commonly used phrases or names. Obviously, the "saving-galley" in any newspaper became a reasonably accurate record of the political persuasion and the personal idiosyncrasies of its editor.

While type preserved in this manner offered questionable economies, particularly if the compositor had to leave his frame, stick in hand, to search for the "saving-galley," the basic idea behind such an attempt to save time was not at all unique, there having been many such equally dubious approaches to speed up the typesetter's task. It is doubtful, however, if in the easy-going atmosphere of the large newspaper composing rooms there ever could have been popular acceptance of any procedure which the modern industry would term as quality control.

The paternal instinct of many newspaper editors, who themselves had worked at the case in their formative years, plus the brotherhood loyalties of the craft, contributed to a rather lax set of standards which would have been much less acceptable in the more competitive commercial printing establishments. A popular anecdote, descriptive of such ideal working conditions, circulated among newspaper printers as late as a half century ago. It concerns a conversation between two compositors on the *New York World,* about the year 1910. A tall gangling comp, clutching a sheet of copy, stopped a fellow comp, who was purposefully striding by also accoutred with composing stick, copy, and the inevitable cheekful of chewing tobacco. The first comp shifted his chaw and inquired, "Say, Mac, where's the 48 Chelt? I've been lookin' for it all morning."

His fellow comp stopped, and squirted a well-aimed stream into the nearest cuspidor. "Hell," he said, "I'm damned if l know. I've been lookin' for the 72 Caslon for six months!"

March 10

"Hearing/Before the/Committee on the Library/House of Representatives/Seventy-first Congress / Second Session / on / H.R. 6147/A bill authorizing the Secretary of the Treasury to pay to the Joint Committee on the Library the sum of $1,500,000 for the purchase of the collection of three thousand incunabula to be deposited in the Library of Congress and known as the Herbert Putnam Collection of Incunabula/March 10, 1930."

So reads the title page of the hearing at which the Library of Congress acquired a magnificent collection of incunabula, including the finest copy of the Gutenberg Bible extant.

Dr. Otto H. F. Vollbehr of Berlin, a book-speculator, had taken an option on the parchment copy of the Gutenberg Bible owned by the Benedictine monastery of St. Paul, in Carinthia, Austria. He had also put together a huge collection of incunabula, which together with a Bible, he offered to the Library of Congress for $1,500,000. It was an exceedingly risky venture. Congressional action would be necessary, and the whims of the legislators when it came to purchasing books for the national library were notorious.

Congress had haggled over the acquisition of the great Thomas Jefferson library and also of the George Washington papers. It had refused to buy Washington's library, which had been sold in London in 1844, although it was later returned to the United States and placed in the library of the Boston Athenaeum. It had lost in the same manner the original manuscript of Washington's Farewell Address. The great library of the historian George Bancroft, consisting of almost twenty thousand books and manuscripts pertaining to American history, had also been turned down by the Congress. Vollbehr was therefore concerned when his speculation finally reached the halls of Congress. He was then so desperate for cash that he approached the great American book dealer A. S. W. Rosenbach for help. Dr. Rosenbach assisted him by taking an option on Vollbehr's option of the St. Catherine copy of the Gutenberg Bible

The Hon. Ross A. Collins, Representative from the State of Mississippi, presented the bill to the House on February 7th, in a lengthy speech in which he traced the history of the Library of Congress and extolled the Vollbehr collection, buttressed by statements by most of the outstanding bookmen and librarians of the country. He ended his dissertation, saying:

"An unusual occasion is now offered to Congress to acquire a wonderful collection of 15th century printing, and at the same time to honor our librarian [Henry Putnam] for his thirty years of distinguished service. This is our last chance to have a copy of the Gutenberg Bible in the Library. It is conceded by all that such an opportunity will never come again. If these books go back to Europe they will be disposed of at auction, and few, if any, will find their way to the Library of Congress. It is a matter of grave doubt if the foreign governments will ever allow another Gutenberg Bible to leave their borders. These cradle books, representing, as they do, the earliest efforts of culture, thought, and printing should be preserved and kept by the United States Government for the people of America."

The minutes of the hearing filled some 61 pages of testimony, and the bill was reported out. Both the House and the Senate passed it unanimously. President Hoover signed it immediately, making it possible for generations of Americans to view the finest known copy of the great Bible of Johann Gutenberg.

March 11

"The rush of office-seekers upon the departments exceeds anything of the kind ever before known. From all morning till late in the evening, Uncle Abe and each of the members of the cabinet are beset by men, women and children."

So said the Baltimore *Sun* of this date in 1861. It was describing Washington where voters of the good Republic wished to cash in on their loyalty to the winning ticket, in this case, the administration of Abraham Lincoln, just one week in office. There was another event on March 4, besides a presidential inauguration and news of Southern secession. That was the opening of a new government bureau called the Government Printing Office. It was very likely, then, that many of those individuals importuning the Congress for employment during that busy and exciting week were printers.

The previous year, on June 23rd, President Buchanan had signed into law the organic printing act which stated, in part:

"[No. 25] Joint Resolution in Relation to the Public Printing.

"Resolved by the Senate and House of Representatives of the United States of America in Congress Assembled, That the Superintendent of Public Printing be, and is hereby, authorized and directed to have executed the printing and binding authorized by the Senate and House of Representatives, the executive and judicial departments and the Court of Claims. And to enable him to carry out the provisions of this act, he is authorized and directed to contract for the erection or purchase of the necessary buildings, machinery, and materials for that purpose, said contract to be subject to the approval of the Joint Committee on Printing of the two Houses of Congress: *Provided,* That the sum so contracted to be paid shall not exceed one hundred fifty thousand dollars."

At the end of 1861, John D. Defrees, the Superintendent of Public Printing, reported to the Congress that the new office had produced $550,887 of government printing, at a saving of some $60,000. The office employed 350 compositors, pressmen, bookbinders, and laborers.

The establishment of a government printing office had been a most controversial proceeding. For sixty years there had been congressional suggestions, resolutions, and investigations concerning the manner of executing printing for the government. A number of different methods had been tried out. Generally, both the Senate and the House had contracted separately for printing, but there had also been schemes in which the printing went to the lowest bidder. The problem was not always that the outside printers were becoming rich with fat contracts. Often enough the printers lost a great deal of money themselves due to their inability to cope with the delivery requirements of the Congress, which made unique demands upon its printers.

A hundred years after its establishment, the GPO has grown considerably, reporting for 1964 6,998 employees, and a total income for printing and binding services performed of $136,058,238. This is in startling contrast to the first report of the Public Printer, with its listing of but a half million dollar production in the first nine months of operation.

March 12

"There is no such thing nor can there be such a thing as 'the ideal book.' " So began an essay on the ideal book, written by Porter Garnett, of the School of Printing at Carnegie Institute of Technology and founder of the Laboratory Press. He was born on March 12, 1869 in San Francisco.

After a thirty-year career as editor and writer in the Bay area, Garnett went to Pitts-burgh to establish a course in fine printing. Here, according to Carl Rollins, "a selected group of young men, turning their back on the complexities of typesetting machines and printing machines, which clattered and whirred on the other side of the partition, worked diligently with hand-set type and hand press to produce a series of broadsides and folders 'as the old printers printed long ago.' "

When the Limited Editions Club offered a prize for the best essay on the ideal book, a distinguished jury consisting of Frederic W. Goudy, Mitchell Kennerley, Frederic G. Melcher, A. Edward Newton, and George Macy went through two hundred entries and agreed to present a joint prize to Garnett and Francis P. Dill. It turned out that Mr. Dill was one of Porter Garnett's students, which made the award unique.

Everything that Garnett stood for as a craftsman and as a teacher finds expression in his essay on the ideal book. The fact that he was a purist detracts not at all from what he set out to do and what he accomplished with the Laboratory Press. The students who took his course have since continued in their own professional lives the strong sense of idealism to which the closing years of Garnett's career were devoted.

"It is difficult," he wrote, "to declare oneself an advocate of fine printing or fine bookdesign without being misunderstood. Such a declaration, however, is not to arrogate superiority. It merely means that one believes in certain principles of craftsmanship and in upholding certain standards based upon a scrupulous and uncompromising observance of refinements and minutiae. . . .

"A fine book of the first order is the endresult of a sedulous effort on the part of designer, printer, and binder to bring to their artifact every care for physical and technical details, every revision in the interest of betterment, of which they are capable, to the end that the finished product shall represent the capacity of each for the fulfillment of his artistic wish, his desire for perfection. To slacken this effort, to compromise wittingly (or wilfully), to surrender to expediency, is to repudiate fineness of the first order. . . .

"It has not been my purpose in this paper to lay down the rules for making a fine book, for, after all, rules are of no use whatever (in an art or in a craft) except to be broken—wisely. . . . Let those who wish to compromise (with popular taste, with outlay and returns, with honesty, with self-respect, or with machinery) do so, but unless the thing they produce represents, with eloquence and beauty, the full and unconditional employment of *every realizable aid to betterment, physical and technical,* it is something other than a fine book of the first order. We must discourage ourselves in order that we may be strong."

March 13

On this day in 1895 a young man named Charles Harry St. John Hornby sat down to tea with William Morris, following an inspection of the Kelmscott Press at Hammersmith. The Press was then engaged in the printing of the great folio Chaucer. Just one year previously Hornby had started a small private press, as he later stated, "solely for the sake of the interest and amusement I expected to derive from it." It was the discussion with Morris which provided the inspiration to go beyond the needs of a simple hobby, however. From that point on, Hornby was conscious of the desire to produce printing which would conform to the highest standards of craftsmanship.

The Ashendene Press, which was to be one of the triumvirate of great English private presses, along with the Kelmscott Press and the Doves Press, began its existence with a few fonts of 12-point Caslon type, an Albion Crown hand press, and the necessary auxiliary equipment. Later on some fonts of the famous Fell type, obtained from Oxford University Press, were used by Hornby. He, with his sisters, a brother, and a cousin, filled in spare hours by setting up and printing several books with extremely short press runs. The first two books were printed on a machine-made paper and a Japanese paper. But from that time on, all of the printing was done with hand-made paper. From 1902 several copies of each edition were printed on vellum.

In 1900, Hornby met Sidney Cockerell, who had been Secretary of the Kelmscott Press and who was then in business with Emery Walker. Walker was a process engraver whose knowledge had made him a guiding force in the design of the Kelmscott types. Cockerell induced Hornby to secure his own type for the Press. After some discussion they agreed to look into a re-cutting of the type used by Sweynheim and Pannartz in 1465 at the monastery at Subiaco, on the outskirts of Rome. Morris had also been interested in this letter, which was a transitional form between blackletter and roman. With the aid of Walker, photographs were made from a copy of Cicero's *De Oratore,* printed at Subiaco, and then in the British Museum. E. P. Prince, who had cut the punches for the Kelmscott types and the Doves type, was persuaded to cut the Ashendene letter. This letter was first used for an edition of *La Commedia de Dante.* The Subiaco type was employed for most of the Ashendene books except for a few set in a type named Ptolemy, cut in 1927.

From 1906 until 1935 the Press issued about one book a year. During the life of the Ashendene Press forty books were printed, in addition to a number of ephemeral items. While a pressman was employed, along with a compositor, Hornby continued to perform a great deal of the work himself. In order to meet costs, subscriptions were taken for each book, beginning in 1902. Throughout its long career, its operation was financed by the books produced. "If the interest," Hornby later wrote, "which it has added to life be put upon the credit side, it has brought a more than rich return."

March 14

John Mansir Wing, compositor, editor, and bibliophile, died on this day in 1917 in the city of Chicago, leaving all of his earthly possessions to the Newberry Library of that city. Born in New York's Oswego County in 1845, Wing served an apprenticeship at the type case at an early age and worked as a compositor in the newspaper offices in Rome and Utica. By the age of twenty he had become a proofreader and editorial writer. It was in this capacity that he journeyed to Chicago to work for the *Chicago Times,* where he remained for nine years.

Following a world tour as tutor to the son of an editor of the *Boston Herald,* Wing shrewdly took advantage of the expanding real estate market then existing in Chicago by founding a trade journal named the *Land Owner.* It became an immediate success, even surviving the great fire of 1871, although Wing had to go to New York to buy new equipment to keep his journal in operation. He made his next venture in trade periodicals with the *Western Brewer* which —along with the *Land Owner*—enabled its publisher to retire from business at the comparatively early age of 43 to devote his life to his one great interest, the collection of books.

This avocation eventually led to an agreement with the Newberry Library by which Wing was to leave his property to the library for the establishment of a collection to be known as the John M. Wing Foundation. The trustees of the library agreed to provide a room in which Wing could work with his books and pursue what had become a passion with him—the extra-illustrating of books. Since he was a bachelor, this arrangement was a most practical one for the library in addition to being pleasant for its benefactor.

In his will, the former compositor directed that the income from his bequest be used to purchase books which treat of "the history and development of the arts of printing, engraving and book illustration from the date of the introduction into Europe of the art of printing with type." In 1920 the first custodian of the Wing Foundation was appointed. He was Pierce Butler, a bibliographic scholar of considerable attainments, who immediately laid out the guide lines which have been followed quite closely by his successors ever since.

In a memorandum which Dr. Butler prepared, outlining his ideas, he stated: "In its particular field of the typographic arts, the John M. Wing Foundation should be what the Newberry Library is in the broader realm of general culture. Concerning itself with the humanities of typography, this Foundation will avoid on the one hand the empirical limitation of the artisan and on the other the finical niceties of the dilettante, to devote itself wholeheartedly to the accumulation of such things as will instruct, correct and inspire the makers and users of books in the higher aspects of typographic arts. Loyalty to this ideal will require no austere refusal to receive into the collection treatises on mechanical processes or curiosities. These will have their place, but they must be acquired and used with a frank recognition of their subordination to other and higher matters."

Butler immediately began to acquire incunabula. His successor, Ernst Detterer, was probably more interested in the aesthetic qualities of his purchases than in their content. The present policy, under the direction of James Wells, now is to obtain works which will provide a solid background for the serious study of the history of printing. For a number of years the Wing Foundation has enjoyed the scholarly counsel of Stanley Morison, the foremost living typographic historian. There are now over 20,000 volumes in the collection, making it one of the truly important collections of its kind in existence. While new acquisitions are becoming more difficult to locate, the library manages to add some 300 new items each year.

March 15

"I think I am dying," wrote Sir Sidney Carlyle Cockerell upon a set of postcards of the spring flowers in Kew Gardens, and sent them to his family and friends, postmarked this day in 1962. The fact that he was then in his ninety-fifth year and had been confined to his bed for a number of years, combined to produce alarm in the minds of those to whom the postcards were addressed. Wilfred Blunt, Cockerell's biographer, lost no time in telephoning, only to learn that his subject was "in excellent form, sitting up in bed and eating a hearty breakfast."

Cockerell did die in 1962, on the first day of May, thus bringing to a close a remarkable career during which he was the friend and correspondent of all of the prominent literary and artistic figures of England from John Ruskin to Sir Alec Guinness. Of them all, to Cockerell the outstanding person was William Morris, founder of the Kelmscott Press, whom he had met through an early interest in Socialism. Asked by Morris to catalogue the library at Kelmscott House, Cockerell remained his associate as Secretary to the Kelmscott Press and upon the death of Morris became his executor.

When Morris became seriously ill in 1896 with a tubercular ailment, he asked Cockerell to make plans to continue the work of the Kelmscott Press. Cockerell wrote in his journal on August 30th: "W.M. asked me whether I should be prepared to carry on the Press after his death, with Walker [Emery], and I said that I was in favor of its ceasing—as otherwise it would fizzle out by degrees, and the books already issued would suffer by inferior ones following them. He said he thought I was perhaps right."

Throughout his long life Cockerell was engaged in some famous quarrels, upon a variety of subjects. On the other hand he was ever ready to act as mediator in the quarrels of his friends. Probably his greatest effort as a peacemaker was put forth unsuccessfully in the dispute between T. J. Cobden-Sanderson and Emery Walker concerning the disposition of the Doves Press type. When Walker had removed himself from the affairs of the Doves Press he desired to continue his own use of the types, for whose design he had been responsible. Cobden-Sanderson refused to allow the removal of the types from the Press.

Cockerell attempted to resolve the disagreement, writing to Cobden-Sanderson: "A modus vivendi has now occurred to me as possible—which is that you should have the sole use of the type for your lifetime, and that if you survive Walker it should remain your property, and that if he survives you it should become his. . . . for whatever your mutual exasperation may make you think of each other, each of you perfectly well knows in his heart of hearts that the other is the best of men and a valiant fighter in the cause of artistic and political progress. . . ."

Cobden-Sanderson unfortunately refused to cooperate, disposing of the types in the River Thames. By this action the private press movement suffered a loss of prestige which might otherwise have been avoided.

Cockerell's greatest contribution to the arts, however, came in the years 1908-1937 when he was Director of the Fitzwilliam Museum at Cambridge, which he transformed—in the words of the art critic, Bernard Berenson—"from the dismal miscellany it used to be, into one of the finest museum buildings existing." His interest in printing sprang from his love of medieval manuscripts on which he had made himself an outstanding authority, and from his activities as a bibliophile.

March 16

A weary Venetian printer named Aldus Manutius on this day in 1503 finally decided that he had had enough and thereupon broke into print to announce the fact. Aldus was primarily concerned with the pirating of his printed works.

One of the great publishers of any era, Aldus had been meticulous in the editing of his texts, using as his correctors only scholars of reputation. Although he had established his press just a few years previously—in 1495—his editions had quickly been recognized as the most authoritative available for scholar or student alike. Thus, no sooner was one of his books published than it was pirated in a dozen localities.

In addition to utilizing the Aldine texts, the imprint of the press itself was copied. Finally even the types were duplicated. Aldus therefore resorted to the warning of all his competitors by appealing to the readers and purchasers of his books.

"When I undertook to furnish good books to lovers of letters, I thought that I need only see that the books issued by our academy should be as correct as care could make them. . . . But four times within the last seven years I have had to protect myself against the treachery of my workmen. . . . I have defeated their plots and punished their perfidy. Yet, in the city of Lyons, books are fraudulently printed under my name. Those books do not contain the name of the real printer, but are made in imitation of mine, so that the unwary reader will believe them printed in Venice. . . . Their paper is inferior and has a bad odor. The types do not please the eye, but have French peculiarities and deformed capitals. The letters are not connected as mine are, in imitation of writing."

Unfortunately the scholarly attributes of Aldus were not matched by his business acumen. His standards of production were so high that he was unable to receive a sufficient return for his efforts. He died in 1515, in financial distress. We owe to his remarkably high standards, however, the small format book, italic type, and cuttings of roman types which surpass in beauty the earlier designs of Nicolas Jenson.

Two well known contemporary types are modern adaptations of Aldine letters, both of which have been cut for the Monotype machine. Bembo is patterned from the type used in *Di Aetna* written in 1495 by the humanist Pietro Bembo. Poliphilus is taken from the types of one of the great books of the Italian renaissance, *Hyptnerotomachia Poliphili.*

March 17

On this day in 1838 the United States Patent Office granted to David Bruce Jr. a patent for modifications on a typecasting machine which greatly improved the original model of 1836. Although not the first American to develop a machine to free the typefounder from the dependence upon the laborious hand-casting of single types, Bruce may be credited with the first fully successful type-caster to be produced in this country.

With tongue in cheek, Thomas MacKellar described the machine in his manual, *The American Printer,* using "cute" terminology, which apparently amused Luther Ringwalt to such a degree that he later reprinted the description almost word for word in *The American Encyclopedia of Printing.*

"Look at one carefully," wrote MacKellar. "The metal is kept fluid by a little furnace underneath, and is projected into the mould by a pump, the spout of which, you see, is in front of the metal pot. The mould is movable, and at every revolution of the crank it comes up to the spout, receives a charge of metal, and flies back with a fully formed type in its bosom; the upper half of the mould lifts, and out jumps a type as lively as a tadpole. You don't see how the letter is formed at the end of the type? True, we had forgotten; well, this spring in front holds in loving proximity to the mould a copper matrix, such as you saw just now in the fitting room. The letter a, for instance stamped into the matrix, sits directly opposite the aperture in the mould which meets the spout of the pump; and when a due proportion of the a's is cast, another matrix with b stamped in it takes its place; and so on throughout the alphabet. Slow work, you say, one at a time? Well, the world is peopled after that fashion; and it fills up fast enough. But just time this machine; it is making small, thin type. Count the type made in a minute. One hundred and seventy-five, you say. One hundred per minute will probably be the average of the ordinary sizes of printing type."

At one hundred types per minute, of course, Bruce's typecaster was far out-producing the hand-casting of types, which

then enjoyed a rate of four to five hundred letters per hour. The Bruce machine, however, was similar to the hand caster in that the type needed to undergo a number of finishing steps, all of which were performed by hand. It was not until the Barth machine of 1888 was developed that a typecasting machine delivered a completely finished type. Additional increase of production also came with power operation.

Bruce attempted to sell his 1838 patent to his uncle, George Bruce, of the famous Bruce typefoundry of New York. The foundry sent its head machinist to look at the caster. He reported that it was not practical. It was instead introduced by the Boston Type and Stereotype foundry, eventually becoming the model for casting machines used by all of the American and several of the European foundries.

March 18

Young typographic designers are frequently cautioned to be careful about the size of the types which they specify in their design. They are told that if they must err, to do so in favor of using larger sizes for body composition of promotional copy, particularly if the message is addressed to a high-priced audience, which may have lost its youthful vision. In 1965 a new publishing venture experimented with the production of quarto editions of currently popular works set in 18-point type "for more comfortable reading." Such a trend is a long way from the styles described by Theodore L. De Vinne in one of his numerous typographic lectures, delivered this day in 1886, in which he discoursed on microscopic types of the past.

The first printers, in their rather slavish imitation of the work of scribes, used types which by today's standards would be described as large. Of course, so were the books, which during the incunabula period were generously proportioned. According to De Vinne, the earliest small type cast prior to 1500, was a black letter of nonpareil (6-point) size, cut by Johann Froben at Basle in 1490 and used in an octavo Latin Bible. He did not believe this to be a well-cut type, however, and described a roman type of 1498 used by Giovanni and Gregorio de Gregoriis in the printing office of the Roman Church as "a remarkably neat letter." This was a considerable feat for the period when the punch-cutter's tools were not as precise as they later became, and casting procedures were inexact. In addition, typefounders had difficulty in obtaining the necessary quantities of tin and antimony with which to assure an ideal cast.

In spite of the prejudice of scholars against small books, the French printer Jean Jannon cut a size of type in 1625 which ran seventeen lines to the inch. This size later became known as diamond (4½ point), and was not uncommon during the 19th century. In fact, De Vinne himself used it, set solid, in a page of his *Plain Printing Types*. Just in case the reader thought he was in trouble, De Vinne followed up with a page of brilliant (4-point) also set solid. Since he used these pages to outline a history of American typefounding, he probably discouraged with one stroke at least several generations of typographical scholars. Jannon used his diamond type for seven books, the first of which was a *Virgil* in 32-mo.

In 1834 Antonio Farino, a Milanese, cut punches for a type which he named *ochia di mosca*, or flies' eyes, but when the foundry attempted to cast the type it encountered so many difficulties that the project could not continue. Twenty years later, however, these types, about twenty lines to the inch, were successfully cast for an edition of the *Divine Comedy*.

Possibly the greatest feat of punchcutting, according to De Vinne, was the type cut by Henri Didot in 1827 when he was sixty-six years of age. The size was called by Didot demi-nonpareil (about 2½-point) and measured twenty-five lines to an inch. These types were used in a 64-mo edition of the *Maxims of La Rochefoucauld*. Didot found it necessary to invent a new mold for this letter. Called a polyamatype mold, it cast many type bodies in one operation.

The most perfect small type in De Vinne's experience was that cast by the Scottish foundry of Miller & Richard in 1873 for a French-English dictionary. The type was cut by John Bellows of Gloucester, England, and measured twenty lines to the inch. The book contained 564 pages measuring 59 mm. square and was printed in two colors. This volume was splendidly printed, and to assure its perfection it required a period of eight years to complete.

Advertising in the *Federal Gazette* of Baltimore on this date in 1812, Samuel Sower, typefounder, and grandson of the earlier founder, Christopher Sower, stated that he was "ready to execute orders for sizes from diamond to French canon, including music, script, and German text."

The tenth son of the second Christopher Sower, Samuel had originally been a house carpenter in Chestnut Hill, Pennsylvania, but turned to the art of apothecary and apparently finding the printer's craft an improvement upon alchemy, he learned that, too. By his twenty-fifth birthday, young Sower was busy producing books and had acquired sufficient skill to set up a press in Baltimore from which he published a German weekly newspaper, adding bookbinding and bookselling to his activities a few years later.

As Samuel Sower had sprung from a family of typefounders who had been pioneers in that trade in America, he had sufficient knowledge of it to be able to cast some type for his own use, and possibly influenced by his fellow printers who needed new types, he enlarged these activities into the establishment of a typefoundry in partnership with William Gwynn in 1804. This firm, which was known as the Baltimore Type Foundry, purchased the equipment of the Fox Foundry from Emanuel, son of Justus Fox, who had been an employee of the first Christopher Sower. Thus some of the original Sower equipment was returned to the family possession.

In a letter which Sower wrote in 1808 he waxed enthusiastic over the fortunes of his business: "The business of typefounding is making great strides,—orders are pouring in from everywhere, so that we cannot fill half of them. We have undertaken to cast the smallest type that have yet been used in the world. You may judge of its fineness when it takes 4-5,000 spaces to weigh one pound. Of this type we have an order from New York for 300 pounds for a Bible. . . . If we could get Antimony enough, we could have work for twelve founders. I am working night and day. We have eleven boys and six journeymen at work and orders for 5,000 pounds type."

Sower's "smallest type" was a diamond size (4-point) and is possibly the first casting in the United States of such a letter. There were few printers then, however, who wished to be concerned with such microscopic type, and fewer still today. The American Type Founders Company presently markets but a single type cast on a 4-point body, called Boxhead Gothic. Most contemporary compositors would be inclined to seek instruction in the operation of the linotype machine if requested to set such a tiny type on a regular basis.

Sower, in his letter, also remarks on a couple of problems which plagued the early American typefounders. They were completely dependent upon Europe for antimony, and this necessary metal was expensive to obtain as the Congress had exacted a high duty on its importation. One of the earliest Congressional lobbies by printers had effected a change in this ruling in 1804, but it remained in insufficient supply for many years.

The Baltimore Type Foundry continued after Samuel Sower's death in 1820 and after a number of changes in ownership it became one of the firms to take part in the amalgamation of foundries into the American Type Founders in 1892.

March 20

The April issue of *The American Mercury,* edited by H. L. Mencken and George Nathan, was published on March 20, 1926. One of the stories entitled "Hatrack," by Herbert Asbury concerned a prostitute. For this the publication was banned in Boston. Its censorship meant that it had run afoul of the Watch and Ward Society, self-appointed guardian of Boston's morals. There had been two previous articles in *Mercury* concerning the machinations of this Society, which for twenty years had held the state of the arts in Boston under almost absolute control. This criticism, coupled with the printing of another detrimental article in the April issue, brought about the decision of the Society, through its secretary J. Frank Chase, to "get" Mencken. Using the article by Asbury as an excuse, Chase notified the Massachusetts Magazine Committee that the April issue of *Mercury* was objectionable. This committee, with the distribution of magazines throughout the state under its control, thereupon requested that the bookshops and newsstands withdraw the issue.

Mencken determined to fight the matter and by doing so try to bring the Society into such disrepute that its influence might be damaged. He secured the services of Arthur Garfield Hays, the lawyer for the American Civil Liberties Union. Hays advised him to go to Boston and risk arrest by selling a copy of *Mercury* on the street. The journalist knew he courted arrest and imprisonment if convicted, but he agreed. The details were worked out that he would sell a copy to Chase himself. To insure that the Watch and Ward Society secretary would appear, the man was informed that dozens of copies of the offending issue would be sold to the crowd that would undoubtedly gather. The press was notified, and on April 5th Mencken went up to Boston.

Mencken had first to secure a license to peddle. This he did with some glee. Then he proceeded in the company of a sympathetic crowd of reporters to the Boston Common. The confrontation was to take place on Brimstone Corner, another item which greatly pleased the Baltimore editor. A large crowd gathered, buttressed by scores of Harvard students, to whom Mencken was the Man of the Hour. A man identifying himself as Chase's assistant asked Mencken for a copy of the magazine but Mencken refused. Finally Chase himself appeared.

"Are you Chase?" Mencken asked.

"I am," was the reply. Chase gave Mencken a half dollar, which the editor tested by biting, to the huge amusement of the spectators.

"I order this man's arrest," shouted Chase, turning to Captain George W. Patterson, chief of the Boston vice squad. Mencken was then escorted to police headquarters and booked. Here he was arraigned and trial was set for the following day.

Since it was unheard of in Boston for a judge of the Municipal Court to find a Watch and Ward defendant not guilty, Mencken spent a worried night before appearing in court. Due to a mix-up in timing, however, the judge scheduled to hear the case was shifted, and Mencken appeared before Judge James P. Parmenter. After both sides had had their innings, the judge announced that he would make his decision the following morning. This he did, finding for the defendant. The clerk of the court then told Mencken that he was free to go.

Mencken was scheduled to lunch at the Harvard Union. Since he had fully expected to be convicted, the lunch was in the nature of a victory celebration, with fully two thousand students waiting to cheer him. The full outcome of the case was that the Watch and Ward Society did find its influence weakened by adverse publicity. The precedent created by the decision was frequently invoked thereafter in similar cases.

March 21

On this date in the year 1794 John Hayes, a printer of Baltimore, Maryland, advertised that he had recently acquired "an elegant and complete apparatus" from Caslon in England. During this period it was quite common for the printers of the young republic to so advise their customers. It is evident that there was need for the establishment of an American typefoundry and that it would be a reasonably successful venture, provided that the product was competitive with the types and equipment being obtained from England.

The English foundries were anxious, of course, to obtain the American business, as the craft of printing was enjoying a time of expansion, making the sale of type quite profitable even with 3,000 miles of turbulent ocean between the typecaster and the printing press. While the English and Scottish foundries received the bulk of the American orders for type, French and Dutch founders were also exporting type to this country. It was not infrequent for the American printers to boast about their sources of types. When, in 1785, the Congressional Secretary advertised for bids to print the *Journals* of the Continental Congress, four of the nine printers submitting estimates sent along typefounders' specimens of the types to be used.

While a few printers ordered type direct from overseas, importing houses and agents were active in the trade. As this business became more competitive, the agent sometimes relinquished his brokerage fee, or so he advertised, as did Robert Browne of New York in 1794, who offered: "The subscriber wishes to inform the Printers in the different States, that he can supply them with Printing Types of every description from Fry's celebrated Foundery, London. The Types shall be de-

livered in New York at cost and charges free of any commission; the money to be paid at the Current Exchange at the time of delivery."

There were, however, numberless delays in shipment, and as the correspondence concerning postponements of orders was equally uncertain, American printers were understandably frustrated in their efforts to secure their types. George Barclay & Company, a London agent, wrote to Mathew Arey of Philadelphia on August 8, 1792: "Thro' the Channels of our Mutual & very good friend Mr. George Meade of Philadelphia we are favored with Your's of the 25 June, Inclosing a Letter with an order for Types which we have forwarded to Dr. Alexander Wilson & Sons of Glasgow & agreeable to your Request have urged them to get it ready as soon as possible & in preference if an opportunity should offer from Greenock, to Ship it from thence—if not to send it up here to be Ship't by one of the New York Traders for we shall have no opportunity Direct for Philadelphia at the same time you mention We hope however it will be nearly the same thing to Send the Types to New York & we shall of Course Pay for them ready Money with a Discount of 7½ pCt. as you seem to wish."

Almost three weeks later, Agent Barclay wrote again saying that the Wilson foundry was so busy that they could not accept the order, but that they could have "an excellent Fount ready for you by the first spring Ships sailing provided that such an Order was handed them soon." Finally on February 4, 1793, Carey received notification that the Scottish foundry had received the order so late that it "would be utterly impossible to execute it in Time to send by the Spring Ships. . . ."

It is obvious that when the American foundries became operative in the closing years of the 18th century, their product was received with little criticism by most printers anxious to replenish cases of well-worn type.

March 22

In 1834 upon this day a new sixteen page weekly named the *New Yorker* was published. It was edited by a young compositor from Vermont by the name of Horace Greeley, then just twenty-three years of age. In his opening statement, the youthful editor wrote, "Our paper is not blazoned through the land as 'The Cheapest Periodical in the World,' or any of the captivating clap-traps wherewith enterprising gentlemen are wont to usher in their excessive experiments on the gullibility of the Public."

Although the periodical began with just fifty paid subscriptions, within a year the number had risen to 4,500, justifying the skill of Greeley as an editor. Just twelve years previously, when he was eleven years old, Horace Greeley had walked eight miles from his home in the village of Westhaven, Vermont to Whitehall in adjoining New York state to ask for the job of apprentice in a printing office. He was turned down as being too young. Four years later, when there was a similar opening in the office of the *Northern Spectator* in East Poultney, Vermont, the boy again applied. This incident was related by Greeley's first biographer, James Parton, in *The Life of Horace Greeley,* written in 1855.

Greeley tramped the twelve miles down the Rutland Road to the home of Amos Bliss, publisher of the weekly, and found him planting potatoes in his garden.

"Are you the man that carries on the printing office?" he enquired.

Bliss later recalled that he saw a boy in rough farmer's clothes, worn-down shoes, no stockings and an old hat that looked more like a two-quart measure inverted than anything else. He admitted that he was the man.

"Don't you want a boy to learn the trade?" asked the stranger.

"Well," said Bliss, "we have been thinking of it. Do *you* want to learn to print?"

"I've had some notion of it," said the backwoods boy.

Bliss gazed at him in astonishment. "Well, my boy,—but, you know, it takes considerable learning to be a printer. Have you been to school much?"

"No, I haven't had much chance at school. I've read some."

"What have you read?"

"Well, I've read some history, and some travels, and a little of most everything."

"Where do you live?"

"At Westhaven."

"How did you come over?"

"On foot."

Bliss sent Greeley over to see his foreman, who sent the boy back with a note saying that he should be taken on. That evening one of the other apprentices asked whether Bliss was going to hire "that tow-head" and the publisher replied, "I am, and if you boys are expecting to get any fun out of him, you'd better do it quick, or you'll be too late. There's something *in* that tow-head."

There was indeed. After his original success with the *New Yorker* Greeley launched the New York *Tribune* which soon became the best newspaper in New York. He went on to become America's most respected editor for a period of thirty years. In 1872 he was nominated to run for the office of President of the United States, against the incumbent, U. S. Grant. He was defeated by a wide margin, carrying only six states. The disappointments and hard work of the campaign, during which he was seriously villified, contributed to his death less than a month after the close of the campaign.

March 23

In the year 1861 on this day, just three weeks before the guns sounded at Fort Sumter, the Kentucky-born publisher of the Indianapolis *Journal,* John D. Defrees, took office as the first Superintendent of Public Printing. In 1869 this title was changed to Congressional Printer, and in 1876 an Act of Congress decreed the office should be titled Public Printer, which it has remained to the present time. Regardless of the title, however, the men who have borne it have had their troubles, with the Congress and with the printers of the republic, who have always felt that the Government Printing Office produced too much printing, thereby letting the commercial printers scratch for a living.

In 1905 the GPO and the Public Printer were the center of an imbroglio that resulted in the discharge—by President Theodore Roosevelt—of Frank W. Palmer, the sixth Public Printer, who had held the office longer than any of his predecessors, a period of over thirteen years. The fuss started when the Mergenthaler Linotype charged that a purchase by the GPO of seventy-two monotype machines had been made without giving Mergenthaler the opportunity to compete for the order.

The Lanston Monotype Company leaped to the defense of Palmer, and both companies enriched the trade periodicals by taking four page ads to inform the nation's printers of the respective merits of their equipment to perform in the GPO as well as to castigate their rivals. The Monotype firm broke into print with their message containing this statement:

"PRINTERS! The President of the United States in the following language has officially stamped the Mergenthaler Linotype Company as a columniator, as an assassin of character; he says: 'Second only to corruption in a public officer in point of iniquity comes making a baseless charge of corruption, and this is what the committee finds the Mergenthaler Company has done in this case. . . .' "

A Committee of Investigation, named the Keep Committee, for its chairman, C. H. Keep, Assistant Secretary of the Treasury, was appointed and conducted a thorough investigation of the charges. The Mergenthaler Company lost no time in announcing in another advertisement, printed on pink paper, that "Linotype Charges of Unfairness Sustained/Public Printer Discharged/Recent Purchase of Type-Setting Machines 'Improvident/Indicates Great Partiality and Bias.' "

Monotype countered with a four-pager printed on yellow stock in which it printed a label alleged to have been attached to all proofs of type set by the linotype machine: "Notice. Composition on this work was done on Linotype Machines. Avoid changes." This was followed by the testimony taken at the hearings, which happened to be favorable to the monotype.

While the Keep Committee exonerated the Lanston firm from all "aspersion as to undue influence," it did recommend that the contract for the seventy-two machines be revoked, a suggestion which President Roosevelt did not act upon. An editorial appearing in the *Journal of Commerce and Commercial Bulletin* stated: "The commission finds that the most serious charges made against the Lanston Monotype Company are not sustained. At a time when much corruption is being uncovered, in the public service and elsewhere, it is a matter for general rejoicing that this corporation should have been able to maintain its integrity. That the Lanston Monotype Company did try, and not without success, to sell its machines to the Government; that it kept them prominently before the principal officers of the public printing

establishment; that it extolled their merits in season and out of season; that it pushed them to the front with untiring persistency—these are the charges that the company's officers may bear with equanimity. With such matters the public has no concern. . . ."

These are, after all, but the commonly accepted principles by which gentlemen conduct business in the United States!

March 24

"I was born at Walthamstow in Essex in March 1834, a suburban village on the edge of Epping Forest, and once a pleasant place enough, but now terribly cocknified and choked up by the jerry-builder."

So wrote William Morris in 1883 referring to his birth upon this day. Born to enjoy a reasonable affluence, Morris never for a moment buried himself in middle-class morality. As a young man he dedicated himself to a "Crusade and Holy Warfare against the age." It is fortunate for those who love the craft of the printer that this 19th century "angry young man" added to his long list of causes the improvement of the poor state of that craft a hundred years ago. It is doubly fortunate that Morris brought to his causes energy and enthusiasm without the accompanying blight of cynicism.

Morris was articled to an architect. However, under the influence of the poet and painter, Rossetti, he decided to become a painter. Shortly afterward he published his first book of verse, became interested in the design of wallpaper and the weaving of tapestries, and began the translation of Icelandic sagas. Involvement with the beginnings of the Arts and Crafts movement and a strong commitment to Socialism followed.

In a lecture delivered in 1881, Morris stated: "Every real work of art, even the humblest, is inimitable. I am most sure that all the heaped-up knowledge of modern science, all the energy of modern commerce, all the depth and spirituality of modern thought, cannot reproduce so much as the handicraft of an ignorant, superstitious Berkshire peasant of the fourteenth century; nay, of a wandering Kurdish shepherd, or of a skin-and-bone oppressed Indian ryot. This, I say, I am sure of; and to me the certainty is not depressing, but inspiriting, for it bids us remember that the world has been note-worthy for more than one century and one place, a fact which we are pretty apt to for-get. . . .

That Morris finally turned his energies and talents to printing was no doubt due to his work with illuminated manuscripts and to interest in the printing of his own works. In addition, about 1888, conversations with his friend and neighbor Emery Walker, the engraver and printer, excited in him the in-terest which eventually resulted in the cre-ation of a typeface and the founding of the Kelmscott Press with which Morris could in-dulge his ideas about typography and the making of books.

The rest is history. Prior to his death in 1896 the Kelmscott Press produced a body of work which captured the imagination of printers and public alike. From this relatively short period has sprung the private press movement which has so influenced typogra-phy in our own time. Present-day writers and lecturers tend to discount this influence. Dis-cussing the revival of the 19th century com-mercial types, such as the sans serifs and the Egyptians, one modern writer was annoyed that Morris had interfered with the logical typographical development of the industrial revolution by agitating for a revival of types of the 15th century.

The fact remains that during Morris's life-time, there was little effort to promote print-ing as a craft, much less as an art. Certainly the many beautifully proportioned roman types presently available to printers might never have been created had not their de-signers received inspiration and guidance from this man who attempted to set the taste for his age.

March 25

On the letterhead of the Department of Fine Arts of Wells College, in the Finger Lakes country of New York State, Victor Hammer wrote to his friend, Howard Coggeshall, the Utica printer, on this date in 1946 and en-closed some specimens of his recent printing at the Wells College Press. The outstanding item was *A Dialogue of the Uncial,* set in the then new American Uncial type designed by Hammer and printed by hand on dampened Van Gelder paper. In the dialogue a printer

(Hammer) converses with a paleographer on letterforms and the craft of printing.

An anachronism in the modern world of automation, Hammer is a craftsman in the medieval sense, believing in the work of the hand rather than the product of the machine. Unlike many men of similar beliefs, Hammer does not advocate this method as an antidote to the tensions of modern life, but merely as one individual's approach to softening their impact.

The *Dialogue* begins with the paleographer coming into the printing office where the printer and his son are at work. "Good eve-ning, gentlemen," he remarks. "It is rather late, I know, but perhaps the best time for me to call at that, for I shall not interrupt you at your work. Would you be so kind as to show me the proofs of your new uncial type-face you spoke of the last time we met?"

"You are most welcome, professor," the printer answers, "and just in time, too; we have now finished the make-ready and are about to pull a few proofs on the very paper we shall use for the keepsake we are going to print. . . ."

"All right," said the paleographer. "I want to know more about the other specimen-cuttings you made. . . ."

"Well, it began with my first year in this country. I approached the director of one of the biggest type foundries. He showed real interest in my uncial; so I cut a 14-point al-phabet and then he had a trial cast made of about 25 letters. With a few pounds of this type we printed a kind of specimen. At the same time my son here had also reached this country, and we began our work at the newly founded Wells College Press."

"I have never seen this type-face, have I?" asked the paleographer.

"No," replied the printer, "it was supposed to be impractical; the director felt there would be no money in it. Consequently it had to be abandoned."

The printer and the paleographer then go on to discuss the qualities of the new uncial form, which the paleographer calls a mon-grel, to which the printer asks, "Do you think I would be foolish enough to copy a hand from an old script and use it for print-ing modern languages?" He then produced a two-paragraph statement which had been printed for the purpose of stating his philos-ophy as a designer of type:

"Language being itself a means of communication in the ordinary sense, as well as a Pegasus on whom we may ride to heaven, has two distinct aspects: a qualitative and a quantitative; sacred language and profane language. Sacred language is forever seeking to fix the expressive forms of the language by an act of creation; profane language, rich with life and change, is forever bringing the language to that point where a new act of creation is required. Sacred language, the language of the poet, defines these changes and registers them. It is this language, indeed, which determines the change of the visual form of the written or, in our day, the printed word.

"Here as I see it, the type-designer's work begins. It is not the reader and his demands that I wish to satisfy, any more than it is the writer. It is my conviction that the type-designer should do his work in the service of language."

March 26

The production record of the Wicks Rotary Type-Casting Company of Blackfriars Road, London, records that on this day in 1901 the firm cast in a single machine 319,284 pieces of minion (7-point) type, utilizing the labor of one man and an unskilled helper, plus a three-horsepower motor. The production for the entire month of March of this quartet was over eight million characters weighing six and one half tons of type metal.

An ecstatic report written by an American observer of the production of the Wicks Rotary Type-Casting Machine states in properly awed tones: "For quite two hours I watched this mechanism vomit type. In every sixty seconds a thousand perfect letters spouted from it. On one side of it a jet of molten metal played steadily; from the other side disgorged a stream of perfect printing types, pouring forth so swift the light gleamed along their surfaces as steadily as sunlight might glow on a spinning reel of ribbon. I saw a jet of metal furiously hot spurt ceaselessly through a mold positively cold; and after an hour of that terrific impact, the mold's parts were chill as cool water. I saw metal at 700 degrees Fahrenheit changed within the two-hundredth of a second to type one held in one's naked palm and felt no burn."

What this enthusiastic chronicler did not see was that the Wicks machine had been passed by, and was, by 1901, just another piece of equipment made obsolete by the inventions of Ottmar Mergenthaler and Tolbert Lanston.

Frederick Wicks, a Glasgow Scotsman, had originally been on the editorial staff of *The Times* of London and had gone to Glasgow, Scotland to help found the *Glasgow News,* where he conceived the idea of a typecasting machine which could cast new types so quickly that the distribution of type would be unnecessary and would be accomplished by the metal pot. About 1889 Wicks returned to London to write novels and to develop his machine. He then formed a company which supplied types for *The Times* and for other periodicals and printers.

By the turn of the century the Wicks foundry was casting and selling some 200 tons of type each week for the English market, and he was ready to arrange for an American branch. An American newspaper publisher, hearing of this, declared that the typefoundries of the United States might just as well go out of business. Wicks' spokesman in America described their patron as a genius: He had known nothing about typefounding when he "conceived his invention." They mentioned that he was without reverence or fear—"reverence for the accepted traditions and the laws of mechanics, fear of the difficulties which might arise in disregarding them."

Lucien Legros, co-author of the informative work on typefounding and composing machines, *Typographical Printing Surfaces,* who knew Wicks personally, wrote of his attempt to change some of Wicks' ideas concerning the mechanics of the typecaster, to no avail. These problems were primarily related to casting temperatures, but even if Wicks had listened to advice, his machine was doomed to obsolescence by the concept of composing and casting in the same machine as was successfully proven by the linotype and monotype machines, which had already been perfected.

The high cost of constructing the Wicks Rotary Type-Caster was a factor in the failure of the typefoundry, along with the technical difficulties encountered in casting different sizes of type, which required constant adjustment for set widths. These problems were so costly that the financial backers of

Wicks became impatient for a return on their investment and withdrew their support.

March 27

The second National Typesetting Tournament ended March 27, 1886 in Philadelphia, with a compositor named Alexander Duguid establishing a record for fast typesetting which has never been surpassed. Among the contestants were the professional swifts, men who engaged in contests for cash prizes in all parts of the country. During the last decades of the 19th century, printers bet their wages on speed typos in the same manner that their contemporaries wager on the four-legged speedsters going for the mile and an eighth. Such excitement was generated at the contests that the International Typographical Union found it necessary to set up rules and regulations for their conduct.

The Philadelphia contest was reported by the *Printer's Circular:*

"At the beginning of the contest, Joseph McCann, of the New York *Herald,* the ex-champion, gave indications of winning the first prize; but after the first day, W. C. Barnes, of the New York *World,* the champion, led for the two succeeding days. He then gradually dropped to third place, which he held to the close. McCann then went to the head of the list, which position he held to the last day, when Duguid put on a little extra steam when he began work in the afternoon, his score then reaching for the hour and a half, 3,388 ems, which he exceeded, however, in the evening, attaining a mark of 3,476 ems, beating his previous record and any heretofore attained anywhere. His total day's work of three hours was 6,804 gross ems, reduced to 6,635¼ ems by 6¾ minutes required for correcting."

As this was the only tournament in which Duguid had ever participated, he was a "busher" in the eyes of the pros. Perhaps to put him in his place by indulging in a bit of grand-standing on the last day of the tournament, the great Bill Barnes of the *World* demonstrated his virtuosity as one of the great swifts of the times.

He set 2,744 gross ems in an hour and a half with the cases reversed, that is, the cap case being transposed to the position of the lower case. During the evening session he set 1,635 ems in an hour and a half while blindfolded, the copy being read to him by another comp. In this feat, Barnes made six typographical errors.

Barnes, Canadian born, had won first prize in a number of contests previous to the Philadelphia match. It was said of him that he used liquor as a medicine only, ate his meals regularly, and slept exactly eight hours per day. To these temperate habits Barnes attributed his better than ordinary powers of endurance, nerve, and speed at forty-three years of age.

Resting upon his laurels, the winner of the event, Alexander Duguid, never again participated in speed typesetting contests, thus retiring undefeated.

Under the rules of the Tournament the type used was nonpareil [6-point], set to a measure of 28 picas. Since most present-day compositors have occasion to set hand type only in display sizes, they would be horrified at having to set even one line of 6-point to a measure so wide. By the turn of the century the speed contests were a thing of the past, Mr. Mergenthaler's machine having taken over straight-matter composition on most of the daily newspapers which had helped to produce the high speed typos.

March 28

By decree of the Council of the Colony of Georgia on March 28, 1763, it was "Ordered That the Secretary of the Province do deliver such Laws to the Printer as the Commissioners shall direct to be printed taking his Receipt for same." Just over a week later, James Johnston, a printer from Scotland, printed at Savannah the first issue of his newspaper, the *Georgia Gazette.* The art of printing had come to the last of the original thirteen British Colonies in America.

Over a year had passed since a resolution had been made which stated among other things: "And whereas James Johnston, lately arrived in this province from Great Britain, recommended as a person regularly bred to and well skilled in the art and mystery of printing, hath offered to set up a printing press in the town of Savannah, if some encouragement and assistance were given to him by the publick, to defray part of the heavy charges and expenses attending the procuring materials and other necessities for setting up the same."

It is probable that Johnston had not bothered to secure equipment until he was assured of being named the official public printer. Since Georgia was the most remote of the colonies, it required a considerable length of time to be ready for printing. Nothing is known of Johnston's career prior to appearing in Georgia. He had been born in Dumfries, Scotland in 1738 and had presumably been apprenticed to the craft in his native country. His first work in Georgia certainly was competently produced. He apparently worked alone in his printing office, as the *Gazette* carried advertisements for an apprentice and a journeyman for its first five months of existence.

Johnston's first official printing for the colony was *An Act to prevent stealing of Horses and neat Cattle,* which had been passed in 1759. This nicely printed job represents the first imprint other than the *Gazette.* The July 7, 1763 issue of Johnston's newspaper carried a letter from London, dated March 27th, which informed his readers of an event which was to considerably influence their lives: "I cannot, however, omit mentioning a matter much the subject of conversation here, which if carried into execution, will in its consequences greatly effect the colonies. It is to quarter 16 regiments in America, to be supported at the expense of the provinces. The money it is said will be levied by an act of parliament, and arise on a stamp tax, excise on rum distilled on the continent, and a duty on foreign sugar and molasses &c. . . ."

When, thirteen years later, the colonies were in open conflict with Great Britain, Printer Johnston was fully on the side of the loyalists. Thus his business was placed in jeopardy. He ceased publication of his newspaper in January of 1776. There is no known printing from Georgia for over a year from that time. In 1778 his name appeared on a list of those "attainted and Ajudged guilty of High Treason Against this State." However, before much could be made of this charge, Savannah was taken over by British troops, and Johnston again began to publish his newspaper, under the revised title of *Royal Georgia Gazette.*

At the close of hostilities, Johnston was banished from the state for a period of three years and his property confiscated. In 1783 he returned, again to publish his paper, this time with the title of *Gazette of the State of Georgia,* which appeared in January 1783. Later Johnston brought his son Nicholas into his business, continuing until the latter's death in 1802. The elder Johnston lived in retirement for six more years, dying in 1808.

March 29

It was undoubtedly inevitable that when the hand press was finally automated, it would be the result of the efforts of a compositor, and such proved to be the case when Frederick Koenig received a patent from the British Commissioners of Patents, dated this day in 1810. Koenig, a farmer's son who had become a printer, was then thirty-five years of age. He had been working on the development of a power-operated printing press for about eight years and had been up to that time frustrated by his lack of success. Koenig's first attempt was, naturally enough, along the lines of the hand presses and was constructed of wood. It received a cool reception with the result that the further capital which the inventor needed to apply his ideas was not forthcoming. He wrote to the Czar, Alexander I of Russia, and was thereupon invited to St. Petersburg to discuss his press. But the politics of the Russian court were so involved that he went to London. Here he was introduced to Thomas Bensley, one of the foremost English printers of his time, who—along with two other printers—agreed to supply the funds which Koenig needed to build his machine.

The 1810 patent was granted for an iron press, an adaptation of the earlier wooden machine. It proved successful, but by this time Koenig's ambition for fame had already driven him to the planning of a power press in which the impression was made by a cylinder rather than by a platen. This second machine was patented in 1811 and was ready for a demonstration by the following year. An important observer of the first trial was John Walter, publisher of *The Times,* who became visibly excited with the press and its implications for the future of newspaper printing. In a discussion with Koenig, Walter learned that the inventor's mind was already on an even more advanced machine, this time a two-cylinder press which would double the output of the original model. Walter immediately ordered two of these machines and, thus subsidized, Koenig set out to prove his theories.

The press for *The Times* was ready in November, 1814, but the publisher found it necessary to resort to a *sub rosa* approach, as he well realized that the pressmen already operating the hand presses in his printing office would be furious at the prospect of technological unemployment and might attempt to damage the new press before it could prove itself successful. On the evening of November 28 he passed the word to the pressroom that he was awaiting important news dispatches from France, which had been delayed. The pressmen therefore sat around all night long, "playing cards, smoking, falling asleep, and cursing the management."

Walter spirited the type forms of the newspaper to the factory where the press had been built, running off an edition at a speed faster than any newspaper had ever been produced before. At six o'clock in the morning, the publisher bravely entered his own press room, with copies of the November 29th issue of *The Times* under his arm. He warded off a possible riot by announcing that every pressman and his assistant would be paid full wages until he could find another job.

The readers of the newspaper were informed in that issue of the momentous technical development by which that morning's paper had been produced: "Our journal of this day presents to the public the practical result of the greatest improvement connected with printing since the discovery of the art itself. The reader of this paragraph now holds in his hands one of the many thousands of impressions of *The Times* newspaper, which were taken off last night by a mechanical apparatus. A system of machinery almost organic has been devised and arranged, which, while it relieves the human frame from the most laborious efforts in printing, far exceeds all human power in rapidity and dispatch."

March 30

In a gloomy cabin aboard the ship, *Nelson*, enroute to England, William Parks who had been Public Printer of both Maryland and Virginia, wrote his will as he lay dying of pleurisy on this day in 1750. He died two days later and was buried in his home soil from whence he had departed in 1728 in order to set up a printing office in Annapolis.

Of the twenty-four years in which Parks labored as a colonial printer, twenty of them were spent in Williamsburg, Virginia. His biographer, Lawrence C. Wroth, writes of his belief, "That Franklin alone excepted there was no printer of his place and period whose service was greater or more distinctive in character than that rendered to the colonies of Maryland and Virginia by this pioneer printer."

Williams Parks had already published two newspapers in England before he set up his press in Annapolis. He brought to the American colonies the traditional intelligence and skills of a literate printer. The first product of his press was an edition of *The Acts of Assembly*. In September 1727 he established *The Maryland Gazette,* the first of four newspapers which he was to publish in America. This was the first newspaper to appear south of Pennsylvania. In its eight years of existence it was an independent journal which in no way reflected its owner's quasi-official standing as Public Printer of the province. It has remained an important source for historians who wish to trace the day-to-day events in the history of the period.

Parks also published literary works, including satire and poetry, and maintained a book shop, a traditional sideline with colonial printers. In 1730 he set up another press in Williamsburg, Virginia, becoming Public Printer of that colony in 1732. He continued to hold the same office in Maryland, but was accused in 1837 of neglecting his duties. Finding that the Virginia business was more lucrative, he moved his equipment there from Annapolis. His first important imprint from Williamburg was *Typographia, An Ode on Printing,* by John Markland, which is the first separate work on printing to be produced in America. A single copy remains, in the John Carter Brown Library of Brown University.

Another American first of Parks' was a book on sports entitled, *A Compleat System of Fencing: or the Art of Defence, in the Use of the Small Sword,* by Edward Blackwell, printed in 1734. In 1742 he produced the first cook book in America, *The Compleat Housewife; or accomplished Gentle-*

woman's *Companion,* written by E. Smith in England, and adapted by Parks for American use. In 1737 he established the *Virginia Gazette,* the first newspaper to be published in the colony.

In 1744 Parks increased his stature as a man of great initiative by building the pioneer paper mill of the South, of which little is now known. None of his wide-ranging activities achieved financial success. After his death his heir, a daughter, was left with practically nothing after the debt of six thousand pounds had been liquidated by the sale of Parks' equipment.

March 31

An agreement "for an entirely new Method of Printing by Machine" was signed in London on this day in 1807 between an immigrant German printer named Frederick Koenig and the noted English printer, Thomas Bensley. The latter arranged to either purchase the "new Method" which happened to be a power printing press or to conclude a contract with the inventor. He further agreed to pay Koenig a penalty of £6,000 if he disclosed the secret in the event he did not wish to support the invention. During the next year and a half Koenig made some headway with his machine. On the strength of what had been completed, Bensley attempted to interest John Walter, publisher of *The Times,* in the project. When Walter was unimpressed, the partners added two other printers, George Woodfall and Richard Taylor, to the group. The partners drew up another agreement in which Bensley was to receive three-eighths of the investment, Woodford and Taylor, three-eighths, and Koenig the remainder. As Koenig wished to be compensated for the preliminary work he had done on the press in Germany, he wanted the sum of £1060. The printers stipulated that if the new press, operated by one pressman to feed and another to remove the printed sheets, failed to reach an output of 300 sheets per hour, Konig would receive no part of this sum. If the press could produce between 300 and 350 sheets per hour, he would get one-third of the money. Should it turn out between 350 and 400 sheets, he would get two-thirds, and in the event that its speed reached 400 sheets per hour, the whole sum would be paid.

The inventor evidently had great faith in his machine, as it easily achieved the maximum as stipulated. The press, patented in 1810, was basically a mechanized hand press, constructed of metal. An important feature was the inking mechanism. Prior to this time the type was inked by devices called ink balls, which had a leather surface. Pressmen believed that the softer the leather, the more receptive the balls would be to the ink. It was therefore the custom to soak the balls each day in various solutions, including urine, an activity which contributed to an overpowering stench in the pressroom. Koenig realized that in order to achieve rapid production he would have to devise a more suitable method of inking the type. He therefore constructed a roller, made of sheepskin and mounted upon a spindle which contained serrations through which steam was forced in order to keep the roller pliable during the period of operation.

Although the press was a success, Koenig of course realized that he had but adapted the principles of the hand press and that he would have to use his new machine merely as the starting point of a completely new technique. The principle of his inking rollers no doubt started him thinking about a really new departure in press design. That was to use a cylinder for the impression rather than a flat surface. Some twenty years previously, an English inventor, William Nicholson, had patented a cylinder press, but being primarily a theorist, he had allowed the patent to lapse. Undoubtedly Koenig had sufficient knowledge of Nicholson's ideas to be able to put them to practical use, which he proceeded to do, and thus must receive credit as the inventor of the first power press.

This second press built in England by Koenig was the first successful cylinder press, in which the type was positioned upon a flat bed and passed under an impression cylinder. In the actual press, which was patented in 1812, the driving mechanism, powered by steam, was larger than the press itself. Koenig was now a successful inventor. With the aid of another German engineer he built several other presses in England, returning to Germany in 1817 to set up one of the great press manufacturing concerns, under the name of Koenig and Bauer, which has continued to supply printing presses to printers all over the world.

April

April 1

In Augsburg, Germany a printer named Erhardus Ratdolt printed a broadside specimen sheet on the first day of April in 1486. Upon the sheet appeared ten sizes of *textura rotunda,* or round gothic, three roman types and one Greek. In the colophon the printer titled his sheet *Indicis characterum diversarum manerierum impressioni paraterum. Finis.*

The only specimen sheet of printer's types which has come down to us prior to Ratdolt's is a publisher's advertisement issued by Peter Schoeffer of Mainz, probably in 1467, according to the historian Stanley Morison. He points out that Ratdolt's use of the word "Index" is important, as it represents the only known application of the term to a catalogue of types during the 15th century.

Many gaps exist in the study of the development of types, owing primarily to the lack of concise information regarding their origin. Bibliographers, particularly, are anxious to have exact sources by which they can determine the origin of texts and their subsequent editions and variations. The lack of precise information is of course more serious for the 15th and 16th centuries, but even in the later periods there are numerous problems to be solved. Modern texts on the development of types must compromise in the reproduction of historical specimens. It is seldom possible to reproduce the originals in the same size, thereby making an exact identification extremely difficult for the bibliographer.

Since the publication of Daniel B. Updike's *Printing Types, Their History, Forms, and Use,* in 1922, great strides have been made in typographical scholarship, but much remains to be accomplished.

April 2

In Leipzig, Germany, upon this day in 1902, was born Jan Tschichold, one of the fine typographers of our times. Just eighteen years later he was teaching calligraphy at the Graphic Arts Academy of Leipzig. In 1923, after attending the Weimar Bauhaus exhibition, he was carried away by the strong protest against the established values made by the Bauhaus architects and artists.

Throwing off his own traditionalism, Tschichold immediately became a leading exponent of the tense, asymmetrical balances called for by the movement. These rigid and geometrical patterns with their strong architectural inclination attracted world-wide attention during the Twenties. As a spokesman for the new trend, Tschichold produced its first important text, *Die Neue Typographie,* published in Berlin in 1928. As an expression of the times *The New Typography* jolted the world of print into controversial reexamination of the existing mores of typographic design.

Naturally enough the greatest effect of the new school was upon advertising and promotional printing. Here the visual aspect of the work of the *avante-garde* typographers reached its most efficient expression. Functional types were needed—and quickly pro-

65

duced. Simplicity demanded that these types be sans serif, but the form of these 19th century letters, called grotesque, required a change which would make them acceptable to the new school of typography. This was done by forming the letters along geometrical principles. The Futura types which have had so much influence upon typography during the past forty years, were the result of the Bauhaus experiments.

By 1933, however, Tschichold was beginning to regret his espousal of experiment and reform. He returned to his traditional birthright. As a designer with a strong historical apprenticeship, he realized that the innovations of the new typography had attracted a host of imitators who lacked fundamental training and who had therefore nothing to contribute to its further development. The new typographers had, in fact, so abused the original concepts of the Bauhaus idea that they had, he felt, destroyed its usefulness.

At about the same time, Tschichold was visited with the disfavor of the Hitler regime. He left Germany for Switzerland, settling in Basil where he remained until 1947. At this time he accepted a request to go to London to restyle completely the Penguin paperback series of books. The success of this venture is well-known. The new Penguins established standards of excellence for mass produced paperback books which have never been surpassed. Their quality proves beyond question that books need not be expensive to be well-planned. By now Tschichold had completely lost his dependence upon the asymetrical form. He was most concerned with the content of print, insuring that nothing interfere with the basic function of being readable.

By this return to traditionalism Tschichold has lost the esteem of many of the younger designers who seek to be innovators but who have little concern for principles. This fall from grace worries him not at all. As a teacher and writer he continues to be a most logical person who remains open-minded to new ideas. His contributions to what is best in present-day typography were recognized by the American Institute of Graphic Arts when it presented him with its coveted medal in 1954.

"There is much boastful talk," Tschichold recently wrote, "about the allegedly high state of typographic design in our time. One can, however, only deplore it."

April 3

The typefoundries of the United States were in the fresh bloom of youth in 1818. They had enjoyed almost unlimited prosperity as there were too few founders for the number of printers who needed type. These conditions were changing, however, and the founders were becoming competitive. In an "Advertisement" bearing this date, appearing in the first American printing manual, *Printers' Guide* by C. S. Van Winkle, the brothers David and George Bruce, stereotypers and printers of New York, who had added a foundry to their facilities, took a few cuts at their fellow Scotsman, the Philadelphia typefounder, James Ronaldson.

"The Art of Printing," wrote the Bruce brothers, "has confessedly received a great improvement within the last twenty years, both in Europe and this country. It was the consequence of a refinement, peculiar to this age, which requires, in every production of human industry, a degree of excellence seldom attempted before, and rarely reached. The specimens of the European type-founders exhibit a striking improvement in the form of their types, which contributed much to the elegance of modern printing; but, in this country, the want of active competition prevented any material improvement in the form and finish of types until within a very few years; and even the attempts at improvement in the foundry which principally supplied the United States, previous to 1812, were mostly so unfortunate as to have been since condemned by the proprietors of that respectable establishment. In this state of things, however well the press-work of our books might be executed, the inelegant appearance of the types destroyed all hope of rivalling the beautiful productions of the European presses.

"Having been long and extensively engaged in the printing business, and suffering from the evil which we have stated, we undertook in 1814 to establish a new foundry, with an expectation of producing better types than were then in use; an undertaking so difficult to accomplish, that the design must in some degree be attributed to our want of accurate information. It was however begun and persevered in, and is now an extensive establishment, furnishing almost every de-

66

scription of types, which might be looked for in an old foundry, and some not furnished by any other. We not only produce better types than were formerly made, but have excited others to improvement; and we have every reason to be satisfied with the encouragement which we have received in our business."

April 4

The journal of Will Ransom contained an entry for April 4, 1903: "Saturday. Before I went to work this morning I went up to see Goudy and he made me a proposition to work with him during the summer. I might make enough to live on, but probably not, and then he may go East within the next sixty days, so that the whole thing is up in the air just at present. However, if circumstances permit, I shall make an awful effort to make it stick. Goudy has been exceptionally nice to me since I came, and if things turn out as I wish I will be indebted to him beyond all hope of repayment."

So Will Ransom, who himself developed into a type designer and one of the nation's finest typographers, expressed his thoughts about the personality of Frederic W. Goudy. Most people who came close enough to the great type designer to get to know him and to understand his motivation, shared Ransom's early opinion.

In 1929 Ransom still felt much the same way about Goudy. In his authoritative *Private Presses and Their Books,* he wrote: "His life work has been, and is, in type design. From the time when, an unknown bookkeeper, he drew an alphabet of capital letters and sold it to a type foundry, he has steadily and consistently produced excellent designs until now there are more than fifty faces to his credit with promise of more and perhaps better to come. It has been said, and with good reason, that Frederic W. Goudy has contributed more to type design than any other man in the history of printing. That opinion is based not alone upon the number and excellence of his types but even more upon a recognition of the fresh viewpoint he has injected into a difficult and limited field of art. The detailed elements of his procedure are largely technical and not pertinent here, but the principle is that letters for type should be drawn by an artist rather than constructed by a mechanic."

At the present time, nineteen years after his death, it is fairly common to hear Goudy denounced as a "period piece." His detractors tell each other that he would "starve to death" as a post-war designer. It is obvious that such remarks are made by people who just don't value the tenet to which Goudy held fast—the integrity of the individual in relation to his work.

Never in his life did the designer give less than he had bargained for. If he continued to design new type, it was primarily because the dream of the perfect roman letter was constantly alive in his mind. He endeavored to reproduce the idea in type metal. Thus, a long flow of roman letters in the 15th century Italian style came from his workshop, each one representing to his discerning eye a definite advance upon the path toward his ideal.

Goudy was right for his time, when there was a revival of interest in classic and traditional forms. Were he alive today he would undoubtedly develop along the lines in which he could contribute most. At present no single standard of typographical accomplishment exists. There are a dozen "schools" with no agreement among them. What is needed to bring them together is an individual with the highest of intellectual standards. Frederic W. Goudy, one of the most admired names of our times in the world of print, was uniquely qualified to fill such a role in his own period, and there is no reason to believe he would not be equally adequate today.

April 5

Upon this day in the happy extrovertish year of 1926 Oswald Bruce Cooper, a Chicago typographer and type designer, wrote a letter in which he predicted that Chicago would become the typefounding center of the country. "In case we fail," he said, "we may be able to touch off right smart red fire, anyway." Cooper was discussing his relationship with the typefoundry, Barnhart Brothers & Spindler, which was then joyfully producing Cooper-designed types by the ton.

In a fond chapter of the still fonder *The Book of Oz Cooper,* written and printed by

Cooper's friends in 1949, the late Richard N. McArthur, former advertising manager of the foundry, detailed the avoirdupois of the matter. "Already Cooper Black was the world's biggest seller in a single type face. If one considers that a 120-point capital M weighs 12 ounces, a capital W tilts a scant pound, the font 81.7 pounds, it can be understood how the tonnage mounted while the orders poured in from all over the roman type-using world and the matrices of the fifteen sizes of this great advertising type were kept hot on the casting machines."

Alas, Chicago did not attain its capital status, and BB&S succumbed in 1929 to the pressure of what was thirty-five years earlier call the Type Trust, the firm of American Type Founders. With the acquisition of the old Chicago letter foundry, ATF then became the undisputed producer of founder's type in the United States. By 1930 the Cooper design had run its course as the darling of the advertiser. Interest had shifted to the revival of the sans serif form as interpreted by the Bauhaus movement in Germany, and its imitators.

The Twenties, though, represented a glorious period for foundry types, perhaps the last that may be recorded. There was no competition from that thorn-in-the-side of the present typefounders, the photo-lettering industry. In 1923 ATF produced its splendid specimen book, containing 1148 pages, in an edition of sixty thousand copies.

The types of this period were wonderfully exotic, and are today even more nostalgic than those produced during the last century. Broadway, Modernique, Gallia, Nubian, Chic, Novel Gothic, and the rest are all long gone, but they did help keep things stirred up and exciting to printers who loved metal types. In the mid-sixties, the typefounders can't afford to be such entrepreneurs. It costs too much to take a flyer on a new design, and even when it is done, the wolf pack of photographic competitors will just copy it under the anonymity of a number, with a small footnote in the specimen book to tell the customer the type to which it is "similar."

April 6

"I am in receipt of your favor of March 25 in which you make inquiry as to my connec-

tion with the Paige Type-setting and Justifying Machine."

So begins a letter written on April 6, 1913 to Messrs. Lucien Alphonse Legros and John Cameron Grant, and reprinted in their monumental work, *Typographical Printing Surfaces.* The writer was David H. Fletcher, of Chicago, a patent attorney responsible for the final specifications of the remarkable machine known generally as the Paige Compositor. Of all the early attempts to set printers' types automatically, this device seems to retain the greatest amount of attention. Perhaps this is due to the association with Mark Twain, its principal backer.

Fletcher went on to state, "You ask 'if this work produced no ill effects upon my mind.' Viewed from a purely human standpoint—yes; viewed from the standpoint that the universe is not a blunder and that man is here for some great purpose—no. This extraordinary creation was both a triumph and a tragedy. Notwithstanding all of the trying experiences and disappointments associated with it, it was in many ways uplifting, broadening, and inspiring. In judging of it as an invention, I have tried to dismiss prejudice and to measure its merits with those of the great inventors of the world, and, as an automatic device, considering the character of the varying problems solved by it, I am of the opinion that it is the greatest thing of the kind that has been accomplished in all of the ages. Commercial failure as it was, for reasons which need not be mentioned, it was an intellectual miracle and its relation to men, as indicating the creative power of mind, is a suggestive verification of the prophecy that 'they shall become as Gods.' "

Fletcher could readily have damned the Paige machine. The patent application was filed in 1887 and took eight years to be approved, during which time one of the examiners died while the case was pending, another died insane, and the attorney who prepared the original case also died in an insane asylum.

Nevertheless the machine worked, and was just about everything its creator insisted it was. Five thousand pounds in weight, eleven feet long, and six feet high, the Paige compositor was a keyboard operated typesetter which assembled and distributed 6-point metal types. This feat was accomplished with the aid of some 18,000 moving parts, a complicating factor which limited its success, particularly at a moment when Mergenthaler's typesetting machine had already demonstrated its capabilities.

In 1895, the year in which the Paige machine was patented, 1,076 linotypes were manufactured. During a twenty year period of development just two Paige Compositors were built, both of which were presented to museums when the Mergenthaler firm purchased the Paige patents.

In 1894, in a sixty day test at the *Chicago Herald*, the Paige outperformed the individual machines in a battery of thirty-two linotypes which had been used by the newspaper for several years. The product turned out was reported to be, "in artistic merit, equal to the finest book-work ever set by hand." Operated by a competent journeyman printer, the Paige Compositor reputedly produced 8,000-10,000 ems per hour.

April 7

"The printers beg leave to acquaint their Subscribers and the Public, that the Types with which this Paper is printed are of AMERICAN manufacture, and should it by this means fail of giving such entire satisfaction to the judicious and accurate eye, they hope every patriotic allowance will be made in its favour, and that an attempt to introduce so valuable an art into these colonies, will meet with an indulgent countenance from every lover of his country."

Thus read a statement in the first issue of *The Pennsylvania Mercury*, published on April 7, 1775, by Enoch Story and Daniel Humphreys, who set up their printing office in Norris's Alley in Philadelphia. The paper was to last only until the end of the year, when the shop which produced it was burned down. It represents the initial work with American types, that is, types which were cut and cast in the American colonies and were actually used for practical purposes.

It has been well established that Abel Buell, a Connecticut silversmith, had cut and cast a font of type in May, 1769, of which only a proof was made. Buell cut a second font, with which he set up a petition to the Connecticut Legislature, but again this type was never put to other use.

At the time of the Buell announcement, Davis Mitchelson of Boston advertised that he, too, had produced types, "equal to any imported from Great Britain," but none of these are actually known to have been used, and in the absence of a specimen little credence may be given to this statement.

About 1770 in Germantown, Pennsylvania, Christopher Sower Jr. imported German matrices and molds and set up a foundry to cast letters to be used for the third edition of the German Bible which his father had originally printed in 1743. The fraktur type which Sower cast allowed him to be somewhat independent of the German typefounders and of imported fonts of type. Sower gave to one of his journeymen, Justus Fox, the responsibility of running the foundry. In 1772 he added Jacob Bay as an assistant. Both of these men learned all of the artifacts of typefounding in addition to simple casting.

Two years later Bay set up his own foundry and started to cast roman types, it was reported by William McCulloch, a Philadelphia printer, who wrote a treatise on the subject. He submitted his findings to Isaiah Thomas, author of *History of Printing in America*, published in 1810. Lawrence C. Wroth, the authority on printing during the colonial period, is inclined to agree with McCulloch's account, as a resolution made by the Pennsylvania Convention in January, 1775 stated: "That as printing types are now made to a considerable degree of perfection by an ingenious artist in Germantown; it is recommended to the printers to use such types in preference to any which may be hereafter imported."

It may be considered that the types of *The Pennsylvania Gazette* represent the first roman letters founded in America which received practical use. The notice published in the first issue made no claim to their perfection, saying, "We are sensible, that in the point of elegance, they are somewhat inferior to those imported from England, but we flatter ourselves that the rustic manufactures of America will prove more grateful to the patriot eye, than the more finished productions of Europe, especially when we consider that whilst you tolerate the unpolished figure of the first attempt, the work will be growing up to perfection by the experience of the ingenious artist, who has furnished us with this specimen of his skill, and we hope the paper will not prove less acceptable to our readers, for giving him this encouragement."

Early in 1891 there was set up in the Parish of St. Bride in London a Foundation which was to be a center for educational and social activities in the area. This spot happened to be also the heart of the district which had contained, from the time of Wynkyn de Worde, the majority of the printing establishments in the city. As one of the functions of the newly formed Foundation was to establish a school for printers, the Secretary of the London Society of Compositors suggested that his organization attempt to secure the library of the eminent printer and typographic historian, William Blades. This library had recently become available following the death of its owner in 1890. A deputation representing St. Bride's examined the library and placed upon it a value of £975.

When the Governing Board of the Foundation met for the first time on this day in 1891, the purchase of the library of William Blades was one of the principal items on the agenda. Since printing classes were to be a part of the program of the Foundation, permission was granted to provide half of the sum needed, with the stipulation that the remainder be obtained from other sources. With the help of printing firms and individuals in the craft, money was obtained and one of the great technical libraries in printing had received its start.

Of the other great libraries specializing in printing, the collection put together for American Type Founders Company by Henry Lewis Bullen is probably the most complete. This library is now the property of Columbia University. The Amsterdam Type Foundry maintains a magnificent collection of printing books, as does Enschedé en Zonen at Haarlem. While privately owned, both of these libraries are available for serious typographical studies. The Plantin Museum at Antwerp contains a fine library which has been virtually reorganized during the past dozen years. It is particularly strong in 16th century material relating to typefounding.

With the number of private collectors of technical books relating to printing growing year by year, it is indeed fortunate that there exist such well-established sources for the study of printing in all its aspects.

Shortly after Charles Dickens called New York City the most prosperous and worst-managed city in America, and another contemporary critic had complained, "She's had, as far back as I can remember, the reputation of being the dirtiest city in the Union!" a reform mayor was elected, on April 9, 1844, in the person of publisher James Harper. A founding partner of the famous firm, Harper & Brothers, James had left the farm just thirty-four years before to become a printer. Possibly his standing as a native-born businessman, Whig, and Methodist had more to do with his election then his skill as a printer, and certainly more than his skill as a politician.

In accepting his nomination, compositor Harper stated: "Gentlemen, I feel highly complimented that the mayoralty convention of the American Republican Party have honored me with the nomination for the office of mayor—I may add that such high honour I never expected—Gentlemen, if our fellow citizens confirm the nomination by electing me it will be my study to discharge the duties in conformity with the principles of our party—being a plain Mechanic I have rather been accustomed to doing than talking—you will therefore excuse my brevity."

The voters also excused it, apparently, as he was elected with a 4,000 vote majority, even though he scarcely campaigned. City Hall was once more safe from the domination of the foreign-born citizens who were at that period beginning to feel their muscles in municipal affairs and who were courted in their ambitions by the Democrats. Possibly the splendid *Illuminated Bible* which the Harper firm was then producing with a great fanfare of publicity had more to do with his election than the few speeches the nominee did make.

Harper did indeed live up to his billing as a reformer by removing the pigs from the city streets and eliminating cattle driving during daytime hours south of Fourteenth Street. He also hired 350 men, presumably loyal Republicans, to sweep those same streets. By ordinance he put in a contract system under which garbage was not allowed to accumulate. Mayor Harper also put the policemen—all two hundred of them—into uniforms for the first time, choosing blue coats with the large letters M.P., standing for Municipal Police, but which quickly converted to "Mayor's Pups" by the more waggish citizens. Another police department innovation of Harper's was the dividing of the city into police districts with a headquarters in each.

Printer Harper's Methodist upbringing apparently was of sufficient strength to make him shy away from a traditional printer's pastime, the enjoyment of the jug. A teetotaling printer was one thing, but the same failing in a mayor aroused indignation in certain quarters when he cracked down on disorderly grog shops, closing the saloons on Sundays and even on the Fourth of July, a day for great, and alcoholic, celebration by the populace. Edgar Allen Poe protested the Sunday closings with the argument that if the saloons were wicked enough to be shut down on the Sabbath, then why not on weekdays too? By decree of the mayor, the huge thirst of the city was to be assuaged by drinking from the large basin in the park which was filled with Croton water and supplied with tin cups chained to the sides. The water was cooled by cartloads of ice dumped in at regular intervals.

At the next election the city lost its printer-mayor. Reform mayors are rarely returned to office in New York.

April 10

The imprint, "Press of A. Colish," was for many years an indication of quality in printing far beyond the ordinary. Its proprietor, who died on this day in 1963, can well be considered one of the fine American printers of his time.

Abraham Colish was introduced to the printer's craft in the '90's when, in his twelfth year, he went to work for a Bridgeport, Connecticut printer for a weekly wage of seventy-five cents. His first job was selling a labor paper printed by his employer. When that periodical failed, he learned the skills of the compositor and the pressman. Within a year or two the boy was earning as much as three dollars a week. As an experienced printer at the age of sixteen, he then decided to try his luck in New York City. Going into a small shop on Canal Street, he was emboldened to ask for a job at $3.50 a week, and was thereupon hired.

After a year with this firm, he took a better paying job as a pressman, but soon tired of this, telling himself that it would be more fun to set type at half the amount he could earn by feeding a press. By 1903 he became the composing room foreman of Post and Davis on Fourth Avenue. Here he remained for three years. Later he took charge of the composing room of Rogers & Company, which was at that time doing work for the new advertising agency business. Colish soon learned that the setting of advertisements was not considered by employing printers to be a lucrative endeavor for a commercial printing firm. With a prophetic look to the future he wrote letters to a number of agencies enquiring whether they would be interested in a specialty composing room devoted to setting advertisements.

When the agencies expressed interest, Colish left Rogers & Company in 1917 to set up what was probably the first firm to engage exclusively in advertising typography. The firm prospered and soon branched out into the production of promotional printing. After a few years cylinder presses were added to the growing pressroom. During the Twenties Colish began to print small editions of books. His reputation as a fine printer became established. Today he is remembered and honored more for the distinguished books which he has printed than for his pioneering in advertising typography.

A most important collaboration took place when Colish was selected to print the 41-volume Shakespeare issued by the Limited Editions Club and designed by Bruce Rogers. A number of other Rogers books were produced, culminating in a splendid joint venture, the printing of a great Lectern Bible.

Rogers and Colish first discussed such a project during the printing of the Shakespeare. Together they produced a dummy for a folio bible, which came to the attention of World Publishing Company, specialists in the production of bibles. This firm then commissioned the printing of the finest bible yet to be produced in the United States. Colish personally supervised every detail in the production of this splendid book, a monument to his skill as a printer. In his description of the making of the World Bible, William Targ wrote, "Only Mr. Colish's enthusiasm and personal interest in the project could induce him to undertake so enormous a labor of love. He is craftsman enough to believe in old-fashioned vigilance. No half measures are allowed, no compromises . . . ." With each passing year there seem to be fewer printers who can measure up to such standards.

April 11

"We cordially wish every book, job, or newspaper printer in America, north, east, west, and south, to consider himself on our free list; and if any time our paper fails to reach him, let him acquaint us with the mishap, and we will do what we can to remedy the evil."

Thus were the printers of the land introduced to Volume 1, Number 1 of *Typographic Advertiser,* mailed to them on this day in 1855. Edited by Thomas MacKellar, a partner in the Philadelphia typefoundry, L. Johnson & Company, this quarterly became the first important periodical to be published for the American printing industry. Some ten years earlier, a monthly specimen sheet bearing the same title had been edited by Samuel Dickinson, the Boston typefounder, but it lasted but a few months. Another quarterly, *Ink Fountain,* published by Lay and Brothers of Philadelphia, was more successful, being first issued in 1852 and continuing until 1856.

The *Typographic Advertiser* was successful primarily because its editor was a first-rate printer, a typefounder of note, and a man with an unbounded enthusiasm to share his love of the printing craft with anyone who had the time to listen to him, in person or in print. He remained as editor until 1884, when he relinquished the task to his son, William B. MacKellar, who finally allowed the periodical to lapse in 1897. For forty-two years the periodical was one of the principal sources of communication among printers, although it contained more advertising for the sponsor than it did editorial columns. It was through the medium of these columns that MacKellar became one of the widest-known personalities in the industry.

In addition to providing "hints to the trade" and a few items of news, Editor Mac-Kellar indulged in his fondness to versify. The very first issue contained a bit of doggerel, entitled *The Printer:*

A mental lamp hung out beside life's wayside
  Unnoticed: yet his unpretending ray
  Shines clearly on man's intellectual way,
And proves to pilgrims an unfailing guide.
He hath within a worthy sort of pride.

April 12

Upon this day in 1870 in Salisbury, Maryland a compositor named Alexander W. Collins was born. He was destined to live but forty-eight years and achieved no great repute during his lifetime. His accomplishments were of an order which could not attract wide notice, but they did happen to receive the attention of a printing historian. Henry Lewis Bullen eulogized him in a short article which appeared in *The Inland Printer,* entitled "Only a Compositor." It was Bullen's hope that Collins would continue to live in the "hospitable pages" of that magazine.

"Only a compositor!" said Bullen. "Only a Gutenberg, a Caxton, a Bodoni, a William Morris, a De Vinne,—a noble company of compositors." What attracted Bullen about Collins' career was his devotion to the craft of the printer as expressed in the writings of the great practitioners. Collins, called by his fellow-comps, "Hair-space Aleck" for his skill at the case, very early in his life became a collector of books about printing. He soon became so knowledgeable concerning these books that he became friendly, through correspondence, with America's great scholar-printer, Theodore Low De Vinne.

Friendship with De Vinne prompted Collins to compile a very complete bibliography of the historian's literary works. De Vinne regarded this as the greatest compliment ever paid to him. Collins set into type his researches and presented them to De Vinne as a Christmas gift in 1912. Bullen apparently couldn't get over the skill evident in Collins' work. He wrote, "All who know the difficulties of bibliographic research wonder at the thoroughness and completeness of his compilation, especially when the isolation of the compiler in the darkest wastes of Pittsburgh is considered."

When Collins died, he left a library of beautifully printed books. It was exceeded only by two other private collections in the United States—those of De Vinne and Daniel Berkeley Updike, the Boston printer.

Bullen was greatly impressed by the breadth of interest shown by the library of the Pittsburgh compositor, stating, "When Bruce Rogers issued his beautiful and masterly translation of Bernard's 'Geoffrey Tory, painter and engraver, first royal printer, reformer of orthography and of typography under Francis I.; an account of his life and works,' published in a limited edition of 300, price $35 per copy, only seven printers did themselves the honor to purchase it, and this learned compositor was one of them."

April 13

"It is an easy thing to talk about the book—but difficult to find words that will give a true picture of the man. His was a character at once so simple that anyone could come to him, yet of such a nature that he evoked a feeling almost of reverence."

This, the opening paragraph in a volume of reminiscences, strives to put into words what all his associates felt about Oswald Bruce Cooper, born this day in 1879 in Mount Gilead, Ohio. Known to everyone as Oz, he nonetheless was generally addressed as Mr. Cooper, indicating the respect in which he was held by his contemporaries.

The Book of Oz Cooper was first mentioned at a meeting of the Society of Typographic Arts in Chicago in 1937, two years before Cooper's death. But it was not until 1949 that it was published. The volume represents a labor of love for its editor, the fine calligrapher, Raymond DaBoll, and its compositor, Edwin B. Gillespie, in addition to such well-known friends of Cooper as Fred Goudy, Bill Dwiggins, Richard McArthur, etc. It had been decided that the book should be set in 14-point Cooper Oldstyle, the first size of that type to be cast by the typefounder, Barnhart Brothers & Spindler. The fitting of many of the letters of this size was less than desirable. Cooper had planned to correct this, but had never completed the task. Gillespie, a compositor who had worked with Cooper for over twenty years, shaved and fitted every letter and proceeded to set the book, spending all his spare time on the task for a period of eleven years.

Cooper himself fitted his early years into a single succinct paragraph: "Born in Ohio, brought up in Coffeyville, Kansas, on the border of Indian Territory and on the edge of the Wild West. At fifteen began as printer's apprentice, during long school vacation (five months). Returned next summer to same job with enthusiasm. No pay; second summer one dollar a week. (Supplemental reading: Mark Twain on Pay for Apprentices.) Quit school at seventeen, making raspberry noise, having flunked algebra, geometry, history, Latin, physics. Still consider mathematics as subject for mathematicians, same as music for musicians. Returned again to print shop to stay until twenty, when swept into Chicago by urge to become great illustrator."

Cooper ended with a sentence saying that it was his loafing at Frank Holmes School of Illustration with Goudy and Dwiggins which gave him the most inspiration for his job in life. This autobiographical note was recovered by Mrs. Cooper from the wastebasket. It was therefore left for his friends to prepare a more adequate record.

It was in the design of letterforms that Cooper excelled. Without question he was one of the best that this country has yet produced. Naturally such skills were utilized by the typefounders, the Cooper series of types being in the main the result of his association with that art. Out of Cooper Oldstyle emerged one of the most distinctive of all American display types, Cooper Black, which was responsible for a trend when it was introduced in 1921, although its designer said of it, "For far-sighted printers with near-sighted customers."

April 14

A series of letters, one of which was dated April 14, 1920, were written between a boy employed as a printer's "devil" and the well-known printer of Salt Lake City, C. H. Porte. In them the numerous problems of the beginner in a printing office were discussed. The boy's questions were plaintive, and the answers he received were expressed in the platitudes of the times. It is doubtful, in fact, whether a contemporary youngster would accept them at face value. Most boys now seeking employment as printers have at least high school behind them and are sophisticated to a degree unknown to the kids who used to start work at the age of twelve.

In his letter of April 14, the boy wrote in part:

"... I am still taking proofs around and delivering packages, and not doing much else, except sweeping out and doing as I have for the last three months. I am wondering when I am going to learn the business. I want to be a printer, and am trying to be one, but Mr. Penrose doesn't seem to be in any hurry about it."

The reply, one of a series entitled *Letters to a Printer's Devil,* could have been a treatise on "How to Succeed, Though Young and Green." It would also have been quite acceptable as the basic plot of a book by Horatio Alger.

The very term, "devil," has now passed on. Its origin has never been exact, but for centuries the boy at the pre-apprentice level who worked for a printer was called the devil. Joseph Moxon, writing in 1683, defined him in this way: "The *Press-man* sometimes has a Week-boy to *Take Sheets,* as they are Printed off the *Tympan:* These boys do in a Printing-House, commonly black and Dawb themselves; whence the Workmen do Jocosely call them *Devils;* and sometimes *Spirits,* and sometimes *Flies.*"

One account attributes the term to the name of one of the first printers, Johann Fust, or Faustus, a partner of Gutenberg. As printing was supposedly a black art, the boys who worked for him were called devils. Aldus Manutius, the great Venetian printer, is involved in a similar story. He had a small Negro boy as a slave who was known in Venice as a little black devil. When the superstition spread that Aldus was invoking the aid of the black art with the help of the boy, Aldus brought his slave to church with him one day and stated:

"Be it known to Venice, that I, Aldus Manutius, printer to the Holy Church and Doge, have this day made public exposure of the printer's devil. All those who think he is not flesh and blood, may come and pinch him."

Still another legend concerning the origin of the word was that William Caxton, England's first printer, employed as his first errand boy the son of a man named De Ville or Deville, which is of course a much more innocent derivation than the necromantic attribution generally used.

The term has been pretty well relegated to the past and is now just one of scores of similar terms which have outlived their usefulness and remain only as an indication of the romantic past of the printing craft.

April 15

Adam Mappa, one of the earliest typefounders to set up and practice his craft in the United States, died on this day in 1828. He was thoroughly convinced that his life had been of no consequence. As a young man he had served in the Dutch army as a lieutenant. When his father purchased a typefoundry in Amsterdam, he resigned his commission in order to learn the typefounding business. A few years later he became involved in the abortive Patriot Party movement against King William V and had to leave Holland to live in France, where he again found himself face to face with a revolution.

It was in France, however, that Mappa met the American Ambassador, Thomas Jefferson, who persuaded him to emigrate to the United States and to start a typefoundry there. Jefferson's enthusiasm for this venture led him to recommend a selection of types which the printers of the new nation were not sufficiently sophisticated to appreciate. Thus, when Mappa with his wife and three children landed in New York after a lengthy seventy-six day voyage, he was prepared to set up a foundry to produce the standard roman types plus a number of the exotic styles represented by the Oriental languages.

Setting up his business at 107 Queen-Street, New York, Mappa advertised in the New York *Journal* of July 16, 1790 that he was prepared to fulfill the orders of the city's printers for "Types of every kind— viz. Roman, Italic, Black Letter, Script, German, Hebrew, Greek, Samaritan, Arabic, English Saxon, Siriac, &c., &c."

He mentioned that "the respective Printers can also be provided with proper Types, in all the learned languages, so that they may satisfy the wishes of the seminaries of learning throughout the continent."

This was indeed a tall order. While presses had been established by that date in all of the original colonies, there were but three printers west of the Appalachians, the great western movement not having really begun. The needs of American printers were simple. There was almost no scholarly printing be-

MARK TWAIN

See January 5, January 18, and December 18 for his story.

ing produced. The product of the press was restricted to the publishing of newspapers and local laws, plus a few primers which represented the closest thing to scholarly publishing.

For a year or so Mappa enjoyed excellent business, but the shortage of skilled help soon caught up with him. In order to provide the type for the printing of the 1792 *Laws of the State of New-York* he had to cast the letters himself. Since he did not possess journeyman skill as a typecaster, the project suffered delays and the types were of poor quality. The editor of the book had to print an apology to his subscribers, in which he attempted to soften the criticism by stating that it was his honest desire "to give Encouragement to the Manufactures of our State," and that "no Cash went to London" for the types.

In 1794 Mappa put his foundry up for sale. It is believed that most of the equipment was acquired by the new Philadelphia firm of Binny & Ronaldson the following year. Theodore L. De Vinne made a comparison of the earliest Mappa types with those later produced by the New York typefounders and could find no trace of them. Thomas MacKellar, when tracing the history of his own foundry, MacKellar, Smiths & Jordan, discovered an 1822 memorandum book which referred to sixteen sets of foreign matrices from Mappa's foundry.

Mappa finished out his life as an energetic agent for the Holland Land Company, performing outstanding service in the re-settlement of many of his former countrymen into New York State.

April 16

In a paper read before the Society of Arts in London on this day in 1890, the English typefounder and writer, Talbot Baines Reed, discussed the revival of interest in typography then taking place. Most of his comments were to the point and bear repeating for the present generation of typographers:

"As artists," he began, "the printer and the letter cutter are responsible to their generation. We live in the midst of a violent reactionary movement against dullness and conventionalism of all kinds. The artist has his three courses. He may sell himself slave to his public, and go where he is driven. He may set himself stubbornly to stem the torrent and fall a martyr to his conservatism; or he may strive honestly to control, even while following, the popular movement, and with his clearer artistic knowledge to direct it along lines of moderation and good taste. . . .

"I must remind you that the perfect model of a letter is altogether imaginary and arbitrary; there is a definite model for the human form. The painter, the sculptor, the architect, have their models in nature. But the man who sets himself up to make an alphabet has no copy but that left to him by former artists. He knows that the symbol which denotes the sound 'I' must be perpendicular, and that that which denotes 'O' must be round. But what should be the height of the 'I' in proportion to its width, how the extremities of the stroke should be finished, on what particular arcs and parallels his 'O' is to be erected —on all that is, which pertains to the fashion of the letter—he has no absolute standard. His own eye must furnish the criterion. If the work of those who have gone before satisfies that criterion, he copies it. If it comes short, he corrects it.

"What, then, is the criterion? It consists, I venture to think, primarily in the legibility of the character, and secondly on its beauty. It may be urged that the two are inseparable, and I am prepared to admit that, as a rule, the truest beauty in art is that which suggests utility. But it is possible for the two to exist without one another. . . . An arrangement of lines and curves and angles may be beautiful in itself, but unless it suggests a form it is valueless. And the more clearly and definitely it suggests that form the more we admire it. Type that is not legible, and in the case of books and newspapers easily legible, however elegant its lines, however delicate its execution, is not a good type. So that the artist of letters finds that his first test of an excellent letter is its legibility, and the second— which may easily be a consequence of the first—its grace and beauty. . . .

"I take it as a hopeful sign that the esthetics of typography are at the present time being studied by men of artistic taste and authority. The result cannot fail to be of benefit. For printing, in all its career, has followed close in the wake of its sister arts. When they have flourished, we have had our most beautiful books; when they have declined, printing has gone down below them.

It is a bad day in the history of any art when it becomes a mere trade, and the 'Art which preserves all other arts' should by all means be saved from that calamity."

April 17

Samuel Rust of New York City was granted a patent on this day in 1829 for a printing press, which he named after George Washington. For several years this machine was manufactured by the firm of Rust and Turney, but in 1835 it was taken over by R. Hoe & Company, the principal builders of American presses. The Washington was a hand press. While it was about the last of this type to be developed, it was destined to be a useful machine for another hundred years. During this whole period it was widely admired as the most popular of the hand presses to be constructed in America.

From the time of Gutenberg in the mid-15th century, the hand press underwent relatively few technological improvements until about 1800, when Lord Stanhope in England produced the first press completely constructed of iron which could print a full-sized form. Stanhope improved the screw principle of the older wooden presses by adding a second lever to actuate the screw, thereby increasing the power of the impression and diminishing the effort of the pressman to accomplish this. As his lordship refused to patent his press and built it "for the good of the trade," so to speak, there were within a few years a number of presses manufactured which applied his methods of actuating the platen to make the impression.

George Clymer of Philadelphia produced the Columbian Press, but finding that American printers did not favor it, he went to England in 1817 to manufacture the press there. Here it became one of the most popular presses of its time. John J. Wells of Hartford, Connecticut patented a hand press in 1819, which utilized a fairly simple toggle joint instead of a screw. This was closely followed by an improved press developed by Peter Smith of New York and then a few years later by the Washington Press. The latter became very quickly the standard hand press in the United States. Over six thousand were manufactured by the Hoe firm prior to 1900. Hoe continued to build the press until

the Thirties, although for the last forty years of this period, it was used primarily for the proofing of photoengravings. Thomas MacKellar, writing in the 1872 edition of his manual, *The American Printer,* stated that, "Hand presses are now restricted to country papers of small circulation, and to book-offices devoted to extra-fine printing."

At the present time there exists a love affair between private press printers and the Washington hand press, making it extremely difficult to find one of the old machines. Many of these establishments have apparently adopted the motto of Porter Garnett, who began his fine article on hand press printing (appearing in Vol. I of *The Dolphin* in 1933) with the sentence: "The hand-press not only records, it glorifies."

April 18

On April 18, 1925, a printer discussed in a radio talk the production of a book which had been printed in his plant. Normally reticent about speaking in public, William Edwin Rudge was perhaps emboldened by the fact that it was also his wedding anniversary.

The Printing House of William Edwin Rudge, then located in Mount Vernon, New York, was one of the notable printing offices of its period. At the particular time, it was at the height of its fame for its production of fine books. In addition it was noted for first class commercial printing, for which there was a somewhat better market.

Rudge, the son of a printer who had operated a very small shop in New York City, had no early love for printing. However, he had, by force of circumstances, become responsible for his family's business at an early age because his father became too ill to continue it on his own. At the age of eleven he had worked in the shop, learning the trade in the fashion of the typical printer's devil. While he found it necessary to leave school in order to help out, he later managed to complete a three years' course in engineering at night at Cooper Union. But increased responsibilities in the small shop interfered with such study, and young Rudge settled down to be a printer.

The quality of printing produced by his shop was quite ordinary and comparable to the output of the countless little plants scattered through downtown Manhattan. In one aspect, however, Rudge slowly acquired a reputation, and this was in his ability to schedule and deliver his work promptly.

Rudge became one of the founders of the Graphics Group which met at the National Arts Club, and included such men as Thomas Nast Fairbanks, Frederic W. Goudy, Hal Marchbanks, and John Clyde Oswald. The intellectual challenge of this group awoke in Rudge a love for the historic values of his craft and a realization that printing could be more than just a livelihood. He enlisted the aid of the best typographic designers. By 1920 he was producing such a volume of top quality printing that he was able to enter over a hundred pieces in the famous National Arts Club Exhibition of that year. Of the thirty-nine medals awarded, his firm won six, with designs commissioned from Goudy, Bruce Rogers, and Elmer Adler.

In 1921 the plant was moved to Mount Vernon. For the next ten years some of the finest printing being produced in America issued from its presses. It was this period that was dominated by Bruce Rogers, who designed eighty books for the firm up to 1931. Among these are several of Rogers' finest books, such as the *Journal of Madam Knight, Pierrot of the Minute,* and *Champ Fluery.* The 18-volume *Boswell Papers* was another design of Rogers which was a unique achievement of the firm.

With his reputation fully established and his dedication to fine printing in full swing, William Edwin Rudge died prematurely in his fifty-fourth year in 1931. In its obituary, the *Inland Printer* stated, ". . . we have in the industry men who are printers because they love their work beyond any other activity in life. Printing to this type of craftsman is an art, a passion, a lifework of consuming interest. It was in this group that William Edwin Rudge towered above most printers."

April 19

"It is one of the more felicitous privileges of the bookman's life to meet in this hall. In the sixty-odd years of the Grolier Club's existence, it has made a distinguished name for itself as an association of book collectors and book makers. And I think it is sometimes overlooked that without book makers, that is to say, without the artisans who print and bind books, there would be no book dealers, book collectors, or book guardians—that is, librarians."

So began a talk given by Carl Purington Rollins, Printer to Yale University, at the opening of an exhibition of his work at the Grolier Club on this day in 1949. Titling his remarks, "Souvenirs of My Inky Past," Rollins, one of the very fine printers of our times, spoke from the viewpoint of a practical printer, reminding the bibliophile audience of the contributions of the craftsmen to the book arts.

"It was Theodore De Vinne and the Grolier Club," he said, "which first in this country emphasized the 'mechanick exercise' of printing and book making as of equal importance, at least, with the sentimental lore of book loving.

"Even the most devoted printer must acknowledge that he must have a text to print, though I have known customers who seemed to labor under the delusion that the printing could begin before the copy was ready! But manners must adorn knowledge, and it is the printer's province to take the raw material of the book, the text, and give it comely form. It has not infrequently happened that the printer tends to mistake his calling, and attempts a primary object of artistic creation, confusing the means for the end. It was probably a fit of exasperation at the *édition de grande luxe* which caused Mrs. Warde to write that 'type must be invisible.' . . .

"The printing press, by its very name, implies that the type is to be impressed into the paper, and by that means rendered readable and permanent. For it is the permanence of print which is one of its great contributions to human development. Permanence, of course, is a relative term, when applied to the handiworks of man, and five hundred years, the life span of the oldest printing, is a short period as compared with the Spanish cave paintings or the Rosetta stone. . . .

"Fond of our archaic cast lead type, accustomed to our uncouth roman letters, preferring the solid, penetrating impression into the surface of the paper made from linen rags, I am by no means sure that these elements of printing are sure to last. Chinese and Arabic symbols are much handsomer than even Jenson's or Bodoni's or Caslon's or Bruce Rogers' type forms. The energetic protagonist of the manuscript hand suggests a new calligraphy. The camera, which was the key to the ubiquitous and loathsome half-tone printing block, has now been harnessed to the composing machine. And finally Senefelder's method of surface printing, developed into the offset press, permits of a much greater flexibility than the printing press. It may well be that before the six-hundredth anniversary of Gutenberg's invention rolls around, the whole process of printing will be changed. The devoted apostles of electronics may even eliminate printer's ink, and the plasticists, paper! But so far as one may see at the moment, printing will still provide us with the readiest, cheapest, most useful and permanent way of recording human thought."

April 20

John Gamble, an English paper mill proprietor, obtained on this day in 1801 a patent for a machine "for making paper, in single sheets, without seams or joinings, from one to twelve feet and upwards in length." Thus, with patent No. 2487, the printing industry marched into the industrial revolution.

While paper had first been used in Europe since the 10th century, it was not until late in the 13th century that paper was first manufactured on the continent. Until Gutenberg developed movable type, there had really been no great demand on papermakers to venture beyond the hand methods of production. The printing press, however, soon increased paper usage to a degree which made it increasingly difficult for paper manufacturers to keep pace. The shortage was not alone in the number of vats in which to form the paper, but in the materials which went into its manufacture. The supply of rags, both linen and cotton, was insufficient for the demand. The use of other fibers became imperative if the presses were to be kept busy.

John Gamble owed his patent orginally to being the brother-in-law of François Didot, a French papermaker and member of the distinguished family of printers. An employee of Didot named Nicholas-Louis Robert—an overseer of the personnel in the paper mill at Essones—had become so discouraged with the bickering and lack of discipline among the workers in the mill that he determined to develop a method by which paper could be manufactured without the dependence upon the papermaker's guilds. He built a model of a machine to manufacture paper, but it was a failure. He would have dropped the matter there and then but for the enthusiasm of Didot who prevailed upon Robert to continue with his experiments, with the result that a second machine was successful.

At the urging of St. Leger Didot, the inventor applied in 1798 for a patent, which was granted with great enthusiasm early in 1799. In the interim Robert was so excited about the possibilities of renown which his invention would bring him that he quarrelled with his sponsors. The economic disturbances of the Revolution contributed to a delay in the manufacturing of the machine, during which time Robert sold his patent to Didot, the payment to be made in installments. When Didot reneged on these payments, the inventor bought back his patent in 1801. It was at this juncture that Didot wrote to Gamble to enquire whether sufficient capital could be raised in England for the building of the first large machine.

Gamble in turn secured the financial aid of two London stationers, Henry and Sealy Fourdrinier. A machine was constructed by a mechanic named Bryan Donkin, using the plans prepared by Robert. The first machine was built at the Frogmore mill, Two Waters, Hertfordshire, at a cost to the Fourdrinier brothers of £60,000. For this considerable sum, the Fourdriniers received relatively little financial return, but the papermaking machine has since borne their name. A flaw in the original patent was responsible for the outcome of their investment, the result being that a number of manufacturers became involved in constructing machines without having to pay royalties. None of the pioneers in the development of this vitally important machine received just compensation for their efforts, but their contributions to the welfare of future generations may not be underestimated.

April 21

H. M. Leydenberg, Director of the New York Public Library wrote, on this day in 1936, to the printing historian and editor, John Clyde Oswald:

"Let me thank you for your note of April 20th about the forlorn widow as the printer recognizes her. The question came up as a routine matter some time ago, and our efforts to run it down led to appeals to various sources. Recently we wrote to half-a-dozen of the outstanding printers in the country, you among them, and we plan to set forth in our *Bulletin* the results of these efforts. We are grateful for your help, and we shall see that a copy of the statement is sent you when it is printed."

The "note" to which Dr. Leydenberg was referring contained Oswald's attempts to explain the typographic widow, in which he stated:

"I have to confess that I have no definition of a *widow*. You ask, 'Does the lady appear only at the top of a page, or would she be so tagged if at the bottom?' According to my understanding, a typographic widow appears only at the top, just as would any other widow, no matter what situation she might find herself in.

"I have delayed answering your letter of the 10 ins. in order to spend some time in research. I have gone over the books in my library in which some references to widows might appear, but find nothing on this subject.

"It is the rule in American printing offices to do away with typographic widows by some sort of surgery, although I have noticed that Mr. Updike must consider the practice an affectation because he does not, himself, observe it, and I think I have seen the same thing in books done by Mr. Rogers and Mr. Rollins.

"Widows are to be found occasionally in the work of the early master printers. I am not sufficiently familiar with the best work done abroad at the present to be able to speak authoritatively about them.

"Regretting that I cannot answer your question more definitely, I am Very Sincerely, John Clyde Oswald."

Mr. Oswald shouldn't have apologized, as none of the other outstanding printers were any more knowledgeable about the matter. While it is recognized by many printers that a widow is a short line, such as a paragraph ending, which occurs at the top of a new page or column, this explanation is by no means agreed upon. Dr. Leydenberg soon found out that his "experts" were of mixed opinions concerning the lady. Almost in unison, however, they rushed to the typographic shelves of their libraries in order to consult with the masters—all with no positive result. David Pottinger, of Harvard University Press, went through all the printer's manuals from Moxon to the present, and couldn't even find the term listed.

Carl P. Rollins, Printer to Yale University, became intrigued. Gathering together a gaggle of typographers he "combed the Grolier Club Library for information, and the result was NIL." Daniel B. Updike agreed with Leydenberg on the general definition, but admitted he didn't know the origin of it.

William A. Kittredge, the Chicago typographer made the most sensible suggestion when he wrote, "Merry widow! Grass widow! College widow! I think we should ask them about their sister."

April 22

At a point in the North Atlantic Ocean approximately Latitude 53° N., and Longitude 32° W., a battleship of the United States Atlantic Fleet was headed this day in 1942 on a zig-zag course. By this route the Navigator hopefully believed the ship would eventually reach port within a half day of the Estimated Time of Arrival which he had handed to the Captain when the vessel had cleared the sea-buoy off Reykjavik, Iceland.

The *U.S.S. New York* had but a few days previously celebrated her twenty-eighth birthday, and was not at that point of her career a ship which could reasonably be expected to do battle with say, the *Tirpitz,* or even the *Scharnhorst.* Her presence in a home-bound convoy, however, was for just such an eventuality. Her sailors, in conversation with seamen of other ships and other navies, proudly referred to how the "Old Queen" would perform in such an encounter, but among themselves they were dubious of the result of a meeting between "this old pig-iron bastard" and the Nazi battlewagons.

At this particular moment, though, no matter how anxiously the lookouts might scan the horizon or the Officer of the Deck might quiz the radar operators, there were some thirteen sailors aboard who were interested in but one objective—one which sorely tried their technical resources. Lord Nelson or John Paul Jones might have quizzically raised their fighting nautical eyebrows at this activity, because it had absolutely no relationship to naval science. The thirteen sailors were, in fact, printers, and three decks down into the warship, they were engaged in a task which couldn't possibly have any bearing upon the outcome of the Battle of the Atlantic. They were printing, folding into signatures, and stitching a twelve-page booklet measuring 3-15/16 inches by 5-3/16 inches, entitled *History of the U.S.S. New York*.

This historic first-edition work is possibly unknown to bibliophiles, even to those few specialists who collect high-seas imprints. That is just as well, as it represents typography at a low ebb. It was set in 8-point solid Century Expanded, with a nonpareil between paragraphs, and in 10-point Century Schoolbook italic for Dedication and Colophon. The typographic *piéce de resistance,* discussed at some length by the sailor-typos, was the use of Typo Upright Shaded for the title on the cover. While the circumstances were perhaps unique, so was the printing office itself. In size, about fifteen by twenty-four feet, it contained: 1 Model 8 Linotype machine, an 8x10 Chandler & Price platen press, 1 Chandler & Price Craftsman Automatic platen press, 1 power cutter (which served an auxiliary purpose as a hide-out behind which a drunk could be slept off), 2 3x5 feet imposing surfaces, 2 twenty-four case make-up banks, plus paper storage bins, a clutter of miscellaneous items such as hell boxes, linotype magazine rack, furniture racks, galley racks, and lead and slug racks. In and around were cots for five of the printers, including the present writer, in addition to their storage lockers.

The *U.S.S. New York* continued her course westward through the long North Atlantic swells, with the lookouts on watch continuing their vigil of seeking out the *Tirpitz.* However, the enemy was not encountered, allowing this naval imprint to be completed and distributed to the ship's company.

April 23

April 23, 1924, Bertram Grosvenor Goodhue, American architect, died. While Goodhue achieved notable success in his profession, the printer's fraternity is most interested in his contributions to the book arts. Beginning his career at the same time and in the same spirit as the William Morris revival, he produced innumerable decorative designs in the medieval style, particularly borders and initials. Goodhue also designed two types, the first of which was commissioned by Daniel B. Updike, proprietor of the Merrymount Press of Boston, and named for the Press. Merrymount type was a bold, solid letter patterned upon the same Venetian originals as the Golden type of Morris. It was ideal for the closely-set and boldly decorated pages of the Kelmscott style.

It was with his second type, Cheltenham, that Goodhue produced one of the best known American typefaces. It was designed originally as a book type for the Cheltenham Press, operated by Ingalls Kimball in New York City, and incorporated Goodhue's ideas concerning a legible type rather than an aesthetic one.

Goodhue reasoned that white space above the line of type increased legibility. Therefore he increased the height of the ascenders of his type, keeping the descenders quite short, an attribute which does increase the legibility of words composed into lines. The serifs of Cheltenham were narrowed, allowing the closer fitting of individual letters, and the contrast between the strokes of each character was minimized.

While all of these facts are important in a type designed for straight-matter composition, and were fulfilled in the Cheltenham design, it is ironic that the great success of the type was in the setting of display matter rather than in book composition. Kimball sold the design to both American Type Founders Company and Mergenthaler Linotype Company. By 1906 it was on its way to becoming the most successful type ever produced and probably the best known face to come from an American designer.

In all this activity, however, Goodhue had no part. Kimball later wrote that while the designer was pleased with the great popular success of the basic letter, he was never willing to forgive the many commercial variations that were made of it by the foundry and the composing machine manufacturer.

Under the guidance of Morris Benton, American Type Founders put Cheltenham in the family way. Starting with the medium weight original, Cheltenham was narrowed, stretched, and generally contorted to meet every demand a printer could make upon a type. The 1923 specimen book of ATF lists

23 variations of what printers soon learned to call "Chelt." As most of these ranged from 6-point to 72-point, and several reached all the way to 144-point, it would require over 350 type cases to hold the whole family.

For long years Cheltenham reigned as the supreme display type for advertising and commercial printing, until during the Twenties, it was supplanted by supposedly more sophisticated types. Following the revival of the sans serif types, Chelt was relegated to the country newspaper shop. It emerges only upon occasion for use in national advertising, at which times articles appear about Chelt being "revived." It is still a useful type, and although just a few of the variations are still available, it will undoubtedly be around for a long time to come.

April 24

On this day in 1911, the "greatest library ever assembled by an American" was auctioned in the first of the nine sessions which witnessed the disposal of 14,996 books, realizing the sum of $1,932,000, and making it by long odds the most important book auction ever held.

The library had originally been gathered by Robert Hoe III of the third generation of the great family of printing press manufacturers which had revolutionized the development of rotary presses. Hoe was no mere rich and ambitious collector of books but was a discriminating critic of fine printing. He was a founding member of the Grolier Club and its first president. In fact it was in his home that the group had originally met. Robert Hoe put together a magnificent library representing the great ages of the printer's art, and including examples of the work of every outstanding historic printer.

Had the auctioneer been a circus barker he would no doubt have burst out with "Not one! But two!" when the greatest of all printed books, the 42-line Bible printed by Johann Gutenberg, was brought under the hammer. Never again was there to be such an event. It is extremely doubtful that even a single Gutenberg Bible will again come up for sale at auction. One copy, on vellum, was sold that night to Henry Huntington through his agent, George D. Smith, for $50,000—the largest amount up to that time ever paid

for a single book. The second bible, on paper, was knocked down to Bernard Quaritch, the London bookseller, whose father had sold Hoe both copies for just $27,500. That particular copy is now at Harvard University.

Present at the auction was the rising young bookseller, A. S. W. Rosenbach of Philadelphia. He had already acquired some wealthy clients, but he found himself outclassed and outbid by such auctionroom titans as the aforementioned Smith, who at this one auction raised Huntington, the California millionaire, to eminence as the premier American book collector. J. Pierpont Morgan was represented by Belle da Costa Greene, and Walter Hill of Chicago bid for Mrs. McCormick, the daughter of John D. Rockefeller. Rosenbach's biographer records that, "Thousand dollar bids were piled up like Ossa on Pelion."

Among the books which found new shelves were the rare first printing of Malory's *Morte d'Arthur* which went for $42,800 to Morgan, the only known copy of a vellum *Helyas Knight of the Swanne,* printed by Caxton's apprentice, Wynkyn de Worde, which Mrs. McCormick secured for $21,000. And so the fabulous sale continued, building the auction into a never-to-be-forgotten legend, its like perhaps not to be witnessed again.

It was Robert Hoe's wish that his books be put up for sale rather than to be donated to an institutional library. "If the great collections of the past had not been sold," he had said, "where would I have found my books?"

April 25

"Since we must have books," wrote Jean-Jacques Rousseau, "there is just one which, to my mind, furnishes the finest of treatises on education according to nature. My son shall read this book before any other; it shall for a long time be his entire library, and shall always hold an honorable place. It shall be the text on which all our discussions of natural science shall be only commentaries. It shall be a text for all we need during our progress toward a ripened judgment, and so long as our taste is unspoiled, we shall enjoy reading it. What wonderful book is this? Aristotle? Pliny? Buffon? No; it is *Robinson Crusoe!*"

Written by Daniel De Foe, *Robinson Crusoe* was published on April 25, 1719. It became an instant success, although in manuscript the work had not been popular with those publishers to whom it had been shown. An account of De Foe's difficulties with his novel was written some twenty years after its publication. "Robinson Crusoe's manuscript ran through the whole trade, nor would anyone print it, though the writer was in good repute as an author. One bookseller at last, not remarkable for his discernment, but for his speculative turn, engaged in this publication. *This* bookseller got above a thousand guineas by it; and the booksellers are accumulating money every hour by editions of this work in all shapes."

Within forty years the novel had appeared in forty-one different editions and some fifteen "imitations." Of the latter, the first of which appeared during the original year of publication, De Foe bitterly protested: "The injury these men do the proprietor of this work, is a practice all honest men abhor; and he believes he may challenge them to show the difference between that and robbing on the highway, or breaking open a house. If they can't show any difference in the crime, they will find it hard to show any difference in the punishment."

While a first edition of *Robinson Crusoe* is today a most valuable piece of property, its prestige is due primarily to its rarity, and not at all to its worth as a prime example of the printer's art. Henry C. Hutchins, in a study of the book, writes: "The year 1719 in which *Robinson Crusoe* appeared under the imprint of William Taylor, at the Sign of the Ship in Paternoster Row, comes in a period which is referred to by most writers on the history of printing in England as the dark age."

There was at the time very little typefounding in England, although the estimable William Caslon was even then contemplating a career in that craft. English printers were almost completely dependent upon Dutch sources for their types, and even those types which were cast in England owed their origin to Dutch founders. The conclusion of authorities on 18th century typography and printing is that the book was composed of letters cast in England by native typefounders, but utilizing matrices which had been imported from Holland, possibly originally cut by Voskens.

"In the choice of books to print I have been influenced partly by my own personal taste in literature and partly by the suitability of a book from the purely typographical standpoint—or perhaps it would be more true to say by a combination of these two factors."

C. H. St. John Hornby, proprietor of the great Ashendene Press, who died upon this day in 1946, so wrote in the foreword to *The Ashendene Press: An Account of its Origin and History.* All those amateur printers who are presently reviving the ideals of the private press would profit from a careful reading of Hornby. He followed to the letter the precepts which he discusses, with the result that the Ashendene books were notable productions, although, of course, far beyond the capabilities of the ordinary amateur.

"My choice," he continued, "has therefore fallen in a majority of cases upon books which gave scope for a certain gaiety of treatment in the use of coloured initials and chapter-headings; or, as in the case of *Utopia* and *Thucydides,* marginal notes in colour. Such books present a more interesting problem to the printer, and as I have worked for my own pleasure and amusement without having to keep too strict an eye upon the cost, personal indulgence in this respect has been easy. There are many books I would have wished to include in my list of work done; the Bible, for instance, and Shakespeare, and Montaigne, and scores of others; but time and opportunity forbade. So short, alas, is the span of a working life measured in relation to what we would each of us fain accomplish before its end."

In the thirty-eight years the Ashendene Press was in existence, Hornby made no attempt to produce books in volume, being satisfied if he could turn out one fine work each year. Perhaps Stanley Morison had Hornby in mind when he wrote, "Fine printing may be described as the product of a lively and seasoned intelligence working with carefully chosen type, ink, and paper. First it must be borne in mind that a fine work is more than 'something to read.' The amateur looks for character in printing. The book therefore which essays to rank above the commonplace will, while not failing in its original purpose, carry the personality of its maker no less surely than that of its author and subject."

All too frequently, the amateur printer violates the principles of good craftsmanship, but these are skills which may be acquired by application. If he wishes, by the intelligent selection of materials, to honor the author whose words he reproduces, he must make every effort to suit his methods to the task at hand. He must at all costs, temper his enthusiasm to print until he has made an adequate study of the correct procedures, in addition to a fully sympathetic understanding of the best traditions of private printing.

Perhaps the words of the French poet Valéry, should be on the wall of every aspiring amateur printer:

"The mind of the writer is seen as in a mirror which the printing press provides. If the paper and the ink are in accord, if the type is clear, if the composition is well looked after, the adjustment of line perfect, and the sheet well printed, the author feels his language and his style anew. He thinks he hears a clearer, firmer voice than his own, a voice faultlessly pure, articulating his words, dangerously detaching all his words. Everything feeble, effeminate, arbitrary, and inelegant which he wrote, speaks too clearly and too loud. To be magnificently printed is a very precious and important tribute."

April 27

Henry Lewis Bullen, one of the most prolific writers on the subject of typography, died on April 27, 1938 in his eightieth year, honored for a unique and outstanding career devoted to the advancement of the printing craft. Indefatigable in his efforts to raise the standards of the ordinary printer, this Australian-born typographic historian and his work remain unknown to most ordinary printers, but he has left a living monument which can never be forgotten—the great American Type Founders Typographic Library at Columbia University.

Bullen was apprenticed as a printer at the age of fourteen in his native Australia. Four years later his nervous energy and boundless ambition led him to make the long journey to the United States where the opportunities for advancement seemed greater than at home. He arrived in New York in 1875. For the next five years he worked in several other American cities as a compositor, finally going to Boston where in 1882 he left the case and became editor of promotional material for Golding & Company, manufacturer of platen presses and printer's tools and supplies. His efforts were so productive that he was named sales manager the following year.

In 1885 Bullen met Henry O. Shepard, publisher of *The Inland Printer,* a recently established trade periodical. This connection led to an anonymous article concerning platen presses which appeared in October, 1885. Until June 1931, Bullen was a constant contributor to the printing journal, probably being best known for the department which bore the title "Collectanea Typographica," that appeared monthly from January 1918 to June 1931, with a few gaps occurring in 1925, 1927-28. His first important article in a series for *The Inland Printer* was "The Discursions of a Retired Printer," written under a pseudonym. The series appeared in a number of issues and the articles remain an authoritative source of information on the history of American typefounding.

In the first "Discursion" article Bullen suggested that American Type Founders Company finance a typographic library. Of course he hinted that he would be happy to cooperate. Robert W. Nelson, president of the firm, became interested. The result of the suggestion was that Bullen became librarian of the nucleus collection of printing books which ATF gathered in its Jersey City plant in 1908.

During the next thirty years Bullen put together the finest typographic library ever assembled in the United States, spending all of his waking hours in the promotion of the books and of the industry which they represented. His enthusiasm for the literature of printing was inspiring to a young assistant librarian he hired directly from the library school of Columbia University. Beatrice Warde has certainly, in the ensuing years, been a loyal pupil of her former mentor in Jersey City.

When Robert Nelson died in 1926, Bullen seemed to lose much of his enthusiasm. During the depression years of the thirties, the management of the foundry listed the library and its upkeep as a liability. Fortunately the magnificent collection was not broken up to be sold piecemeal, but has since remained intact at Columbia University where it continues to enhance the heritage of the printer.

April 28

"Take it, therefore, in good part, and it please you, O devoted and worthy lovers of well-made letters, and believe that what I have done has been done with zeal and hearty good-will. Praying our Lord JESUS to give you all increase in well-made letters and excellent virtues, withall sound health of body and soul. At Paris this XXVIII day of April on the Petit Pont at the sign of the Pot Cassé."

And so did Geofroy Tory, man of the Renaissance, professor, proofreader, engraver, publisher, bookseller and first of a long line of *Printers du Roi* in France, close the introduction to his book, *Champ Fleury*, published in 1528. In *Champ Fleury*, Tory attempted three things: he wished to bring rules of good taste and sound diction to the French language; he next treated the proportion of roman letters "compared with the natural body and face of the perfect man," and finally gave directions for the construction of fine roman letters. Altogether, a tall order and one which had already been attempted by such earlier writers as Feliciano, de Pacioli, Verini, and Dürer. Tory's great contribution was to bring to the study of typography sound scholarship, and the ability of a fine teacher to inspire his contemporaries to look to his ideals. His typographic skill is evident in the construction of his magnificent roman initials with floriated backgrounds to match the other decorative materials of a book.

Tory began his introduction to *Champ Fleury* with sonorous phrases: "Geofroy Tory of Bourges offers humble greetings to all true and devoted Lovers of well-formed Letters. Poets, Orators, and others learned in Letters and Sciences, when they have made their studious diligence and toil, are wont to present it to some great lord of the Court or the Church, lifting him up by letters and laudation to the knowledge of other men; and this to flatter him and to the end that they may be always so welcome about him, that he seems to be bound and obliged to give them some great gift, some benefice, or some office, as reward for the labours and vigils they have put to the making and composition of their said works and offerings. I could easily do the like with this little book; but considering that, if I should present it to one rather than to another, some feeling of envious despite might be caused, I have thought that it would be well of me to make of it a present to you all, O devoted Lovers of well-made Letters, without placing the great before the lowly, unless it be so far as he loves letters more, and is more at home in virtuous things. Thus the Prelates and great Lords, who are eminent, all in goodly virtues, will have their part therein, whilst you will not lose yours."

April 29

The journal of Thomas James Cobden-Sanderson contained for this day in 1900 the following entry: "I have in hand now: (1) Organization of Printing Press. We are in treaty for No. 1 in the Terrace, and propose to install our printing press there. . . . And we have engaged a compositor, J. H. Mason, sent to us with a superlative character by Miss Sheepshanks. . . . He began work last Monday week on *Agricola,* at the Bindery, in the attic over my room. This has at last set us in motion; we have ordered 'oddments' of all 'sorts' and an additional fount to keep going, and finally a press and paper. . . ."

Cobden-Sanderson, who had come late to printing, was, according to Ruari McLean writing in *Modern Book Design*, a "proud and fanatic character, to whom the Book Beautiful was some kind of mystical and magic Ideal." He had become interested in establishing a private press through his relationship with William Morris. He was a distinguished amateur binder and Morris had commissioned his work for the Kelmscott Press. In company with the engraver, Emery Walker, Cobden-Sanderson launched his enterprise under the name of the Doves Press. Walker had also collaborated with Morris in the creation of the Golden Type, patterned from the type of the 15th century Venetian printer Nicolas Jenson.

It was Cobden-Sanderson's desire to produce books which were to be read, as those of Morris were not. To this extent, the Doves Press books were rather austere and without decoration other than calligraphic initials produced by Edward Johnston and Graily Hewitt. They were thus a challenge to the overly decorated Kelmscott Press books. In his essay on the Ideal Book, Cobden-Sanderson wrote that "The whole duty of Typography, as of Calligraphy, is to communicate. . . ."

The great book to issue from the Doves Press was the five volume bible, called by one authority, "one of the noblest books ever made." It will long stand as the monument to the whole idea represented by the Doves Press.

April 30

The title page of a 12mo (pp. iv, 156) London, 1797 reads:

"Typographical antiquities. History, Origin, and Progress of the Art of Printing, from its first invention in Germany to the end of the 17th century, and from its introduction into England, by Caxton, to the present time; including, among a variety of curious and interesting matter, its progress in the Provinces, with chronological lists of eminent printers in England, Scotland, and Ireland: together with anecdotes of several eminent and literary characters who have honoured the art by their attention to its improvement: also a particular and complete history of the Walpolean Press, established at Strawberry Hill; with an accurate list of every publication issued therefrom, and the exact number printed thereof. At the conclusion is given a curious dissertation on the origin of the use of paper; also a complete history of the art of woodcutting and engraving on copper, from its first invention in Italy to its latest improvement in Great Britain; concluding with the adjudication of literary property; or the laws and terms to which authors, designers, and publishers are separately subject. With a catalogue of remarkable Bibles and Common Prayer-books, from the infancy of printing to the present time. Extracted from the best authorities."

The compiler of this encylopedic volume was Henry Lemoine, who died on April 30, 1812. A modern book with such a wonderfully descriptive title page would certainly make life simpler for the copy writer who was entrusted with preparing the blurb for the jacket, or even for the critic trying to fit the book into an already crowded reading schedule. On the other hand, the designer might find it exceedingly difficult to attempt an asymmetric treatment which would be looked upon kindly by the jury for the Fifty Books of the Year.

But such a title was quite typical of the period, and Bookseller Lemoine was no doubt delighted with the finished result.

No doubt the view of Lemoine as an eccentric sprang from his pro-American prognostication upon the future of printing in the United States, contained in an article which he wrote upon that subject for *Gentleman's Magazine* in 1796. In it he stated, in part, "Such is the literary portrait of a country which threatens to surpass all others in the great and useful science of politics, as well as the liberal arts. This is but the glowing that evinces a kindling flame; which, from what we have seen, we have a reason to expect may some future day enlighten and instruct the Old World, whence they have withdrawn themselves."

May

May 1

"On the first day of May, 1826, we set our initial stickful of types, followed by three more on the same day, all in brevier, besides laying a font of job type. It was our first day in any printing-office, and a high day it was, for we believe we leaped deerlike over every housetop and cellar door on our way homeward at dark. What happened between that day and this we may not here tell, save that some hours were so bright that earth was almost heavenly; others were not so, but, though very dark, the hereafter may show that they had important uses, nevertheless."

With this one paragraph autobiography, one of the great American printers of the 19th century resigned the editorship of *The Typographic Advertiser* to his son, in 1886. He was Thomas MacKellar, typefounder, for long the head of the principal American typefoundry, MacKellar, Smiths & Jordan of Philadelphia—an outgrowth of the first American foundry, Binny & Ronaldson.

During the final thirty-five years of the last century, nearly every apprentice in the land learned his trade with a copy of MacKellar's *The American Printer* at his elbow. First published in 1866, this manual went into eighteen editions before it was supplanted by De Vinne's four-volume *Practice of Typography,* appearing in the years 1900-04. *The Typographic Advertiser,* first published in 1855, was a printing journal which, although it served as a house organ for the foundry, was according to the printing historian, H. L. Bullen, the first journal to be devoted exclusively to printing. In its pages MacKellar indulged in flights of poetry, of which he later published two volumes. His best known bit of versifying, still from time to time reprinted in the printing periodicals, is *The Song of the Printer,* beginning, "Pick and click/Goes the type in the stick."

In the July, 1863 issue, published on the eve of Gettysburg, a notice appeared: "The lateness of the present number of the *Advertiser* is due to the interruption of business caused by the rebel invasion of the State. We had previously contributed about a company to the grand army of the Union, and we felt that we had filled our quota, but when the tramp of hostile footsteps profaned the soil of our good old State, we gave a God's-speed —(as we had before to our only son)—to those of our remaining operatives whose patriotism impelled them to shoulder the musket to meet the new emergency. About a third of our entire force have gone to the battlefield in defense of the Union and Constitution of the Land."

MacKellar's interest in retired and indigent printers was unusual in a day when geriatrics was an unknown science. He wrote in his magazine as early as 1855 about the establishment of an "Asylum for Decayed Printers." His sympathetic interest excited the cooperation of George W. Childs, the Philadelphia newspaper publisher, who later endowed the Union Printers' Home in Colorado Springs. This institution has for the past seventy years taken excellent care of indigent members of the International Typographical Union.

Wooster College, in Ohio, presented MacKellar with an honorary Ph.D., possibly the first honorary degree ever to be given to a member of the printing craft in the United States.

May 2

Eleven hair trunks were delivered to the city of Washington on the second of May in the year 1801 and were placed in the office of the Clerk of the United States Senate. The trunks contained the first purchase of books for the newly formed Library for "the Use of Both Houses of Congress." There were 740 books in the collection, all of which had been selected from the shelves of London booksellers.

The year previously, the federal government had been in the midst of the hectic period during which it moved from Philadelphia to the newly established site on the Potomac. At that time it became the responsibility of Representative Robert Goodloe Harper of South Carolina to prepare legislation for a Congressional appropriation to provide the necessary funds for the purchase of the furnishing of the various chambers and offices required. The fifth section of Harper's bill, which was passed by the Congress and signed by President John Adams, contained the provision for the purchase of books "as may be necessary for the use of Congress at the said city of Washington, and for fitting up a suitable apartment for containing them, and for placing them therein." The sum of money voted to provide the books was five thousand dollars.

The books remained in the aforementioned trunks until the Congress convened and a joint committee of the House and the Senate met to organize the library, an accomplishment which was completed in January, 1802. It was decreed that the books should be placed in a room in the north wing of the Capitol and were to be made available only to the President, the Vice President, and the members of both Houses of the Congress. The President was authorized to appoint a Librarian who was to receive a salary of not more than two dollars for each day of necessary attendance.

A dozen years later, the library, enjoying a quiet and almost anonymous existence, was destroyed during the British occupation of Washington in 1814. This act of vandalism,

to use the words of Thomas Jefferson who was living out his retirement in Monticello, "enraged the literate citizens of our country," with the result that the existence of the library became widely known, albeit belatedly. To form the foundation of a new library, Jefferson offered to sell to the Congress his own magnificent library, containing 6,487 volumes, unquestionably the finest in the United States. All of them had been lovingly acquired during his lifetime by the literate former president. The Senate immediately accepted Jefferson's offer, but the House haggled for two days over the expense. Daniel Webster, then in his first term, objected to the purchase because the books were more literary than legal or historical. Finally, by a margin of ten votes, the Jefferson library became the property of the United States for the sum of $23,950.

From this modest beginning the Library of Congress has grown to be one of the great institutions of its kind in the world. In his report to Congress for 1964, Librarian Mumford stated that the collection included over 13 million books, 18.9 million manuscripts, 2.7 million maps, 3 million volumes and pieces of music, 1.7 million photographic negatives, prints, and slides, 163,000 reels and strips of microfilm, 78,000 reels of motion pictures, 130,000 reels of microfilmed newspapers, and 150,000 bound newspaper volumes.

May 3

In a letter to the Editor of *The Times* of London, dated this day in 1917, Gerard T. Meynell, publisher of *The Imprint,* and a director of the Westminster Press, fine printers, wrote:

"Sir—It would be interesting to know what Mr. Emery Walker thinks should be done with the Doves Press punches and matrices. The attitude of mind of the owners of private presses is interesting and peculiar. Morris himself was if anything a democrat, even when he gave up his active work with the Socialists, but he spent a considerable part of his life in turning out things that nobody but the rich could ever attain to, and the principle is carried on today by the whole Arts and Crafts movement. The small editions of the works of the Kelmscott Press were bought almost entirely by collectors and speculators, and I wonder how many of its books, or any other private press books, have ever been opened."

Having thus set up the target, Meynell then tossed his brick: "Let us remember that there is nothing very original about those who run private presses; they nearly always, as I have said, steal the designs for their type, and they nearly always steal the matter they print."

Emery Walker replied at length in a letter appearing on May 17th. He stated in part: "Is there nothing to be said for the craftsman who, from that impulse from within which spurs all artists without thought of profit, desires to print as beautifully as may be some masterpiece of literature? The idea, for instance, is grotesque that the text of Homer was 'stolen' when the monumental edition of the Odyssey was issued by the Oxford University Press in the late Mr. Robert Proctor's type, the making of which was a labour of love, if ever there was one.

"A good deal of the work done by private presses has been of what Ruskin used to call an 'exemplary' nature, and it has its influence on current book production. More than that could not be expected from pioneers. . . ."

May 4

At the tenth session of the Lateran Council, Pope Leo X issued a bull on this day in 1515, entitled *Inter sollicitudines,* which became a part of the long struggle by ecclesiastical authorities to control printing. All books were to be submitted to the Cardinal Vicar and the "Magister Sacri Palatii" if printed in Rome, or if elsewhere to the bishop of the diocese or to a professor appointed by him and by the local inquisitor.

A fine of 100 ducats, along with excommunication, confiscation, and public burning of the books were the penalties for offenders, in addition to the loss of license to print for one year. This edict resulted in a certain amount of confusion, particularly outside of Rome, as the books which were acceptable to one inquisitor might be condemned by another. A Neapolitan censor, Gregory Capuchin, wrote that his practice was to burn such bibles as were defective in text. His method was to examine the third chapter of

Genesis, and if he found the words, *"in sudore vultus tui, vesceris pane donec,"* he directed that such copies were not to be corrected but were to be committed to the flames.

The books which were condemned were listed in an *Index* kept in each area. The judgments of the local inquisitors were so uncertain that, as in the example of Arias Montanus, Chief Inquisitor for Antwerp and compiler of the *Index* in that city, his own writings were placed upon the *Index* in Rome. It became necessary for the various censors to maintain lists restricted to their own use. The practice was to have each inquisitor insert in the indices the statement: "I do say that this present book, thus by me corrected, may be tolerated and read, until such time as it shall be thought worthy of some further correction."

Even these inquisitors' indices underwent their own form of censorship. Sandover, archbishop of Toledo, prohibited in 1619, "under pain of the greater excommunication, any one to print the index, or cause it to be printed; or when printed, to send it out of the kingdom, without a special license."

In general, the bull was assumed by most printers to refer to theological works only. Increasingly, after the incunabula period, secular printing came to form the bulk of the output of the press, and the shackles of censorship became less difficult to bear.

May 5

On May 5, 1637 William Laud, Archbishop of Canterbury, informed the Vice-Chancellor of Oxford University, "You are now upon a very good way towards the setting up of a learned Press." His Grace was referring to the code of statutes, called the Laudian Code, set up eleven months previously, under which a printing office could be efficiently operated. Above all it defined the duties of the printer-in-chief. A paraphrase of the sonorous Latin of the statute reads:

" 'Tis provided by an University-Statute, That there be a Person set over the Printers, who shall be well-skill'd in the Greek and Latin Tongues, and in Philological Studies, with the title of *Archi typographer,* whose Office is to supervise and look after the Business of Printing, and to provide, at the University Expence, all Paper, Presses, Types, &c. to prescribe the Module of the Letter, the Quality of the Paper, and the Size of the Margins, when any Book is printed at the Cost of the University, and also to correct the Errors of the Press."

In a number of these duties the architypographus in actual practice disdained to observe the letter of the statute, leaving the more onerous tasks to the "mechanic warehouseman," or technical foreman. A Corrector of the Press, Thomas Hearne, wrote out in 1715 what he believed to be the duties of the First Printer: "The Architypographus, or chief Printer, is to be a learned man. The rest are barely styled typographi, and one is not mentioned to have more Power or Authority than the rest. The Architypographus is to be a Governour & to præside over the rest, & he is to manage, as a Scholar, all things for the Honour and Credit of the University. And what they style a Ware-House Keeper is to be put in by the Architypographus, & is to act under him as his Servant."

At the period of the formation of the Laudian Code, the University was plagued with a most inefficient chief printer, named William Turner. The Vice-Chancellor petitioned for Laud to prevent Turner from competing with the London booksellers. Compositors at the press enjoyed considerable freedom during this period and were men of some means in the community, being property owners. It was even said of them that "their daughters might marry a parson." The compositor would be responsible for the production of a book, planning the format and setting the type, and even ordering the paper. He was then paid directly by the outside customer. On occasion compositors took orders for books without the permission of the Delegates who had authority over the conduct of the Press. In the light of such conditions there was constant pressure from the scholars at Oxford that the Press be brought up to a level of efficiency to do justice to the University.

It was not until 1649 that the University agreed to combining the offices of chief printer and architypographus. A further delay came until 1658, when Samuel Clarke, the Orientalist and M.A. from Merton College, was appointed to the post, which he held with distinction until his death in 1669. He too, however, had difficulties with the printers. But a start had been made, and the groundwork had been laid for the continuing selection of a scholar to be architypographus.

May 6

"Typography may be defined as the craft of rightly disposing printing material in accordance with specific purpose; of so arranging the letters, distributing the space and controlling the type as to aid to the maximum the reader's comprehension of the text. Typography is the efficient means to an essentially utilitarian and only accidental aesthetic end, for enjoyment of patterns is rarely the reader's chief aim."

This introductory paragraph from *First Principles of Typography* is possibly the most widely quoted definition of the art to appear in our times. It was written in 1930 by Stanley Morison who was born this day in 1889. He wrote it for the seventh volume of *The Fleuron*, an English journal of typography of which he was the editor. Morison is today preeminent in the field of typographic history, with a volume of published work behind him which is notable for its breadth and historic judgment.

Morison was twenty-three years of age and a clerk for a missionary society when he read the famous Printing Number, the 40,000th issue of *The Times* of London. He was attracted to a new monthly printing periodical named *The Imprint*, which was advertised in this issue and which was expected to begin publication shortly, under the editorship of F. Ernest Jackson, Edward Johnston, J. H. Mason, and Gerard T. Meynell. In the very first number of *The Imprint* an advertisement appeared, seeking "a young man of good education," as an editorial assistant. Morison applied for the position and was accepted. But the new magazine lasted only a year. However, the young man was presented with an opportunity to begin a career of service to the printer's craft. Fifty years later, he is still continuing. The last issue of *The Imprint* contained his first article, entitled "Notes on Some Liturgical Books," which became the first item in the now lengthy Morison bibliography.

Following the brief period with *The Imprint,* Morison designed books for a Catholic publishing firm and was encouraged to develop both his editoral and critical abilities. He next assisted Francis Meynell at the Pelican Press and spent two years with the Cloister Press of Manchester. In 1922 he joined with Oliver Simon in the publishing of *The Fleuron,* of which Volume I was produced in 1923. Six additional volumes were printed, the last four under Morison's editorship. Unquestionably this journal has been one of the most influential printing publications ever to be published. The series of monographs on type which Morison wrote remain outstanding contributions to the serious study of typography which had received its impetus from the two-volume work of Daniel Berkeley Updike, *Printing Types,* published in 1922.

Simultaneously, with his work on *The Fleuron,* Morison took on the responsibilities of Typographic Advisor to the Monotype Corporation. Here he made a contribution of even greater moment than his essays. At his direction the firm undertook a program of cutting new book types for machine composition, based upon historical examples. From this program there emerged such outstanding types as Garamond, Poliphilus, Bembo, Baskerville, and Bell. Eric Gill, the contemporary English artist, was encouraged to cut the popular series of sans serif types which bear his name. Possibly the most successful type to stem from the Morison program was his own Times New Roman, designed for *The Times,* now one of the universal types.

He took on the typographic restyling of *The Times* and at the same period became Typographic Advisor to Cambridge University. In 1935 he began the editing of *The History of The Times,* which appeared in four volumes, 1935-52, almost entirely written by Morison. In 1946-47 he edited the widely circulated *The Times Literary Supplement.*

When in 1950 the University of Birmingham honored Morison with the D. Litt. degree, the Public Orator concluded his citation, "It is high time that we made him in name what he has long been in fact, Doctor of Letters."

The Morison bibliography presently contains some two hundred items, many of which have been written anonymously or as introductions to other books. There has been a wide and consistent demand for "a Collected Morison" by typophiles all over the world.

At ten minutes after two o'clock on the afternoon of this day in 1915, the Cunard liner *Lusitania* was torpedoed by a German U-boat. It sank in the Irish Sea with a loss of life of 1,257. Among these were Elbert Hubbard of East Aurora, New York and his wife Alice.

Hubbard, the self-styled Fra Elbertus, Sage of East Aurora, was a controversial figure upon the American scene for almost twenty years preceding his death. Fra to some and fraud to others, he had organized in the little upstate village an establishment which he called the Roycroft Shop, after the two 17th century English printers. Here were produced standard authors in special editions and the voluminous writings of Hubbard himself in addition to a widely-circulated magazine called *The Philistine.* The shop also contained craftsmen who produced furniture and wove fabrics. The idea behind the venture was that the workers would learn a craft at the Roycrofters, earn a wage and live in a community of craftsmen. By 1910 over 400 people were working at the shop.

In appearance Hubbard was a rather odd individual, affecting long hair, a flowing windsor tie, and a wide-brimmed black hat, but he took his business very seriously. He was proud of his reputation as a self-made man.

During a trip to Europe he visited the famous Kelmscott Press in London and talked to William Morris. From this point his life seemed to take shape, as he returned home to set up an American Kelmscott Press. He began to lecture on the lives of famous people and very quickly became a feature on lecture circuits, earning over ten thousand dollars from that source yearly. His greatest success as a writer was the well-known *Message to Garcia* which the Roycrofters turned out by the hundred thousand.

His books were all rather heavy-handed in appearance and very close in general structure to the Kelmscott printing. They were criticized by the more sophisticated typographers of Hubbard's time, and even today they are considered to be superficial copies of Morris books. They were, however, widely circulated and were undoubtedly admired by their many purchasers.

May 8

"Dear Sol," wrote Frederic W. Goudy on May 8, 1947 in what was to be the last of countless letters which had come from the hand of the great type designer, "I would have written you long ago except for an acute attack of neuritis which has kept me in the house *since* early in *March,* and finally culminated a few weeks ago in a heart block so that until the past few days the Dr. wouldn't even let me go upstairs to bed. I am better just now but unable to do any work yet. Thank you for sending the photo to the professor in Evanston, Ill. I had a letter from him but wasn't strong enough to look up a photo or write to him. I get requests for autographed portraits 3 or 4 times a month, but only occasionally do any enclose postage. They seem to think I do nothing but pose for photos. Can you or will you have two or three more like these I am sending you made for me and *send* me the bill for them? They will give me something to use when such a request comes that I *want* to accept. Am glad Harvey is looking better, tell him "hello" for me when you next see him. Regards to my friends at the Mono."

Three days later Fred Goudy was dead, on the eleventh of May. So passed the man who was probably the last of the great individualistic type designers this nation shall ever see. From the time fifty-two years ago when he had sent a most tentative set of sketches for an alphabet of type to the Dickinson Type Foundry of Boston and had secured in return a check for ten dollars, Goudy had been a type designer. He had also been a letterer, a typographer, a prolific writer, and the operator of a most distinguished private press. But it is as a type designer that he will be best remembered.

By 1944 when he completed his last design, 123 types had come from his drawing board. A number of these were never actually cut or otherwise cast into printer's types, but they had been conceived by the designer as finished letterforms. Out of that vast output some forty-three types are still available, a number of them being in everyday use. It is unfortunate that Goudy never produced a type specifically for the linecasting machine, the dominant typesetting machine in this country, a factor which has limited the wider use of his types. Almost all the Goudy designs were made for the monotype machine. This has in one respect been useful to the small printer, enabling him to have in his cases of type for hand composition a selection of the Goudy types.

Very far from being "the boastful old man who has designed a hundred types," as Henry Lewis Bullen described him, Goudy was a man of considerable modesty obsessed by a dream—a dream of beautiful letters, and his role in their creation. It is for this reason that his types speak for themselves and he shall ever be honored as their designer.

May 9

The proprietor of the *Northern Whig* of Hudson, New York engaged this day in 1809 in a controversy with the local postmaster over the employment of an apprentice to fetch the mail, the postmaster demanding a written order from the editor upon each occasion that the boy appeared in his post office.

The poor apprentice of the period who was engaged by a country printer as often as not found life exceedingly difficult. Service as an errand boy was just one of the seemingly infinite responsibilities laid upon his shoulders. He had to sweep out the office, keep the fire going in the winter by chopping wood or carrying in the coal, and of course he must deliver the weekly newspaper to its customers.

Practically every printer, however, who survived such an apprenticeship during the 19th century spoke later of his ordeal somewhat nostalgically. Lewis G. Hoffman, who served under Jesse Buel at Albany, told of the most onerous task allotted to him, that of "treading pelts," or preparing the skins to be used on the ink balls:

"A Pelt was a dried sheepskin, divested of the wool, immersed in the *slop pail* until well soaked, then taken out, rinsed by hand of the surface water, as far as practicable, for *treading.* It was then rolled up in old newspapers and rolled under the foot, changing the papers as was required until every particle of moisture was expunged from it, which rendered the skin as pliable and soft as a lady's glove. Then it was in order for a Printer's ball. Treading out a pair of skins was an epoch in a printer's devil's life which he will always remember until *odor* is lost in forgetfulness."

Hoffman also mentioned the fact that "the eight hour system was not then in vogue." He wrote, "In winter we ate breakfast by candlelight, took dinner at 12 (except publication days), supper at 6, returned to the office, and set type until 9."

Sometimes the apprentice found conditions to his liking, and his employer an understanding man anxious to teach the craft properly, but generally he could not expect "home" treatment once he had been bound. Edwin Scrantom, apprentice to A. G. Dauby, the pioneer printer of Rochester, New York, recalled "the rough box, or bunk, that was rigged up on the floor under one of the counters, for this was the sleeping room for the apprentices—two of us—and coming to this scanty provision, as I did, from a bed that my mother had always in her love provided . . . the contrast was so great . . . that it brought homesickness, sighing and tears."

There was little agreement concerning the wages a boy could earn during his apprenticeship, over and above board. Fifty dollars per year could be considered adequate, although some masters stipulated that the payment vary during each year of the apprenticeship, in most instances a period of five years. Although learning the "art and mystery" of printing was deemed a sufficient liberal education for a boy, a few masters allowed their apprentices to attend school during their first period of indenture, but this was not a common practice. That printing did actually provide a liberal education is borne out by the many distinguished men whose only education was that of the apprenticeship to a printer.

May 10

It might have been Thin Space McGill, but more likely it was Small Cap Jones, who—feeling poorly on this day in 1881—did something mighty unusual for a peregrinating printer; he stopped off to visit a doctor. The sawbones examined him and suggested that all he needed was a little more fresh air while sleeping. "Hell, doc," spluttered Small Cap, "what do you want me to do, kick out a few spokes? I'm sleeping under a wagon now, these nights!"

The predicament was not an uncommon one for that independent breed of man, the itinerant printer, euphemistically called journeyman, but more frequently labeled tramp. Ever since the invention of movable type, printers traditionally accepted the term journeyman to mean just that, spending at least part of their careers in traveling from place to place. In the United States the tradition reached its peak in the post-Civil War period. It declined after the turn of the century, when the introduction of the linotype made it possible for the daily newspaper to maintain a steady work force without dependence upon the wayfaring typo who might pop in at any moment and leave just as quickly.

It was a colorful period in the history of the craft. Many an old-timer recalls somewhat nostalgically the romantic stories he heard in his youth from fellow workers who had either "tramped" or knew many printers who had. Many of the tourist typos objected strenuously to the appellation of tramp, insisting that they were simply journeymen. Indeed a number of them were just that, being sober and industrious printers who brought skill and experience into many a small town printing office. Their traveling was in such instances more footloose than fanciful, and they did not readily accept inclusion in the questionable reputation of many of their fellows. Even at that, they could not accept the disapprobation of their group in some sections of the country, primarily the East and the South, where social mores were more solidly established.

A majority of the tales of the traveling typesetters have to do with their phenomenal ability to handle the jug. Of course drinking has been a traditional pastime of the fraternity of printers, due in part to the long hours and arduous labors common to the craft. Joseph Moxon, the first writer to record working conditions in printing offices, wrote as early as 1683 that a newcomer could not become a member of the chapel unless he paid a "benvenue" which amounted to treating the journeymen to beer. It was common until late in the 19th century to "rush the growler" during the working day; that is, to send the apprentice out for beer for the journeymen, to give them the stamina to complete their labors. Benjamin Franklin wrote that he was considered odd when he worked in London and refused to drink beer.

A compositor working on the New York *Tribune* wrote that, "No one familiar with the route of the morning daily marveled at the proverbial dissipation of the old-time printer. He came from under the hot gaslight in the morning, exhausted and pale as a church bug. No wonder his coppers got hot pretty often. He needed rest, but was prone to substitute stimulants. . . ." The saloons in the vicinity of a large daily newspaper office did a roaring business at the close of the working shift. When the thirsty printers ran out of money they signed chits. It was not unusual to see bartenders lined up with typos at the pay window each week.

The excuses brought forth for the hard drinking did have some basis in fact. Printers were afraid of lead poisoning. Other prevailing diseases in printing offices in the hand-set days were tuberculosis and rheumatism. Up until the first decades of this century, the life expectancy of the printer was but forty years, giving some justification to the printer who sought relief in alcohol, while at the same time interfering with the longer life he hoped to attain

Many of the tales of the tramp days are concerned with the addiction to the cheering cup. From this distance it now seems that perhaps undue emphasis was given to just one of the problems encountered by printers at work a century ago. The touring typo is still around, but in nowhere near the numbers of earlier times. The present-day traveler is today more likely to be seeking broader trade experience before settling down. His last desire would be to appear romantic or to participate in a tradition.

May 11

In the tiny village of Hatchel (pop. 400) in Germany was born this day in 1854 a man destined to revolutionize the printing industry of his time. Ottmar Mergenthaler was the son of parents who were both teachers. It was their desire that he also train for that profession but since the boy was more interested in mechanics, he was apprenticed to a watchmaker. At the close of his period of indenture he decided to emigrate to the United States. His employer's son was engaged in the manufacture of instruments in Baltimore, so young Mergenthaler journeyed

to that city and went to work for the younger Hahl, becoming foreman of the shop within two years.

It was to this shop that James O. Clephane, a public stenographer, came with a model of a typewriter in which he had become interested. Unfortunately it was a failure, a fact attributed to poor workmanship in the model. He brought the machine to Hahl's shop where young Mergenthaler examined it and believed that he could eliminate the flaws. The device printed characters on a paper ribbon which was then transferred to a lithographic stone for printing. Mergenthaler improved the model, but its basic difficulties remained.

Clephane, believing the lithographic method to be at fault, next suggested that the machine be adapted to impressing letters into a papier-maché strip in order to form a matrix for the casting of the characters to form a stereotype. Mergenthaler did not have any faith in this idea, but he built the machine Clephane directed. It worked, insofar as the impression was concerned, but the problem was the casting of metal. At this point Mergenthaler removed himself from the development but Clephane worked for several more years on this device.

In 1883 Mergenthaler left the Hahl shop and set up his own establishment. His first customer was the same Clephane who still was convinced that a type machine could be developed. Mergenthaler decided to adapt the matrix impression to an entire line and built a machine which worked upon that principle. The finished model was the first machine to bear his name. Since there were still defects, another model was constructed, and this was the last one to utilize the principle of a papier-maché mold.

Mergenthaler next tried metal matrices to form the characters of the line, and in 1884 built a machine which produced a finished line of type. The justification was performed by hand, a laborious process. The following year the wedge-shaped steel band, the invention of Jacob W. Schuckers, was incorporated into the machine. Then Mergenthaler added a distribution system by which the matrices could be used over and over again.

On July 3, 1886 the machine was demonstrated in the office of the New York *Tribune* with the inventor at the keyboard. Whitelaw Reid, the publisher, took the first slug which emerged from the machine, calling it a line of type and thereby giving the machine its name.

Thus a dream of scores of inventors was brought to fruition—the fully successful and economical mechanization of typesetting. Mergenthaler was amply rewarded for his efforts, living in considerable affluence before his early death in 1899. There have been numerous stories that the inventor ended his career destitute, but actually he became a millionaire. A director of the Mergenthaler firm, talking before a group of printers in 1908, told them that Mergenthaler's heirs had received not less than $50,000 a year in royalties from the company since the inventor's death.

May 12

An advertisement appearing in the Philadelphia *Aurora* on this spring day in 1797 read: "TYPEFOUNDERS — Wanted, *five* or *six* journeymen typefounders, to whom the highest wages and constant employment will be given—Also an apprentice wanted. Apply at Binny & Ronaldson's FOUNDRY, in CEDAR at the end of ELEVENTH Street, PHILADELPHIA, where any quantity of old type will be received for money or exchange.

"The printers of newspapers thro'out the Union will encourage this establishment by publishing the above."

Considering the lack of typefounding facilities in the United States at that period, it would seem that Messrs. Binny & Ronaldson were optimistic in the extreme of finding *any* journeymen founders, but at the same time, the advertisement did inform the public of the existence of the firm, and the hint that other newspapers might publish the notice was a canny bit of promotion on the part of the two Scotsmen.

The year previously, what became the first permanent typefoundry in the United States had been established by Archibald Binny and James Ronaldson, both from Edinburgh, Scotland. Binny, who arrived in Philadelphia in 1793, had been a printer in Edinburgh and had also learned the craft of typefounding. Ronaldson, a baker by trade, emigrated to Philadelphia in 1794, setting up a biscuit bakery which he ran for about two years until it was destroyed by fire.

Meeting Binny by chance in an alehouse, Ronaldson renewed an acquaintance which had begun in Edinburgh. The two men quickly became good friends, agreeing to go into business together as typefounders, in November, 1796. Ronaldson put up the capital, while Binny supplied the practical skills necessary for the successful operation of the foundry, in addition to contributing his stock of typefounder's tools and equipment, without which the enterprise could scarcely have had any chance of success.

In 1806 Binny and Ronaldson purchased the typefounding equipment which Benjamin Franklin had acquired from P. S. Fournier, son of the great French typefounder, Pierre Fournier *le jeune*. Franklin had hoped to establish his grandson, Benjamin Franklin Bache in that business in Philadelphia. Bache did set up a small foundry and printing office and issued a specimen sheet some time after 1890, but he had little interest in typefounding, preferring to remain a printer. After his early death the French tools became the property of William Duane who had married Bache's widow. Duane offered to lend them to Binny and Ronaldson. Upon examination of the equipment, Ronaldson was so delighted with it that he made an immediate purchase and fearing Duane would change his mind forthwith borrowed a wheelbarrow and transported his tools to the foundry, "during one of the hottest days in the summer of the year mentioned."

The Binny & Ronaldson firm was immediately successful, producing excellent types which soon won over the printers in the new nation, previously so dependent upon European sources, particularly the English and Scottish foundries. Binny retired in 1815. Ronaldson continued the business until his own retirement in 1823, when his son Richard carried it on for another ten years. At that time it became known as Johnson & Smith. The line of succession then went on to L. Johnson in 1843, becoming Johnson & Company in 1845. In 1867 the firm was called MacKellar, Smiths & Jordan, becoming incorporated in 1885. Finally in 1892 the founders became one of the most important elements in the merger which produced the firm known as the American Type Founders Company, which still retains in its vaults some of the original Binny & Ronaldson matrices, the best known of which is Roman No. 1, now called Oxford.

May 13

In the Mohawk Valley village of Little Falls in upstate New York was born this day in 1844 a boy named Linn Boyd Benton. He was destined to live for eighty-eight years and to add considerably to the technological advancement of the printing industry. Benton's father was a lawyer who became interested in a career as a newspaper publisher, moving to Milwaukee in 1853 to assume the editorship of the *Daily News* of that city. Through this association young Benton was first introduced to the printer's trade. His "formal" education was obtained during two years at Galesville College, followed by private tutoring in Latin and Greek, all of which was completed by his sixteenth year. He later acquired greater proficiency in a printing office in La Crosse, Wisconsin when his father was named a circuit judge there.

Deciding that the compositor's art was not to his liking, Benton became a bookkeeper for the Northwestern Type Foundry, operated by a former partner of his father. When the foundry went bankrupt a short time later, Benton purchased it in company with a partner of his own. Thus at twenty-nine years of age he became the owner of what he once stated was "the worst equipped typefoundry in the United States." The firm later took the name of Benton, Waldo & Company. By this time the former bookkeeper had discovered a passionate interest in precision mechanics and in its application to typefounding. Out of his experiments came the idea of "self-spacing" types.

In this system all of the characters of the font were assigned to six unit widths, as against the thirteen or fourteen of standard types. The set widths were in multiples of one-sixth of the body, which with the spaces of the same multiples allowed for automatic justification. According to Bullen, the types were tested by the Curtis Publishing Company of Philadelphia. A compositor named Stoddard was chosen for the trials. He set type about thirty-three per cent faster with the unit-width letters as against the non unit-width types. It was Stoddard who named the type. After being questioned about the justification he said, "I never thought of that—why, the damned thing spaces itself!" The system, while completely practical, foundered upon the principle of good letter proportion, since necessarily each character had to conform to the unit system, creating a letter of questionable aesthetic value.

Benton next turned his attention to the invention of a type-setting machine. Faced with the problem of having to cut some three thousand punches, with no punch-cutters available, Benton designed a machine to perform this laborious task. Thus he freed the typefounders of their dependence upon hand-cut punches, almost four and one-half centuries after the invention of movable types. Based upon the method of the pantograph, the Benton punch-cutter was patented in 1885 and was an immediate success.

Without this device the composing machines being developed during the same period could scarcely have been practical. The machines of Mergenthaler and Lanston needed a rapid method of punching matrices in order to sell them in quantity to accompany the machines, and hand-cutting the punches would have been impossibly laborious. The Benton machine was therefore purchased for this purpose by both the Linotype and Monotype firms. The same device, with variations, is now used by all of the world's typefoundries and manufacturers of composing machines.

When Benton's foundry was merged with the American Type Founders Company in 1892, he brought his machine with him to New York. The first type to be cut there was the famous Century type, in collaboration with Theodore Low De Vinne. The machine was later adapted to the direct engraving of matrices, the practice now universally followed by the typefounders.

May 14

In a sense, Bruce Rogers, who was born on this day in 1870, was both the first and last of America's great artists of the book, enjoying an international reputation for over a half century. During his active career he designed over 700 volumes, among them some of the outstanding books of our times. No other designer can approach the high level of accomplishment represented by such production, and Rogers is rightly honored as the finest artist-printer which America has yet produced.

After his graduation from Purdue University's Art School in 1890, BR as he became familiarly known served as an illustrator for a newspaper, followed by free-lance art work.

His career really began when he joined Houghton Mifflin of Boston in 1896, remaining with that firm sixteen years and designing over 200 books bearing the imprint of the Riverside Press. He then went to England, where he became typographic advisor to Cambridge University, returning to the United States in 1919. His next great period of accomplishment was with the printer William Edwin Rudge, during the twenties. At the end of this time he returned to England to work on the great lectern folio bible which was completed by Oxford University Press in 1935 and which is undoubtedly his greatest monument.

For the remainder of his life he chose to work on a free-lance basis, selecting projects which suited his tastes, such as the 39-volume edition of Shakespeare which was published by the Limited Editions Club, and the fine folio bible printed in 1949 by the World Publishing Company. He remained active up to the time of his death in 1957. Such is his life in outline. His achievements as a book maker are of such an order, even in a time when technological factors appear to dominate the typographical, that his name will continue to be honored wherever books are admired and loved for their appearance.

Bruce Rogers was a traditional printer. He was at his best under conditions which allowed him free rein in his selection of materials. Some of his contemporaries had a way of referring to his work as "ivory tower" when they attempted to defend their own production-conscious approach to book design, but he followed his own precepts and refused to lower his standards at any time. Another criticism leveled at him was that he was happy only with the design of "period" books, a matter which he discussed in an address at the Grolier Club in 1938.

"Even a casual look round the room will show that apparently no basic principle has actuated the production of all these books, no new organic theory has been demonstrated. They are as miscellaneous as they look to be; and therefore, as a collection, not nearly so impressive as a set of Kelmscott or Ashendene or Doves Press books. Yet there *has* been a sort of principle on which I have worked, however mistaken it may have been. It is to have, conceivably, pleased the *author* of the work that I had in hand, by the form which I gave it. This has indeed actually happened, when the book was by a writer still living, as several letters in my possession will testify. But as it has been my fortune to have been frequently called upon to print authors of the past, rather than those of the present time, it seems logical to have cast their words in the forms that were familiar to them in their own day, instead of trying to impose upon them any of my own typographic interpretations or peculiarities. My contribution has been mainly to take advantage of modern improvements, to print their books better if possible, than they were done in their own times."

May 15

An edition of Cicero's *Letters,* from a printing of 300 copies at Venice by Wendelin Da Spira, was presented this day in 1471 to the Dominican convent in Nürnberg, by Friar Peter Schwartz. This volume, set in roman type, is an indication of the spread of the humanist ideas into northern Europe by way of the printed word.

When the period which we call the Renaissance began, about 1400, such scholars as the poet Petrarch became vitally interested in the interpretation of the ancient classics of antiquity. This involved the re-copying of numerous early manuscripts. As the scholars were often enthusiastic calligraphers they rejoiced in their labor, consciously attempting to follow the basic structure of the Carolingian miniscule, thus paying tribute to the ancient authors whose works they were reviving. The then-current gothic hand was viewed with suspicion by the humanists who were more concerned with classic curves in letterforms than in the proved economy of the tightly controlled gothic.

It was generally felt by the humanists that to copy Cicero or Tacitus in a gothic hand was a desecration. It soon became common practice to letter the classics in the roman hand, although such texts as law books, prayer books, medical books, and the like were done in the gothic. There soon existed a brisk market for beautiful calligraphy which existed well into the period following the introduction of movable type. Indeed, the rich collectors preferred the manuscript copies to the "cheap" printed editions. The great bookseller, Vespasiano de' Bisticci, employed dozens of scribes in a copying establishment which had for its clientele the most distinguished bibliophiles of the period. It has been said that one of his customers, the Duke of Urbino, boasted that his library contained not a single printed book. Such disparagement of printed books was carried to an extreme when calligraphic copies were made of printed books.

The established success of the roman hand through the distribution over all of Europe of the classic Latin texts was primarily responsible for the cutting of roman types rather than the blackletter forms when printing was introduced into Italy. The first printers there, Conrad Sweynheim and Arnold Pannartz, were brought from Germany by the classical scholar Giovanni Andrea de' Bussi, Bishop of Aleria, and placed under the patronage of Pope Paul II, also a humanist, primarily to produce the books for which the Roman classicists were pressing.

Within a few years there were many printers in the Italian city states, all engaged in the production of multiple copies of classics composed in roman types. The result was a glut of the market. A number of printers became bankrupt, including the reputable Nicolas Jenson of Venice. In order to restore their finances, many of these printers turned to the gothic types, and began to print law texts, for which this style was particularly suited. By the year 1500 the printing trade was assuming the form in which it was to be most successful. Standards were set by competition rather than by privilege granted by decree, a factor tending to limit production. However for many years in numerous locations throughout Europe the number of establishments was still controlled by law.

May 16

It was a happy day, indeed, for authors with writers' cramp and for typesetters who had to follow copy, when on May 16, 1893 Patent No. 497560 was issued to a Brooklynite named Herman L. Wagner, who in company with his brother Franz developed the first typewriter with a visible front-strike design. The writer could observe, in other words, the material which the contraption was turning out. The brothers Wagner sold their machine to John T. Underwood, son of the man who pioneered the carbons and ribbons business and thus was the famous Underwood typewriter born.

In the relatively sophisticated terminology of the 1960's, this "visible image" from the typewriter is known as hard copy. But it appears that writers may soon find themselves back in the pre-1893 era, with no comfortably-read record of their efforts in front of them and with no Wagner boys to help them out. This problem became apparent when the technology of typesetting became automated to such an extent that ordinary composing machines such as linotypes and monotypes were simply not efficient enough to do the job by themselves.

In the old—and more golden—days, the author produced his manuscript in double-spaced typed lines on 8½ x 11 inch bond paper, and more or less hopefully submitted the finished result to the publisher's office. Depending upon his skill in placing his ideas on paper there would occur at this point some changes in the manuscript, but eventually it would be sent off to the printer who then placed one sheet at a time on the copy board of a typesetting machine and transcribed the typed characters to metal type. A post-World War II innovation was the transfer to film characters, but the essential details as far as the writer was concerned did not change.

The publisher's production manager, cautious of author's alteration charges for photoset type, laid down some stringent rules for the editors, when a manuscript was to be set on a film machine, since last minute changes in this medium could be exceedingly costly. A year or so ago, the computer was harnessed to the typesetting machines of the hot metal variety and the more recently arrived phototypesetters. Not only did it become necessary for the author to be so very right at the beginning, but it became too costly to let him have fun with proofs. The poor scribbler was informed about coded tape, both paper and magnetic, tape blending, tape conversion, tape merging, and a host of other technical details about computer "hardware" and "software." The problem, it seemed, was that corrections made upon completed typesetting were becoming so expensive, that unless the author cooperated he might find his manuscript gathering dust on the publisher's desk.

The hard copy produced upon the tape-punching device is evidently to become the "proof" which the author is to correct—a stupefying situation for any writer to face, as anyone who has ever toiled away producing a manuscript can attest. By this method the writer can no longer enjoy the rebirth of his original copy into the printer's types. Solid, well-inked galley proofs can make a considerable difference in refreshing his viewpoint when it has become jaded. How can *another* typed manuscript take the place of the so-beautiful type of the proofs. Oh! So *that's* how it's going to look! And out comes the blue pencil, to be applied with religious fervor.

But the damage has been done. Perhaps the top writers of a publisher's list will be allowed their old freedom, but for the rest it's going to be a new way of life. The computer engineers have said that the completed tape will be in the image of the hard copy, as the electronic guts of a computer simply cannot commit errors once the signals have been passed. The writer will have to learn to read another version of his original manuscript. He will have to make corrections on it, if he can think of any, so that a correction tape may be punched, which will automatically merge with the original to put the copy into type—and at such savings in production costs!

May 17

The passage of the infamous Stamp Act was announced bitterly by the *New-Hampshire Gazette* in its issue of May 17, 1765. The editor placed heavy black rules around the announcement, in which he declared that the new law would "oblige the Printers on this Continent to Raise more Money every Year, than was ever raised at the year's end, and perhaps be obliged to pay the Stamp Duty weekly."

The uproar from the colonial printers resounded through the land, and with some reason, as the precarious financial position of most printing offices was already a cause

for concern. The Stamp Act assessed a tax of a halfpenny on each copy of a newspaper printed on the size of paper called a half sheet, and a penny on the larger size. On top of that each advertisement was to be taxed two shillings, which was about half the usual charge of an insertion in most newspapers. The job printing was to be charged a half-penny for every pamphlet printed, twopence on each almanac, and from three pence to £6 on legal and business forms. Foreign language printing was to be taxed at twice the regular rate, which meant that the Pennsylvania German printers would be taxed out of business.

The penalties for violations were severe, ranging from forty shillings to £10, with the stipulation that these fines were to be enforceable in admiralty court without a jury trial. The ordinance also dragooned the printers into a toll of 2½ to 5 per cent on apprenticeship indentures.

The British Parliament had passed an act which contained political dynamite. There appears to be no evidence that the law was meant to interfere with the freedom of the press, but the reaction of the colonial printer proved that he believed this to be the case. David Ramsey in *The History of the American Revolution,* published in 1789, stated: "Printers, when uninfluenced by government, have generally arranged themselves on the side of liberty, nor are they less remarkable for attention to the profits of their profession. A stamp duty, which openly invaded the first, and threatened a great dimunition of the last, provoked their united zealous opposition."

A number of newspapers attempted to evade the Stamp Act by changing their names slightly, running the risk of double penalty for anonymous publication. Quite a few papers suspended publication, but irate subscribers soon complained. Andrew Steurt, editor of the *North-Carolina Gazette,* was forced by a mob to resume publication, "at the Hazard of Life, being maimed, or having his Printing Office destroy'd." Another editor was informed that "should you at this critical Time, shut up the Press, and basely desert us, your House, Person, and Effects, will be in imminent danger."

Newspaper publishers quickly learned that in most instances the public supported them when they wrote outraged editorials against the tax. In turn, the people of the colonies learned which papers rushed to the defense of the colonists. Even more important was the realization that the press constituted a solid front when faced with a situation which threatened its survival. This factor in the long run was to represent a stabilizing influence in the long battle of the American colonies to gain their independence.

May 18

On this day just sixty years after Earnest Elmo Calkins set (and promptly pied) his first line of type in 1890, he received the medal of the American Institute of Graphic Arts, with the following citation:
"To Earnest Elmo Calkins, Printer
Writer, Collector, Dean of Advertising Men;
Founder of the Advertising Agency
As we know it today; eye and ear in the use
of effective illustrations and
typography in advertising."
As a young man Calkins set out from Galesburg, Illinois, bound for New York carrying a compositor's card. But instead of working at the case he became an advertising copy writer, a career so successful that he was able to begin his own advertising agency in 1902. For the next thirty years the profession was to know and admire a strong creative force in the preparation of first-rate copy, joined with stimulating typography.

At the age of four Calkins became excited about books in spite of the restrictions of tiny, illegible typefaces, poor printing, and shoddy illustrations. His "passion for beautifully printed books and for fine printing and paper" grew until, at his death in 1964, the former Galesburg comp owned a library of almost four thousand books. He once described his attitude toward books by saying, "I can never be indifferent to the way a book is made. I do not enjoy a wretchedly made book, however enthralling."

With an associate, Calkins set up the first advertising agency art department and was responsible for attracting a number of well-known artists to the field, such as Edward Wilson and Walter Dorwin Teague. In 1958 he looked back down the years and compared the typographical standards of his formative period with those of the post-World War II era, and heartily disliked what he there observed.

"Now a new influence of typography has arisen" he wrote, "which may just possibly be a threat to advertising typography, at least, if not to higher forms. Briefly, there is a tendency to consider typography as an art by itself, apart from, and at times inconsistent with, its real purpose. While it is not advertising but really literature, I cannot help noting a book of poems designed by Guillaume Appollinaire. 'It is a typography of fantasy,' says the catalog, 'in which words, syllables, and even letters are arranged according to rhythm or take external shapes that depict the spirit of the text. Such experiments disobey all rules of printing. In one example entitled *Il Pleut* (It Rains), the letters fall down the page in a shower.'

"Literature can take care of itself, but for advertising it is absolutely necessary that printing should be read. Typography is not an end, but a means to an end. Pictorial art is an end and contains within itself the materials for its own criticism. It is far more logical to compare printing with architecture, for architecture is also a means to an end. To design a building, however beautiful, that cannot be successfully used for its purpose is no worse than designing an advertising folder that cannot be read."

May 19

An advertisement in *Liberty Hall,* Cincinnati on this date in 1807 announced the forthcoming publication of a book which was bound to titillate the frontier population: "For Publishing by Subscription, in one volume royal duodecimo, *The Long and Interesting Trial of Charles Vattier."* Written by two "Gentlemen of Law Knowledge," this volume took advantage of the widespread public interest in the sensational trial of Mr. Vattier, who was accused of burglary and larceny. The publisher of this book—considered to be the first non-utilitarian book to be published in Ohio—guaranteed that the book would be printed at the earliest opportunity and would be set in small pica type and that there would not be an additional charge even if it was necessary to exceed the 250 pages originally planned.

During the 19th century, there would have been few publishers willing to risk their capital without assuring a first printing that would cover their costs. The procedure followed in most instances was to advertise a title in the newspaper, and then send out agents into the hinterland, each armed with a prospectus in which the subscriber signed his name, agreeing to pay the price requested upon receipt of the copy. Many of the books produced in such a manner were histories—local, state, and national—and of course religious texts were exceedingly popular. It was rare indeed that subscribers were offered the opportunity to purchase books which would eventually become valuable. One of the exceptions was the edition of *The Birds of America,* by the naturalist John James Audubon, which was issued in one hundred parts at a dollar a part.

A Connecticut Yankee, Henry Howe, who had been born to a bookseller's family and who had walked the length and breadth of New York state two times collecting historical data for a subscription book, came to Ohio early in 1846 and repeated the process. Howe's *Historical Collections of Ohio,* a 581-page book, sold eighteen thousand copies at three dollars, a record which not even General Grant's *Memoirs* could exceed. On the strength of this venture Howe settled in Ohio where he became the leading publisher in the west of subscription books.

Howe wrote in the preface of one of his subscription books, *Travel and Adventures,* published in 1853, his philosophy as a publisher of subscription selling: "This, like our other publications is intended to be disposed of by subscription only. This mode of circulating literature, as practiced in this country, is peculiarly an American invention. In Europe it is adopted to assure, in advance, the expense of costly works—with us, as a method —for the convenience of the purchasers—of engaging sales after a book has been issued. . . . for it should be remembered that the regular book merchant—the trader in ideas—is the very last man who emigrates—the very last to be established in a young community. Taking the whole land through, doubtless a thousand establishments have been reared to supply the animal appetite for liquid stimulus to one erected to minister to the intellect, by the sale of books; and further, millions of our people never in their lives have even entered a bookstore, and millions upon millions do not annually average the possession of a single new book. With all our self-congratulated civilization, the mass of even

our most enlightened communities is far behind a proper standard of cultivation, as is illustrated by the universal desire for tinsel and display. . . . In fact, Ignorance everywhere rears his stupid front, and among the best weapons with which to vanquish him are books, and in the interior, with a vast number, the habit of obtaining and of using these will not be acquired unless brought to their very doors."

May 20

Caleb Stower, printer, dedicated his lengthy work, *The Printer's Grammar; or, Introduction to the Art of Printing: containing A Concise History of the Art, with the Improvements in the Practice of Printing, for the Last Fifty Years,* to his patron, Lord Stanhope, in a letter dated this day in 1808:

"To the Right Honourable Earl Stanhope, My Lord, The appropriation of the time and talents of a Peer of the Realm to the improvement of the Arts, merits the thanks of a British Public. It is not to any one solitary branch of these arts that our Lordship's attention has been devoted—your indefatigable and persevering genius has investigated almost every article of human ingenuity which is connected with the welfare of mankind.

"But, my Lord, it is the object of this dedication to notice your Lordship's improvements in the invaluable *Art of Printing.* Your merits in this respect are detailed in the subsequent volume; which is both enriched and decorated by the fruits of your diligence. Nor let this circumstance be forgotten by your Lordship, which I mention with peculiar pleasure, that your success has been eminently distinguished in the *Art,* which possesses the power, and which will most cheerfully employ that power, of conveying down the name of Stanhope to the latest posterity. I have, my Lord, the honour to remain, Your Lordship's humble Servant, C. STOWER."

Stower produced an informative handbook which—although following the basic precepts as laid down for manuals of printing by Joseph Moxon's *Mechanick Exercises* of 1683—nevertheless contains a considerable amount of new material concerning early 19th century practices. *The Printer's Grammar* contains, in Chapter XII, "On the Construction of Printing-Presses," a thirty-eight page account of the standard wooden press of the period, with some twenty-nine wood-block illustrations. From Stower's description, a modern printer could construct his own press.

The chapter on fine printing was written by John McCreery, who some years later was to write the memorable poem about printing entitled *The Press*. Among the other then current authorities prevailed upon to write sections of the book, the account of proofreading was written by Joseph Nightingale, a prominent Corrector of the Press of the period. Unquestionably, Caleb Stower's *Grammar* belongs on the shelf with other notable printing manuals of the past, which together help to perpetuate the long history of this honorable craft of printing.

May 21

On May 21, 1948 Bruce Rogers was honored with the gold medal of the American Academy of Arts and Letters. Chauncey Brewster Tinker, who had made the presentation, stated in part:

"I have the honor to present to Bruce Rogers, designer of books, the gold medal of the Academy for special distinction in the arts. This award is made on certain occasions in recognition of the whole output of the recipient. This is the seventh award. In the present instance the corpus of the artist's work is as extensive as it is distinguished. The designing of books is, like architecture, one of the indispensable arts; life may go forward, after a fashion, without poetry, painting, sculpture, or even music; but shelter and books man must have. For better or worse the arts of building and book-designing must live on."

In his acceptance of the award, BR said:

"Though I am, as the citation states, a designer of books, and not, in the accepted sense of the term, a printer (as Benjamin Franklin was proud to assert of himself), I would like to speak of the art in its broader aspects. Design is but one factor in printing; but even as a designer I can still get a thrill out of taking a dingy rectangle of type, smearing it with still more dingy ink, laying on a sheet of paper, and pulling a lever. The thrill comes when you lift the paper and

find you have perhaps a page of Professor Tinker's mellifluous writing about *The Wedgwood Medallion of Samuel Johnson,* or about *An Unknown Portrait of James Boswell. . . .*

"I hope that the question of my age did not enter into this award; for it is said that so long as a man retains his illusions he doesn't grow old; and after sixty-five years of trial and error I still labor under the delusion that someday I shall produce a perfect book. In that length of time I have used millions of words, chiefly as raw material for working up into pages of type. But when I started to gather together some fitting ones to express my feelings of appreciation on this occasion, I found that of those millions very few could be unearthed from the printer's hellbox that constitutes my vocabulary. . . .

"This is a great day for printing, and a red letter day for me as an exponent of that art. Had I the production of the invitations, programmes, and other matters connected with this day's ceremony, you may be sure they would all have been printed in red.

"Printing has had many great days—when Gutenberg (or somebody) pulled the first proof from movable types; when Caxton set up his press in Westminster; when Jenson first used his beautiful Roman type in 1470; when the King James Bible was finished in 1611; when *The Freeman's Oath* and the *Bay Psalm Book* came off the press at Cambridge in 1639 and '40; when Franklin issued his handsomest book, *Cato Major,* in 1744— these are a few of printing's great days. And now, by your formal recognition of the art and its admission to the company of the other arts which this Academy so eminently sponsors, another great day has been added to the printer's calendar."

May 22

"Perfect typography is a science rather than an art. A thorough grasp of the craft is indispensable but it is not all, for the sound taste which distinguishes the perfect is based on a clear knowledge of the laws of harmonious form. It is true that it springs, as a rule, even though only in part, from an original feeling, but feelings are of little worth as long as they cannot be expressed as reasoned opinions; they have to be changed into knowledge about the consequences of decisions on artistic construction. There are, therefore, no born masters of typography: only by gradual training can such a status be reached."

The American Institute of Graphic Arts paid tribute, on this day in 1954, albeit belatedly, to Jan Tschichold, the author of the above statement, by presenting to him its medal for distinguished services to the graphic arts.

As a young man, Tschichold visited the Weimar Bauhaus exhibition in 1923 and was inspired to apply the precepts of the Bauhaus artists and architects to typography, utilizing type as a constructional element of design. The typography of the period was unimaginative, the greatest stress being placed upon the use of supposedly exotic types rather than upon creative design. The principles of the Bauhaus movement, being at variance with established habits, were slow to make headway among typographers, but a small group of young designers began to discuss the possibilities of the new concepts. Herbert Bayer, El Lissitzky, and others, among them Tschichold, adopted the new ideas as representative of the creed of the era.

Tschichold's contribution was major. He published, in 1928, *Die Neue Typographie,* which blew like a typhoon through the typographical world, creating about as many critics as adherents. But that it had tremendous effect on typographic design for a generation there can be no doubt. The book was also to come under political approbation. When Hitler came to power in Germany it was banned as "cultural bolshevism" and its author taken into protective custody.

In 1933 he left Germany to live in Switzerland. Here he was to work and teach for a period of twenty years, except for a two-year period in England following the war when he was typographic director for the famous Penguin editions. The format for these books may be credited to him. It has undoubtedly had a significant effect on the typography of pocket books in the United States.

In his mature years Tschichold has reversed his field somewhat, to the dismay of the avant-garde typographers. He now believes in the lasting values of traditional design, stating: "As typography is addressed to everybody, it does not allow of revolutionary alterations. . . . Comfortable readability is the paramount rule of all typography; but judgment on this matter can only be pronounced by one who is really trained in reading. . . . A perfect knowledge of the history of printing types is an indispensable precondition of perfect typography. Still more precious is a practical knowledge of calligraphy."

Tschichold is now back in Germany as a teacher, continuing to influence the new generation of typographers. He has published some forty books, too many of which have unfortunately not been translated into English for the benefit of the younger designers who need so much to listen to such a wise counselor.

May 23

In the year 1752 upon this day a printer died in his ninetieth year, honored as the man who had introduced the art of printing into the middle colonies of British America. William Bradford thus occupies a distinctive place in the history of the craft in the United States.

Bradford was apprenticed to his trade in England. Through an association between his employer and William Penn, he was selected to journey to the Colonies in 1682 with Penn to set up a press. He survived a three month voyage, during which smallpox broke out aboard the vessel, killing thirty of the one hundred passengers.

Bradford spent some time in traveling, but there is little record of just what he did before he returned to England to secure equipment for the project of establishing his printing office. He returned to Philadelphia and began printing, in his twenty-second year, for the middle colonies. His first issue was an Almanack for 1686, which was printed in the autumn of the previous year.

In 1689 Bradford was charged with printing an edition of the Penn Charter without authority and was warned not to do any other unauthorized printing. Two years later he was again in trouble for printing an address by the superintendent of the schools who was then out of favor with the authorities. All of those arrested were convicted and fined, but Bradford's case was not resolved. The type form which had been used to print the so-called libelous material was brought into court but when it was brought before the jury for identification, a juror inadvertently pied the form, thus destroying the evidence against Bradford.

At about the same time, the Assembly of New York met and offered a resolution: "That if a printer will come and settle in the City of Newyorke for the printing of Our Acts of Assembly & publick papers he shall be allowed the summe of fourty pounds Current money of Newyorke per annum for his salary & have the benefite of his printing besides what serves the publick."

Bradford appealed for the dismissal of the case against him, as his printing equipment had not been returned to him. The governor examined the records and dismissed the case. Bradford, feeling his usefulness at an end in Pennsylvania, secured the appointment as Royal Printer at New York, where he set up his office in 1693, thus making himself the first printer in both Pennsylvania and New York. He added Printer to New Jersey to the list in 1703.

In 1725 Bradford published the *New York Gazette*, the first newspaper to be produced in that city. He also printed a book during the same year, in partnership with John Peter Zenger, to whom he had taught the printer's craft and who later was involved in the influential freedom of the press issue.

He retired in 1744, after fifty years as Public Printer of New York, and died in 1752. In addition to his work as a printer, Bradford is credited by Lawrence C. Wroth, the historian of the colonial period of American printing, with being the founder of paper making in the United States. In 1690 he set up the first paper mill and secured the services of William Rittenhouse as the papermaker. He later owned a mill in Elizabethtown, New Jersey.

May 24

"The wildly enthusiastic youngster from Snohomish, Washington," who helped Fred Goudy start the Village Press and then went on to a long and distinguished career in typography, died this day in 1955.

Will Ransom's interest in printing came about when as a boy he wrote out by hand his favorite stories, decorating them in the art nouveau style of the period and binding them in ooze-leather. He used the hectograph to obtain multiple copies for presentation to his friends and relatives. Thus motivated, it was natural that his first job should be in printing. He went to work for the Vancouver (Washington) *Weekly Tribune* for the wage of one dollar per week. At the same time he continued his interest in bookmaking projects.

In September, 1901, he started the Handcraft Shop with the production of Tennyson's *Lady of Shalott,* containing line photo-engravings hand colored by Ransom's aunt. The edition of ninety-five copies was quickly sold, encouraging the young designer to do another book, which was also successful and received several favorable reviews.

In 1903 having saved enough money to attend art school, Ransom went to Chicago and enrolled in the school of the Art Institute. In Chicago he met Goudy and soon became quite friendly with him. Goudy was then a free-lance designer and teacher of lettering and had not yet acquired his later reputation as a type designer. At Goudy's request, Ransom became a partner in the foundation of the Village Press, but when Goudy decided to move east, Ransom elected to remain in Chicago. During the next nine years he took up the vocation of bookkeeping, which offered a more substantial income than printing design.

After his marriage in 1911 he was encouraged to return to his first love, setting up as a letterer and free-lance artist. Soon he began to acquire some important customers. A style of lettering which he used for Carson Pirie Scott & Company, the Chicago department store, was noticed by the typefoundry, Barnhart Brothers & Spindler, and resulted in the design of a type named Parsons in 1918. It became an immediate bestseller and remained popular for commercial printing for a number of years.

In 1921 Will Ransom's love of books prompted a venture in the printing of limited editions, but by 1925 he found it necessary to return to commercial work. During this period he had continued to correspond with the operators of private presses. He accumulated a great deal of information which was published by R. R. Bowker in 1929 in a volume called *Private Presses and Their Books,* probably the most authoritative text yet written on the subject. For the remainder of his life Ransom continued his interest in the private press movement, adding to his original work with the publication of *Selective Check Lists of Pressbooks*, completed in 1950. He also edited the Typophile Chap Book *Kelmscott, Doves, Ashendene.*

From 1930 to 1935 Ransom worked at the Printing House of Leo Hart in Rochester, New York, as supervisor of the book department. During this time his notable books were *Venus and Adonis*, hand set in Lutetia type and illustrated by Rockwell Kent, and *Dissertation on Roast Pig*. The next four years were spent with a commercial printer in Buffalo. Finally Ransom went to New York to head up the celebration of the 500th anniversary of the invention of printing, sponsored by the American Institute of Graphic Arts.

In 1941 he went west to the University of Oklahoma Press as Art Director, and stayed at that post for the remainder of his life, being responsible for the high quality of the hundreds of books produced during that period by the Press. Will Ransom's contribution has placed Oklahoma high up on the list of fine university presses. Without question, the fourteen years spent there were the happiest of his life. He felt himself to be a part of the academic atmosphere of the university, and he had the opportunity to continue his world-wide correspondence with private press operators and the many friends he had acquired within the craft of printing.

The records of his inquiries and much of his correspondence are now at the Newberry Library in Chicago, where they will continue to be of use to those bibliographers who wish to further their knowledge of private press operations.

May 25

"Dear Sir," wrote John P. Sheldon, founding editor of the *Michigan Gazette* on this day in 1829 to Andrew Jackson, seventh President of the United States, "This is a specimen of the printing done by me on Mr. Burt's typographer. You will observe some inaccuracies in the situation of the letters; these are owing to the imperfections of the machine, it having been made in the woods of Michigan where no proper tools could be obtained by the inventor. . . . I am satisfied, from my knowledge of the printing business,

as well as from the operation of the rough machine, with which I am now printing, that the typographer will be ranked with the most novel, useful, and pleasing inventions of this age."

On the reverse side of this letter, the first ever produced by a typewriter device in the United States, was a note from the inventor himself: "I, William A. Burt, being duly sworn, depose and say that I am the inventor of the machine, called by me the TYPOGRAPHER, and intended for use in families, offices, and stores, and further that such invention and any parts thereof, have not, to the best of my knowledge and belief, been known or used in the United States or any foreign country."

Burt, then thirty-seven years of age, was the embodiment of that typical 19th century mechanic, the self-educated inventive genius. When he was twelve years old, and had just completed his formal schooling, he found that the chores on his father's farm in the Mohawk Valley town of Broadalbin in upstate New York, interfered with his love of books. Putting his mind to the problem, he invented a bookholder which allowed him to continue his reading while working on shingles with a drawshave. His great love was the sea, and he read every book on the subject which he could find. He instructed himself in this manner in the science of navigation, but lacking a text in astronomy, he resorted to a mathematics text book, along with several farmer's almanacs to provide himself with a sufficient background to enable him to construct a sextant—an instrument which he had never seen—and to accurately compute the latitude and longitude of the farm.

From the study of navigation Burt taught himself surveying. Following military service in the War of 1812, he went as far west as Michigan, where he became a surveyor and a builder of saw-mills, and a member of the Territorial Legislative Council, all of which kept him busy. In fact he found that the paper work, which he detested, kept him from endeavors in which he was more interested. Determined to do something about this state of affairs, he visited the printing office of the *Gazette*. Procuring a font of type, he set about building a writing machine.

Constructed primarily of wood, the machine contained a semi-circular disc upon which the type was mounted. This disc was rotated until the letter desired was positioned in the proper place, whereupon it was pressed into the paper with a lever. The paper was in the form of a roll, and when the number of lines equalled page length, a clock dial on the front of the machine indicated that it was time to tear it off. Actually, the product of the Typographer was fairly neat and clean, but unfortunately it was slower than writing.

The letter to President Jackson resulted in a patent being granted on July 23, 1829, but Burt was unable to raise sufficient capital to produce the machine. It therefore died aborning, but word of it did get around. From that moment inventors became interested in writing machines. Burt in turn became more interested in devices closer to his heart. He constructed a surveyor's compass which became standard equipment for the United States Government surveys for seventy-five years. For the remainder of his life he always had enough new projects kicking around his workshop to make him forget that he had invented the first American typewriter.

May 26

The renowned Theodore L. De Vinne was asked to state his views on the changing technology of the printing industry during the 19th century. In a broadly reasoned statement De Vinne expressed on this day in 1889 his attitude toward what critics were then calling the destructive forces which endangered the future of the industry. His words could well be appropriate today, when the threat of automation of typesetting by computer is upsetting to many traditional printers.

"Much of the present disquietude," said De Vinne, "is unnecessary. That typesetting by machine may or will reduce the cost of work on reprints and cheap books and papers is probable. That it will ever drive any large body of good workmen out of business is absurd. The machines will surely make more work for workmen. So far from decreasing the standard of workmanship, they will elevate it. In this country there has never been any active hostility to new machinery in the printing business. There have been no moves or strikes against inventions, but workmen look on all new devices with

suspicion and unfriendliness. They do not see that the invention which temporarily throws one man out of work, ultimately, makes work for two or more men.

"What would be the state of the trade if we had no stereotype or electrotype, no composition rollers, and no printing machines: the daily newspaper as we now have it would be an impossibility. An edition of two thousand or twenty-five hundred copies of a small sheet would be the highest performance of the hand press, and what severe work this paltry performance would impose on the wretched hand pressman who had to print this edition in a hurry! The illustrated magazine of large edition and low price, filled with fine wood cuts, could not exist at all in the days of hand presses. One could go on and show how hand presses would curtail the production not only of the popular but of the artistic forms of typography.

"Processes and machines that were once dreaded are now used by every printer, and they are welcomed as much by the journeyman as the master. No one will pretend that they have reduced the number of workmen. Where there was one printer fifty years ago, there are at least twenty printers now. As a rule, the average piece compositor is a better educated man than the average pressman. Under equal conditions he should and would earn higher wages, but his superior intelligence and education do not increase his production. This production is limited by the slowness of his hand, which is now as it was fifty years ago. If the compositor was employed on a type setting machine, he would get some of the benefits of the increased production.

"One reason why the modern pressman is better paid than the old pressman is because he is a better workman. The machine is more complex than the hand press, and it compels the pressman to exercise more forethought and intelligence. As a rule, the mechanics who bitterly decry machines are those who have been found incompetent to handle them. The men who refuse to learn the theory or the practice of new processes—who are content to do work as it was done when they were boys—who 'don't want to be bothered' by the study of new problems in handicraft—who evade or shirk responsibilities—are the very men that employers do not want to employ upon their machines. That they may and probably will suffer for their persistent refusal to adapt themselves to changed conditions is much to be regretted; but are they blameless? Is it the fault of the master, or the machine, or the workman himself?"

May 27

A faded statement, written in pencil on a piece of paper with the single word "Memorandum" set in the left-hand corner in 18-point Gretchen caps, was attached to a page torn from a copy of *The Inland Printer*. Under the date of May 27, 1913 were the words, "Be sure the new boy sees this!" The page carried the story of a compositor named Henry Nidermaier whose life represented a paragon of virtue, and a model for any printer's devil to follow. It is indeed difficult to imagine the present-day teenager inspiring a similar panegyric:

"For one month Henry Nidermaier had been feeding press, sweeping the floors, running errands and doing the other duties usually assigned to the beginner in the office of the Tazewell Printing Company, of Tazewell, Virginia.

"Then he asked for a raise. He thought that $3 a month, together with board and room, was insufficient, considering the amount of effort that he was putting forth.

"Naturally this request was refused. Apprentices seldom get a raise at the end of the first month of their apprenticeship.

" 'Well,' said the proprietor, 'I suppose you'll quit now.' "

" 'No sir,' replied young Nidermaier. 'I want to learn the printing business, and I am going to learn it, raise or no raise.'

"And right there he made good with the boss. After that it was not necessary for him to ask for increases in salary—they came unsolicited.

"He worked hard, too. After being in the shop from eight to twelve hours he had extra work to do in the evening—feeding chickens, feeding and cleaning the horse, carrying in coal and kindling, etc. Occasionally he was given the opportunity to set type, at which he displayed so much aptitude that in the third year of his apprenticeship he was receiving the regular scale of $10 a week. When he had spent six years with the Tazewell Printing Company he left, and after a

course of bumps and knocks throughout the South he finally landed in Cleveland. Here he came into contact with a new class of printing—the tariff—his first page of which, when returned from the proofroom, 'resembled a Balkan war map.'

"Some time during the fall of 1908 there appeared at The Inland Printer Technical School one who looked more like the advance agent of prosperity than a student of job composition. Not that the job printer as a rule fails to present an appearance in conformity to his position as a craftsman, but this student went the most fastidious one better. As a result of his manner and appearance, the student had been in the school less than forty-eight hours before he was dubbed 'The Duke'—and as 'The Duke' Nidermaier has been known since that time.

"His sojourn at the school was not as is the ordinary relationship between the student and the instruction department. Rather was it an interchange of ideas—for 'The Duke' is another proof of the statement that the more a man knows the more he wants to know and the more susceptible he is to new influences. The broader a man's mental horizon becomes, the smaller, relatively, are the things which he already knows.

"As might be expected, Nidermaier made good from the start. Whatever there was in the course of instruction that he was not already familiar with he readily grasped and applied to his work."

The social historians are all fond of telling us that America "came of age" with the advent of the first World War. Unquestionably the story of Compositor Hank Nidermaier is typical of the period of our youth and has been repeated countless times by those who believe that we lost our sense of values when we did reach our majority.

May 28

William A. Kittredge was born into the family of a Lowell, Massachusetts printer on this day in 1891. Just fourteen years later he was beginning his apprenticeship as a compositor at the Parkhurst Press, Chelmsford, Massachusetts. Afterwards he undertook the traditional journey, working as far away from New England as Elk River, Idaho. By 1914 he was back, however, doing a stint at the case in the famous Riverside Press, during the last year in which Bruce Rogers was connected with the great Boston printing office. No doubt this exposure set the direction which Kittredge's life as a printer was to take. The following year he became, at twenty-four years of age, Art Director of the Oswald Press in New York City. In 1918 he assumed similar responsibilities for the Franklin Printing Company of Philadelphia, and finally in 1922 he became Director of Design for R. R. Donnelley & Sons Company of Chicago, a position he held with distinction until his death in 1945 at the age of fifty-four.

While at Donnelley's, Kittredge of course was responsible for a wide range of printed materials, most of which was promotional, but he is best remembered as a book designer. No fewer than forty-three of the many books which were produced under his direction were selected for the Fifty Books of the Year Exhibitions sponsored by the American Institute of Graphic Arts. Four of these may be singled out as examples of American bookmaking at its finest. All printed in 1930 to represent the craftsmanship of the firm, they were, *Moby Dick,* illustrated by Rockwell Kent, and still considered one of the great American illustrated books; *Two Years Before the Mast,* illustrated by Edward A. Wilson; *Poe's Tales,* illustrated by W. A. Dwiggins, and *Walden,* with illustrations by Rudolph Ruzicka.

It was Ruzicka who addressed the American Institute of Graphic Arts in 1940 on the occasion of the presentation to Kittredge of the Institute's Gold Medal: "Kittredge accepts the materials as well as the life of his time and in this sense his work is modern; the conscientious regard he has for the purpose of the work in hand and a certain natural reserve save him from the modish. For its sparsely ornamented simplicity, dignified use of materials, fitness to purpose, his work can be placed not so much in time as in quality: it is good printing."

Kittredge became involved in the 1923 controversy between the friends of Frederic W. Goudy, and the typographic historian, Henry L. Bullen. Following a long article by Bullen in which Goudy was characterized as having an "unfortunate tendency toward megalomania", Kittredge wrote a scathing reply, which appeared in the *Ben Franklin Monthly,* a periodical for which he had ear-

lier written several fine monographs on the history of printing types.

"Because Frederic W. Goudy," he stated, "has obtained just recognition and honor in his own time is conceivably a thorn in the side of Bullen. The most that Goudy has ever claimed for himself is that of the simple effort of an honest craftsman to do good work. . . . A man of accomplishments in literature, music, on the stage, or in politics, equal to Mr. Goudy's accomplishments in type designing would receive vastly more wealth, honor and publicity because of it. Can Mr. Goudy subdue, smother, or hold back those eager friends of his who would do him honor while he is yet with us? Who but our verbose 'publicist' and contemporary, Bullen, could begrudge the doing of honor where honor is due? The name, fame and reputation of Goudy will endure long after his enemies and detractors are forgotten and have become less than dust."

May 29

"Gentlemen," wrote James Watson to the Printers in Scotland in the preface of his book, *History of the Art of Printing,* published this day in Edinburgh in 1713, "That Men are not born for themselves, but for the Republick, is an ancient and universally applauded Maxim. And it is so agreeable to right Reason, that the wisest and best Part of Mankind, in every Age since the Creation, have endeavor'd to lay the foundation of a lasting good Name, by every Action of their Life; whereby they might improve the Body or Society of which they were members. To this Principle it is, that we owe the Invention or Improvement of all the Arts and Sciences that are instructive or beneficial to Man. 'Mongst which the Invention and vast Improvement, of the no less honourable, than useful and admirable Art of PRINTING, which we profess, deserves a very eminent Place: Since by It, all sorts of Learning, Sacred or Profane, and every Kind of profitable Instruction and Invention are both publish'd and preserv'd; as my Author, I here give you a Translation of, shews clearly and copiously enough."

Actually, Watson's history was a translation of Jean de la Caille's *Histoire de l'Imprimerie et de la Librairie,* which had been published in Paris in 1689. There are possibly three other histories of printing which preceded it in Great Britain: *The Original and Growth of Printing Collected out of History and the Records of the Kingdome,* by Richard Atkyns (London, 1664); *Some observations on the use and original of the Noble Art and Mystery of Printing,* by Francis Burges (Norwich, 1701); *Observations concerning the Invention and Progress of Printing,* by Humphrey Wanley, which appeared in *Philosophical Transactions of the Royal Society,* No. 228, 1703.

The Watson work appeared some thirty years after Moxon published his famed *Mechanick Exercises.* It is of interest today primarily because Printer Watson wrote his preface, in which he discusses the state of the art in Scotland at that period, along with some of its practitioners. It is also very well printed for its period. Of further interest is the 48-page specimen of the types which Watson owned, although Talbot Baines Reed, the historian of British typefounding, wrote of them as being "indifferent Dutch types."

That Watson had a different opinion of these types is obvious from the last paragraph of his preface. He writes:

"I have affix'd to this history a Specimen of what Types I have now by me; in a few Weeks I am to be provided with a greater Variety, and of the best in *Europe:* I shall always be ready to acquaint my Countrymen of the Place and Founder I have them from. 'Twas not from any ostentation that I plac'd this Specimen here, but to undeceive some People, who were made to believe, That the last Specimen I printed about Six Years ago, was done for me Abroad, and that I had no such Types in my Work-house: But most of you know the Falsehood of this Assertion. I wish none of you may have your Country's Honour less at Heart as to PRINTING, than I have had it: and spend as much of your Money and Time for reviving PRINTING in This Part of the Island, as I have done."

May 30

James Conner, one of the important typefounders of the 19th century, died this day in 1861. Born near Hyde Park in New York's Dutchess County, Conner became apprenticed to a printer at the age of thirteen. His indentures were interrupted the following year when he ran off to fight in the War of 1812. He continued in New York City at the conclusion of hostilities, working in a number of different printing offices, in one of which, operated by John Watts, the first stereotyper in the United States, he learned that craft in addition to setting type and operating the press.

Gaining a reputation as a stereotyper, Conner was offered a large salary to become foreman of the newly established Boston Stereotype Foundry, where in a relatively short period he saved $3,000, a sufficiently large sum of money to enable him to return to New York to establish his own stereotype foundry in 1827. The practice in all of the earlier stereotype plants was to set the type which was to be molded. To this Conner included the publishing of such standard items as the Bible, Shakespeare, and encyclopedias.

As business prospered, Conner decided to add typefounding to his services, although such a move was received coldly by the other New York typefounders. As he knew little about this new craft, other than actual casting, he secured the help of Edwin Starr, who had some twenty-five years earlier gained employment in the foundry operated by Binny & Ronaldson in Philadelphia, for the express purpose of "stealing" the firm's information concerning the construction of a type mold. This knowledge Starr had imparted to Elihu White, a Yankee inventor anxious to start his own typefoundry in Hartford, Connecticut.

Conner's first important contribution to American typefounding was the successful introduction of a type known as Light Face Scotch. Some sources credit Conner with the actual cutting of the punches for this type, while others claim Starr was responsible. It has also been stated that Conner purchased the matrices for the type from William Hagar, another founder who had not been successful with the design. In any case, Conner popularized the use of light-face roman type in America, the Scotch letter becoming the standard type of the period.

Working again with Starr, Conner next introduced the construction of matrices by the electrotype method, an invention which revolutionized type manufacturing, allowing any foundry to pirate its competitor's designs at random. A side effect of this development was the consequent reduction of opportunity for the designing of more original and imaginative type styles, particularly in the field of roman types for book composition. This procedure is still occasionally utilized by typefoundries, particularly when original matrices or punches have been lost or destroyed, and a customer wishes to replenish a case of old and rare type.

Following Conner's death, his sons continued the business under the name of James Conner's Sons. William C. Conner, the eldest son, became widely known in the political life of New York City, holding a number of offices. It was while he was Sheriff of New York that the notorious Boss Tweed was imprisoned and placed in Conner's custody, from which he escaped. In order to regain his own good name, Conner had to spend a great deal of his own money to apprehend Tweed, finally locating him in Spain and returning him to New York.

Two other sons, James M. and Charles S. Conner, devoted themselves to the running of the typefoundry, but upon the death of their elder brother in 1881, the business declined. James Conner gained full control. Following his death in 1887, his sons succeeded him, selling out to the American Type Founders Company in 1892, thereby bringing to a close a fifty year period of significant contributions to the typefounder's craft in America.

May 31

A tiny bookplate, measuring 10½ x 5½ picas, containing the name of Samuel Phillips and dated May 31, 1652, might very well stand as a prime example of a well-designed bookplate. In addition it has historic value as probably the earliest known authentic American bookplate.

This bookplate, simply designed with a border of acorn ornaments, stands in strong contrast to the arty bookplates of our own time. Most of the latter are far too large for their purpose, which is primarily to denote the ownership of a book. Commercial bookplates have assumed the proportions and appearances of posters and have long since lost the bookish appearance which would appear to be a functional requirement. Such is the influence of the current variety, that

should a bibliophile need a properly designed plate he will have to seek out a good printer. Even then he may have to insist that it be kept simple—and of course small.

The Phillips plate is still rather controversial historically. It was discovered about twenty-five years ago in a New York antique shop by Edward Naumberg, Jr. who happened to be looking for whale-oil lamps. It had been affixed to the back fly-leaf of a pocket notebook owned by the Rev. Zachariah Greene, who had died at Hempstead, Long Island in 1858 at the age of ninety-nine.

Collector Naumberg had traced the bookplate to the Stephen Day Press in Cambridge, Massachusetts, during the period when it was operated by Samuel Green. Up to the year 1652 the Cambridge Press had produced thirty-five books or broadsides, of which just six are extant, the *Bay Psalm Book* of course being the principal item. This small scrap of printed paper is thus a unique example of early American printing.

There are three known dated book labels earlier than 1652, but these were printed in England, as they predate the establishment of a Press in the Bay Colony. There remains but a single plate, with the name of Steven Day, and dated 1642, which challenges the Phillips label as the first American example. (Day had changed the spelling of his name from "ph" to "v" after his arrival in the Colonies.) This label contains a *fleur-de-lis* border of individual ornaments which were fairly common in England at that time but were not seen in any American printing until 1693. On the other hand the acorn ornament, or dingbat, as the printer would term it, was frequently used by Samuel Green at the Day Press before and after the printing of the label.

The 1642 plate thus remains doubtful of its place as the first American bookplate, although Dr. R. W. G. Vail, Director of the New York Historical Society, so lists it in his paper on American book labels which appeared in the *American Book Collector*, Vol. 4, 1933. He demonstrated that a single type ornament in the Day label later appeared in the labels of Walter Price and Joseph Mors, dated 1693.

No matter whether the Phillips label was the first or second, however, it still remains a wonderful model for contemporary bookplate designers, in spite of its badly cast ornaments and poor type.

June

June 1

At Manchester, England on June 1, 1839, Charles H. Timperley completed his preface to *A Dictionary of Printers and Printing,* an octavo containing in 1,002 pages of brevier type, a storehouse of factual information concerning the progress of the craft of printing. The authoritative bibliographers of printing, Messrs. Bigmore and Wyman, say of it, "One of the most interesting works a printer can possess; while laying no claim to originality, it is full of anecdote and historical facts."

Indeed, Timperley went to some length in his preface to deprecate his contributions to the Mystic Art: "In April, 1828, that portion of the work which now forms the introduction, was delivered as one of two lectures before the Warwick and Leamington Literary and Scientific Institution; and the very flattering commendations then bestowed induced me to pursue the subject further, as a means both of self-instrucion and amusement for my leisure hours. . . . Not aware of the labours that others had performed, and without an assistant, I had many obstacles to contend with; and soon became well convinced, that the design I had formed was above the bibliographical acquirements of a journeyman printer."

"My aim," he further stated in his prefatory remarks, "has been to record, with as much fidelity as possible, the names and deeds of ancient and modern typographers, who have benefitted literature by their labours—society by their exertions—and whose conduct it would be easy to adopt, and desirable to emulate. Nor will it, I hope, be deemed presumption for having introduced the names of many of our humbler artists, whose meritorious conduct when living obtained the meed of praise; and whose honourable industry deserves to be recorded as a laudable example to the young typographer, who wishes to obtain respect from his fellow-men."

Timperley had been apprenticed to a copperplate engraver. However he entered the army in 1810 where he soon learned that a military career gave "few opportunities for self-improvement." Wounded in the Battle of Waterloo, he was discharged in 1815 and returned to his trade. Disliking it, he indentured himself instead as a letter-press printer, "with the view of affording me that literary information which I so ardently desired." His first compilation was *Songs of the Press,* one of the best selections ever put together of printer's songs and poems. At the present time Timperley's *Dictionary* is not readily obtainable, and the collector who runs across the volume in a second-hand bookshop may consider himself fortunate.

For a printer with such scholarly attributes, Timperley did not have a distinguished career following the publication of his dictionary, primarily because he was the victim of a 19th century con game operated by the publisher of his book. To pay his debts as a responsible employee of the publisher he consigned his entire stock of dictionaries to an auctioneer who ran off with the proceeds of the auction leaving the author heartbroken and quite destitute. He ended his career in a comparatively minor job.

June 2

In Berwyn, Illinois on this date in 1897, Frederic W. Goudy, a bookkeeper of sorts, married Bertha Sprinks, whom he had known for about seven years. He thereby acquired a helpmate who exerted a most powerful influence on his subsequent career, as Bertha Goudy became one of its motivating forces.

Almost immediately she was helping him to obtain recognition in the craft of lettering, which was then just a side line to Goudy. Working as cashier of *The Michigan Farmer* in Detroit, he was studying book design and lettering. He received a commission to draw some initials for a St. Louis typefoundry. He drew the letters in pencil and Bertha inked them in. When the work lagged she insisted that it be completed.

When the Village Press was formed, Bertha was the bookbinder, but in a short time it was realized that there would not be sufficient income for the Goudys and also for Will Ransom, their partner. Fred bought Ransom's interest and thus by default Bertha Goudy became the compositor for the Press. She attained such proficiency that Ransom later said of her, "She gave to the Village Press not only intense enthusiasm and magnificent courage but also a deft craftsmanship already well developed in other media. She turned from a hand-loom to a case of type with certain assurance and, from the first, showed a rare natural aptitude for composition, which has remained her special forte."

In a moving memoir of their lives together Goudy wrote:

"She had an intuitive sense of spacing—a sense almost uncanny in her ability to judge the amount of matter that would or would not go in a line—and if by chance she omitted a word or a letter, I frequently marvelled at her success in getting the omitted words in without extensive running over and without spoiling the general effect. Her setting was very accurate because she invariably read the lines in the 'stick,' but occasionally she would repeat inadvertently the last word of a line at the beginning of the next. She liked to leave out commas, and many were the arguments on this point. I was a stickler for typesetting traditions and she delighted in disregarding them."

Paul Bennett, a good friend of the Goudys, observed at one time that Bertha was "one of the greatest of women printers, one with a longer and more prolific record in private press annals than any other woman—and the most valuable."

Four years after her death in 1935, her husband wrote of her, "For nearly two-score years she unselfishly aided me in every way in my work in the fields of type design and typography, and enabled me to secure a measure of success which I, alone, never could have achieved."

June 3

On this day in 1693 William Anderton, an unfortunate printer, stood at the Bar of the Old Bailey before the august members of the Court, which included the Lord Chief Justice Treby, Mr. Justice Powell, Sir John Fleet, Lord Mayor, and Sir Salathiel Lovell, Recorder of London. Anderton was charged with high treason in the composing, printing, and publishing of two malicious libels.

He was accused by a fellow printer of operating a press in a hidden location, of owning a trunk filled with seditious papers, and of calling King William, the reigning monarch, "Hooknose." The evidence presented to the Court was circumstantial. It became evident that Anderton was to be made a scapegoat. C. H. Timperley, writing in satiric vein almost a century and a half later, tells of the trial:

"In summing up the evidence, two or three old, musty, impertinent precedents were brought in, which had not seen the sun for many ages, the chief of which was that of Sir John Oldcastle, Lord Cobham, and he might as well have urged the case of the Man-in-the-Moon: for what was my Lord Cobham's place to printing? That famous Wicklivite lived in the reign of Richard II, some scores of years before printing was thought on, which came not into England until the reign of Henry VII; . . .

"In short, every thing was aggravated to the utmost, every little punctilio was made use of, which was thought might be any thing serviceable to beget in the jury an hard opinion of the prisoner. . . . After two hours debate, the greater part of the jury became well inclined to have found not guilty; but there was one amongst them who loved mischief, and he was for hanging Anderton for being a Jacobite, not for being guilty. . . . He readily acknowledged that the evidence did not amount to the proof of the fact; but saith he, what of that? I believed he was guilty, and I shall hang a hundred of them for half so much evidence. Some of the jurymen, by way of complaint, said thus, 'My lord, our foreman is of the opinion this fact is not proved.'—Court: 'Whether it be proved or no, you ought to determine; the bare finding the books in his custody would not be treason; but the case is, gentlemen, here is a man who has a printing-press, to which no man has admission but himself; and this man is found with an errata, and &c., so that he must needs print the treason.'

"To this a juryman answered, 'Tis a very strong presumption, my lord.' And then Baron Powell clenched the nail with this grave saying, 'a violent presumption is as much as if a man had been there and done it himself.' These answers being returned to questions, the jury were sent back again, where almost three hours more were spent in debating the matter, before they could come to a conclusion; they then complied and brought in the prisoner guilty. The matter now lay wholly before the City Recorder, Sir Salathiel Lovell, who after a flourish or two of empty rhetoric, proceeded to pronounce that dreadful sentence which the law allots to treason; to have the heart and bowels torn out, and burnt, and the body dismembered, and the quarters set up, or disposed as authority orders."

Timperley concludes his account with the statement that the sentence was carried out thirteen days later, "except for the disembowelling." It was later established that the government had at the time of the trial, already taken into custody the actual culprits who had committed the treason. Thus the unfortunate Anderton's trial and execution remains but another landmark in the long history of the freedom of the printed word.

June 4

At the age of seven years Isaiah Thomas was indentured to a Boston printer named Zechariah Fowle, on this day in 1756. The articles provided that:

"The said apprentice, his said master and mistress, well and faithfully shall serve; their secrets he shall keep close; their commandments lawful and honest everywhere he shall gladly obey; he shall do no damage to his said master, etc., or suffer it to be done by others without letting or giving seasonable notice thereof to his said master, etc.; he shall not waste the goods of his said master, etc., nor lend them unlawfully to any; at cards, dice, or any other unlawful game or games he shall not play; fornication he shall not commit; matrimony during the said term he shall not contract; taverns, alehouses or places of gaming he shall not haunt or frequent; from the service of his said master, etc., by day or night he shall not absent himself."

Printer Fowle agreed on his part to furnish the lad with room and board and clothing and to instruct him in reading, writing, and ciphering. Isaiah was to remain an apprentice until his twenty-first year, with the provision that when he reached his fourteenth year he could break the contract if he decided that he did not wish to be a printer.

Fowle was a lazy and ignorant printer who earned his living by printing and hawking on the streets licentious ballads and what would probably now be called pornography, a practice not at all unusual for the 18th century, even in Boston. Thomas' biographer relates that, "Then babies, ladies, and even the most saintly of the clergy, in jest and in ordinary conversation, used language which today would startle an aviation mechanic. Fowle could not have corrupted his apprentice by his 'licentious' ballads for the simple reason that there was nothing which he could teach anyone who lived a few years in the eighteenth century about those subjects which we today consider taboo."

While the printer treated his bound boy with relative kindness, he did subject him to all of the chores of a household in addition to those of a printing office. The boy had to stand on a bench in order to reach the cases to set type, a task which he was required to do almost immediately upon becoming apprenticed. No doubt his learning in "reading" was self-acquired as Fowle never did honor his part of the bargain about teaching young Thomas to read and write. In his first job of composition Thomas matched the letters with the words which he had to set. It took the lad two days to set the fifty-six lines of the ballad entitled *The Lawyer's Pedigree* which was sung to the tune of *Our Polly Was a Slut.*

Isaiah Thomas was possessed of character, however. He remained with Fowle until he was seventeen years of age, finally leaving secretly. He traveled to Halifax, with the intention of continuing to London to complete his education as a printer, as he had learned, in spite of his tutor, to love the craft. Thomas eventually became the best known printer of his time and one of the most properous. He wrote the first history of printing to be published in the United States, *History of Printing in America.* He retired from printing in 1802, devoting the balance of his life to scholarship and to founding the American Antiquarian Society, of which he was the first president. He died in 1831.

June 5

Across Harvard Yard at the commencement exercises on this June day in 1947 came the sonorous phrases of a recitation citing a printer for an honorary degree: "William Addison Dwiggins: Typographical designer whose skill and creative imagination have left a lasting impress on the pages of time." Thus America's oldest university honored with a Master of Arts degree a man who without question, of all living graphic designers, most deserved the accolade of "Master of Arts."

Many years previously Dwiggins had written out for Carl Rollins, Printer to Yale University, a standard biography: "Dwiggins, William Addison, Typographer and Carpenter-Artist; Black and White-Smith. b. Martinsville, Ohio, 1880; Richmond, Ind., Cambridge, Ohio; Chicago, Ill., Boston, Mass. Res. Hingham, Mass. Mem. Boston Art Club, Boston Society of Water Color Painters, the Society of Printers. No school. Secretary, the Society of Calligraphers . . . that is all."

That is all—except for the place in the hearts of everyone who knew him, personally or through his work, or through the expression of his ideas by means of his most facile pen. No one can properly recount the history of printing in the first half of this century without discussing his competency. As a typographer Will Dwiggins was one of the best of his time, primarily in the area of book design. He had said in 1925, "I want to make a few books—somehow—into which I can put the best I have. Do as finished and competent a job as I know how."

The "few books" turned out to be many hundreds, and a "competent job" resulted in thirty-seven of these being honored by selection in the Fifty Books of the Year Exhibitions sponsored by the American Institute of Graphic Arts. This group also made him its medalist in 1929. Most of these books were designed for the firm of Alfred A. Knopf, who still publishes a score of books each year with the colophon note: "Typography based upon the designs of W. A. Dwiggins."

Dwiggins' reference to being a Carpenter-Artist no doubt springs from his ability to create patterns of design using hand-cut templates. In themselves they were simple, but as combined into finished art they were WAD's trademark, and so completely individualistic as to be inimitable. No doubt it was his use of decoration which prompted one of George Salter's students to ask the question, in 1956, "Is Dwiggins supposed to be good?" In Salter's judgment Dwiggins was a genius in his work. "The character of his line is entirely his and only his. It does not derive from any existing style, past or present. Yet in an intangible way it is related to either."

As a Black and White-Smith, Dwiggins was a great calligrapher, and through the medium of lettering he became a type designer of note. Most of his types were for book composition—probably the most challenging form of letter design since the artist must merge his individuality to his design. There can never be a "look at me" attitude in a good book face, and the Dwiggins' types meet the test. Caledonia, designed in 1939, is now one of the most widely used types and would be on any compilation of the fine types available to modern printers. Also widely admired is Electra, his first book type, while his sans serif Metro is still most popular with newspaper printers for heads and advertising display.

The whimsical scrap of biography written for Carl Rollins by the future Harvard Master of Arts was then but a whispered outline of a great career, which made a lasting impression in every area of endeavor he chose to enter.

June 6

Academicians but rarely descend to the level of bestowing honorary degrees upon printers for their contributions to our civilization. There come to mind but a half-dozen instances when an American college or university has called to a convocation platform a craftsman representing the industry, other than a rather steady flow of newspaper and magazine publishers. This day in 1949 was therefore unique, when tiny but long-established Transylvania College in Lexington, Kentucky, honored the American type designer, Robert Hunter Middleton, with a Doctor of Fine Arts degree.

Now considered to be the "dean" of his craft (in a time when type designers represent a group scarcely of sufficient number to fill a hotel room should they ever hold a convention), Middleton has demonstrated his longevity by remaining on the job with a single firm, the Ludlow Typography Company, for his entire professional career. He was brought as a child from his birthplace in Glasgow, Scotland to Alabama in 1908, following a path worn smooth since the early days of the republic, when the typefounding industry was populated almost exclusively by Scotsmen.

While attending the Department of Printing Arts of the Art Institute of Chicago, young Middleton was fortunate in having as a teacher Ernst Detterer, to whom he later dedicated his little book, *Making Printers' Typefaces.*

It is probably unfortunate for Middleton's reputation as a creative designer that he has served one firm so long and faithfully, particularly since the nature of the machine for which he designs type precludes originality, which is not to say that Middleton lacks imagination as a type designer. The Ludlow machine was devised to produce display type primarily for newspapers and periodicals, utilizing hand-assembled matrices. It became the custom to inform purchasers of Ludlow machines that all the "currently popular" hand types would be made available. This factor has therefore prevented Middleton from attaining the individuality of an independent designer, but within this framework he has had to exercise mature judgment about the types which are valuable enough to warrant adapting to the Ludlow machine, and to evaluate typographic trends in advance, a task at which he has been remarkably successful.

Beginning with an outline capital named Delphin cut in 1928, Middleton has now reached the impressive total of over ninety types, most of which remain in everyday use by the nation's printers. Of his Garamond, modeled on the types appearing in the famous Egenolff-Berner specimen of 1592, Bruce Rogers was most enthusiastic, calling it one of the best of the modern Garamonds. Rogers used it in the 18-point size for the setting of his edition of *Gulliver's Travels* for the Limited Editions Club.

Middleton has become internationally known, also, as the proprietor of the Cherryburn Press, from which has been issued printing of a high order. The name of his private press, reminiscent of the time of the engraver Thomas Bewick, has appeared in a number of modern editions of Bewick's work, as Middleton owns one of the largest collections of the original engravings now extant, and has spent countless hours perfecting the process of printing by which they are best reproduced.

June 7

Whenever contemporary pressmen discuss "wild" printing presses, the conversation invariably turns to the Hoe Patented Ten Cylinder Type-Revolving Press, illustrations of which appear in most histories of printing. The inventor of the machine, Richard March Hoe, died on this day in 1886 in Florence, Italy. He was the inventive genius of the Hoe family of press manufacturers who contributed so much to American press design during the 19th century.

The type-revolving press was the first fully successful rotary printing machine, revolutionizing the production of newspapers. In 1846, the first model—a four-cylinder machine—was installed in the office of the *Public Ledger* of Philadelphia. At the time, 3,600 impressions per hour were the maximum obtainable on any cylinder press, but Hoe's machine—with four men as feeders, each turning out 2,000 impressions per hour —was 8,000. Publishers who had not been able to produce sufficient quantities of newspapers to meet the demand were wildly enthusiastic, not only in the United States but in Europe, where it became necessary to build a manufacturing facility to maintain production.

An early Hoe catalogue perhaps best describes this machine which became the standard newspaper press for twenty years, until the web-fed presses were introduced:

"It is," stated the catalogue, "as its name indicates, on the rotary principle; that is, the form of type is placed on the surface of a horizontal revolving cylinder of about four and a half feet in diameter. The form occupies a segment of only about one-fourth of the surface of the cylinder, the remainder being used as an ink-distributing surface. Around this main cylinder, and parallel with it, are placed smaller impression cylinders, varying in number from two to ten, according to the size of the machine. The large cylinder being put in motion, the form of types is carried successively to all the impression cylinders and receives the impression of the types as the form passes. Thus as many sheets are printed at each revolution of the main cylinder as there are impression cylinders around it. One person is required at each impression cylinder to supply the sheets of paper, which are taken at the proper moment by fingers or grippers, and after being printed are conveyed by tapes and laid in heaps by self-acting flyers, thereby dispensing with the hands required in ordinary machines to receive and pile the sheets. The grippers hold the sheet securely, so that the thinnest newspaper may be printed without waste.

"The ink is contained in a fountain, placed beneath the main cylinder, and is conveyed by means of distributing rollers to the distributing surface on the main cylinder. This surface, being lower, or less in diameter, than the form of types, passes by the impression cylinder without touching. For each impression cylinder there are two inking rollers. Each page of the paper is locked up on a detached segment of the large cylinder, which segment constitutes its bed and chase."

June 8

Issuing from the United States Patent Office on this day in 1869 was Letters Patent No. 91,175, entitled *Improvement in Machinery for Sewing Books,* in which the inventor stated: "Be it known that I, David McConnell Smyth, of Orange, in the County of Essex, and State of New Jersey, have invented certain new and useful improvements in Machinery for Sewing Books and Pamphlets; and I do hereby declare that the following is a full, clear, and exact description thereof, reference being made to the accompanying drawings, making part of this specification, in which . . . ."

A veteran of Gettysburg, David Smyth was that type of 19th century American who can only be described as a compulsive inventor. He was brought as a boy from the County Down across the sea to the northeastern corner of Pennsylvania by his blacksmith father who settled in the Susquehanna County town of Harford. Here he served an apprenticeship at the blacksmith trade. At the age of fourteen he turned out his first invention, the gimlet screw-point. Finding it necessary to finance the patent for this device, he purchased a supply of colored lithographs, which he sold from door-to-door throughout the surrounding countryside.

Smyth then attended Franklin Academy for a year. Still unable to raise the money for a patent, he started out for New York City hoping to develop his device further. He walked the entire distance, supporting himself by odd jobs on the way. For almost two years he was in financial difficulties, but his skill as a blacksmith eventually secured him a position with a carriage and street-car builder. At this time he received a thousand dollars for his gimlet-screw. He found himself classed as an up-and-coming young man by such inventors as Elias Howe, inventor of the sewing machine, and Samuel F. B. Morse, perfector of the telegraph.

Smyth's next invention was a platform scale, which brought him over two thousand dollars for half-interest. In the tradition of the creative mechanic, he always had great problems in managing his money. Consequently he was frequently short of cash, and from time to time had to return to his work in order to recoup his finances. No doubt his friendship with Howe started him thinking about devices for sewing, as he next constructed a machine to sew on the sides of shoes, which was not successful. He then built a machine to sew spangles in hoop skirts, selling it for a pittance to an entrepreneur who later cleared over a quarter of a million dollars a year with it.

After military service during the Civil War, he produced an improved method of making toothpicks, an adjustable carpenter's miter-box, and a machine for making paper collars. Finally a machine for sewing the fancy stitching in shoes brought him very comfortable royalties. But again he found himself in financial difficulty, so he determined to produce a device which would maintain him securely into his old age. This turned out to be a book-sewing machine, which with subsequent improvements was his most successful invention. He formed the Smyth Manufacturing Company in Hartford, Connecticut, and at the age of forty-seven had finally achieved his goal.

The sewing-machine revolutionized the manufacture of books at a period when power presses and stereotyping had far outdistanced the bindery in production speeds. With the Smyth machine a good operator could sew up to seventy books per minute. Such a rapid output found immediate favor with book manufacturers all over the world. One practice which the Smyth device relegated to the scrap heap, to the cheers of most of the bibliophiles, was the sewing of books by stabbing holes in the inside margin, which made it impossible to open a book flat.

It also eliminated the "long rows of girls" described by a little volume on publishing printed by Harper & Brothers in 1855: "The sewing of books is a great work. The ranges of tables devoted to it are so extensive as to furnish accommodations for one hundred girls. . . . Every visitor who sees these girls at their work is struck with the extreme rapidity and dexterity of their movements, and with the healthy and happy, and highly attractive appearance which they themselves and the scene of their labors exhibit."

No doubt the girls were even happier and more attractive when Mr. Smyth relieved them of their healthy labors.

June 9

"Nos, laus Deo, omnia absolvimus qua ad Biblia regia pertinent," wrote the great Antwerp printer Christopher Plantin on this day in 1572, in a thankful and weary statement which may be translated, "Praise be to God we have finished everything pertaining to the Royal Bible."

Plantin had reason to be weary, as he had just completed one of the great undertakings of any printer up to his time and for centuries afterward—a Polyglot Bible, composed in parallel columns of Latin, Hebrew, Greek, Syriac, and Aramaic. Twelve hundred copies of this 8-volume bible were printed on paper and thirteen on vellum, which alone required some 35,000 calfskins, more than were available in all of the Low Countries.

The idea of printing a bible in its original languages, with an annotated text from the great theological authorities of the day, and the whole to be produced in a style fitting to its content, had been a continuing thought in Plantin's mind for some years. In 1565 he suggested such a project to Don Gabriel de Zayas, one of the two foreign secretaries to Philip II, King of Spain, to whom the Netherlands had been given as a gift in 1555.

The King was not immediately disposed to finance Plantin, but he placed the proposition before the Council of the Inquisition for examination. While this body was deliberating, Plantin was instructing his compositors in the setting of the Syriac and Aramaic types. The period was one of famine in the Netherlands, and Plantin found it necessary to sell much of his stock in order to keep his bible moving ahead. The French punch-cutter Granjon cut the Greek and Syriac types, and Plantin had begun to acquire the paper for the job when word to proceed was finally received from Spain.

From that point Plantin maintained some forty printers on the one task and set aside four presses exclusively for the bible. From 1566 until 1572 the printing of the bible was the principal work of the office, although Plantin found it necessary to continue his normal printing in order to pay for the tremendous undertaking.

When the work was finally printed, it needed only be published, and as Philip wished to have the highest authority to approve the text, he sent the Spanish ambassador to Rome to petition the Pope. Pope Pius V refused to grant his permission to publish the bible. The Pope stated that he had no way of knowing whether the Syriac translation contained material which could be attacked as uncanonical. Montana, the editor, was then sent to Rome with a vellum copy for the Pope, but before he reached his destination Pope Pius V had died. The new Pope, Gregory XIII accepted the bible and granted a privilege for twenty years.

June 10

"Being frequently censur'd and condemn'd by Different Persons for printing Things which they say ought not to be printed, I have sometimes thought it might be necessary to make a standing Apology for my self, and publish it once a Year, to be read upon all Occasions of that Nature."

So began an article published by Benjamin Franklin in his *Pennsylvania Gazette* on this day in 1731. In using the word Apology, Franklin of course meant explanation. It is interesting to note that his apologia keeps the terms printer and printing uppermost. Present-day newspaper owners never think of themselves as printers, being more conscious of their importance as molders of public opinion. To most of them, printers are just the craftsmen who are necessary to mechanically produce the newspaper.

Some of the high points of Franklin's remarks follow:

"That the Business of Printing has chiefly to do with Mens Opinions; most things that are printed tending to promote some, or oppose others.

"That hence arises the peculiar Unhappiness of that Business, which other Callings are no way liable to; they who follow Printing being scarce able to do any thing in their way of getting a Living, which shall not probably give Offence to some, and perhaps to many; whereas the Smith, the Shoemaker, the Carpenter, or the Man of any other Trade, may work indifferently for People of all Persuasions, without offending any of them: and the Merchant may buy and sell with Jews, Turks, Hereticks and Infidels of all sorts, and get Money by every one of them, without giving Offence to the most orthodox, of any sort; or suffering the least Censure or Ill-will on the Account from any Man whatever. . . .

"Printers are educated in the Belief, that when Men differ in Opinion, both sides ought equally to have the Advantage of being heard by the Publick; and that when Truth and Errors have fair Play they chear-fully serve all contending Writers that pay them well,

without regarding on which side they are of the Question in Dispute.

"Being thus continually employ'd in serving both Parties, Printers naturally acquire a vast Unconcernedness as to the right or wrong Opinions contain'd in what they print; regarding it only as the Matter of their daily labour: They print things full of Spleen and Animosity, with the utmost Calmness and Indifference, and without the least Ill-will to the Persons reflected on; who nevertheless unjustly think the printer as much their Enemy as the Author, and join both together in their Resentment.

"That it is unreasonable to imagine Printers approve of every thing they print, and to censure them on any particular thing accordingly; since in the way of their Business they print such great variety of things opposite and contradictory. It is likewise as unreasonable what some assert, *That Printers ought not to print any Thing but what they approve;* since if all of that Business should make such a Resolution, and abide by it, an End would thereby be put to Free Writing, and the World would afterwards have nothing to read but what happen'd to be the Opinions of Printers.

"I consider the Variety of Humors among Men, and despair of pleasing every Body; yet I shall not therefore leave off Printing. I shall continue my Business. I shall not burn my Press and melt my Letters."

June 11

In a letter written upon this date in 1886, from New Brunswick, New Jersey, John F. Babcock, a compositor in the office of *The Fredonian* wrote of the earliest known contests of speed in typesetting in the United States. The letter was addressed to William C. Barnes, one of the great "swifts" of the period:

"In consequence of absence from home for several days, I have not found time to answer before your communication of May 25, relative to a typesetting contest in which Robert Bonner was engaged forty years ago. At that time Bonner and I were compositors in the *American Republican* office, a morning daily, printed and published in Ann Street, New York, on the southeast corner of Nassau. It was in the summer of 1846. But a few weeks previous Bonner had arrived from Hartford, Conn., and was probably not more than twenty-one years of age—I think less. He was then a very slim youth, and probably did not weigh more than 100 pounds, if as much.

"He soon gained a reputation as a fast compositor, and frequent races took place between him and the other comps. Almost invariably Bonner came out ahead. The results of these contests were published frequently in the *Republican* and other newspapers, and there was considerable excitement among the craft in regard to them. There were several typos who would exceed 2,000 ems in an hour for an hour or two at a time, but when the contests exceeded five or six hours Bonner invariably came out ahead. Finally, there was a small wager that no man could set 24,000 ems, solid matter, in twenty-four consecutive hours. Bonner accomplished the feat in something over twenty hours, and stopped. Then a wager of ten dollars was raised, or rather a purse (for Bonner would not bet) that he could not set at the same average rate for the whole twenty-four hours. The number of ems fixed was 33,000. The type was solid minion [7-point], reprint copy, twenty-five ems wide, all breaks to be omitted. The proof was to be read by copy, and the whole finished within the twenty-four hours. Work commenced at 12 o'clock, noon, and continued until the next noon. Lunches, in the shape of sandwiches, were placed within reach of Bonner, and he occasionally took a bite and a drink of coffee. Bonner was a very clean compositor, and did not average more than two typographical errors on a galley. When the City Hall bell struck 12 the following day, Bonner threw down his stick, emptied his last lines and the type was measured—it having been agreed that there should be no measurement while he was at work, thus avoiding excitement. It was found that he had set up 32,997 ems, lacking just three ems of the amount set for his task. By universal consent, the judges permitted him to receive the ten dollars."

June 12

The earliest press to be established in Italy completed on June 12, 1465 its fourth book,

De Civitate Dei of St. Augustine. The press then removed to Rome from its first location, the three Benedictine monasteries at Subiaco which make up the Abbey of Santa Scolastica. In 1454 the reigning Pope, Calixtus III, had appointed the Abbot of Santa Scolastica a Cardinal Commendatory. The first to hold this title was the scholarly Spanish priest, Juan Turrecremata.

When news of the invention of movable type filtered down into Italy, the Abbot— no doubt realizing the exciting possibilities inherent in a new method of spreading the gospel—set about to secure practitioners of the art who would be willing to work with the Benedictine monks. He obtained the services of two printers, Conrad Sweynheim of Mainz and Arnold Pannartz of Prague, both of whom are reputed to have been fugitives from the sack of Mainz in 1462.

The first book produced by the German printers was a *Donatus pro Puerulis,* a Latin grammar, of which no copy has survived. The first dated book to be printed in Italy was the *Lactantius,* which was issued by the press in 1465, followed by Cicero's *De Oratore,* not dated, and finally *De Civitate Dei* of June 1467, unquestionably the great work of the press. The type used in this volume is a vigorous letter which follows the tradition of the humanist roman letters, but with very definite gothic characteristics.

When this book was completed, the German printers were lured to Rome by the princely house of Massimo, where they no doubt expected a richer patronage than they enjoyed in the stark surroundings of Santa Scolastica. However, they evidently brought with them to Rome at least a few copies of the books which they had printed for the Benedictines, as the copy of *De Civitate Dei* at present in the Bibliotheque Nationale in Paris is inscribed by Leonardus Dathus, Bishop of Massanus, who wrote, ". . . bought for himself and his grandson, Georgius, with his own money, for eight gold pieces and two papal coins (three pence each), from those Germans staying at Rome, who are accustomed not to writing many books of this kind but to making them. In the year of grace 1467, in the month of November."

In their new location in the Palazzo Massimo, Sweynheim and Pannartz produced a number of fine editions of such standard classics as Apuleius, Livy, Ovid, Pliny, etc., along with theological works. Their business was so successful that they ventured an edition of the *Biblical Commentaries* of Nicolaus de Lyra, in five large volumes. The printers quickly found themselves in difficulty, being unable to finance such an undertaking. Even the House of Massimo could not be of assistance beyond its own capabilities, so the printers—through the Bishop of Alleria—petitioned Pope Sixtus for funds. The Pope, however, was more interested in manuscript books than in printed ones and refused his aid, thus forcing Sweynheim and Pannartz to discontinue their press in 1472.

June 13

Not at all content to allow his works to speak for themselves, the great Venetian printer Nicolas Jenson wrote into the colophon of *De Veritate Catholicae,* "Moreover this new edition was furnished us to print at Venice by Nicholas Jenson of France, a true Catholic, kind towards all, beneficent, generous, truthful and steadfast. In the beauty, dignity and accuracy of his printing, let me (with the indulgence of all), name him the first in the whole of the world; first likewise in his marvelous speed. He exists in his own time as a special gift of Heaven to men. June 13th in the year of the Redemption, 1480."

The practice of inserting a paragraph concerning the printing of a book began with the publication of the great *Psalter,* printed in Mainz in 1457 by Johann Fust and Peter Schoeffer. The *Psalter* is also notable for being the first dated book and the first to carry the device of its printer, the well-known crossed shields now so widely known as the emblem of the International Club of Printing House Craftsmen. Prior to the invention of printing, manuscript books usually began with the words, "Here beginneth" and contained no title page. Rarely were they dated.

In the early days of the craft, when numerous printers were competing in the printing of scholarly works, the colophon became exceedingly important to the purchaser, assuming the present-day significance of the publisher's imprint. Printers were therefore in the habit of pointing out that their texts were authoritative and free from error. It was upon such precepts that Aldus Manutius built his sound reputation, succeeding so well that even his colophons were pirated.

The writing of a colophon sometimes presented an opportunity to printers with poetic aspirations, as is evident from a book published in Naples in 1472 by Sixtus Russinger:
"Sixtus the copies printed with much care,
Now twice revised by Dr. Iliviere;
The happy purchaser in vain shall look,
Yet find no error in this faultless book."
A 1507 colophon represented an essay into humorous verse:
"May this volume continue in motion,
And its pages each day be unfurled;
Till an ant has drank up the ocean,
Or a tortoise has crawled round the world."
There are several explanations of the derivation of the word colophon. That it comes from the Greek word meaning summit, or finishing stroke, appears to be the most logical, but another legend offers more fascinating possibilities. In this explanation the word is taken from an Asiatic city of the same name, as the home of artists of every description who were possessed of great skill in completing their projects. Such proficiency promoted a proverb, *ulliman manam imponere,* or to put the finishing hand to anything.

Bruce Rogers, in the colophon of his wise and informative book, *Paragraphs on Printing,* writes: "Christopher Morley once said it was most appropriate for book printers to name the finishing stroke of their work after the ancient Ionian city of Colophon, because the cavalry of that town always concluded an engagement with a furious charge. (In this instance ten dollars.)"

June 14

In the wake of the Conquistadors the art of printing came quickly to the New World. To Mexican printers must be given the credit for a number of notable firsts in the history of American printing. It was upon this day in 1544, just forty-two years after Columbus stepped upon the shores of the Western Hemisphere, that the House of Juan Cromberger completed the printing of *Doctrina Breve Muy Provechosa de las Coasa que Pertenecen a la Fe Catolica y a Nuestra Cristiandad,* by Bishop Zumárraga, which is considered to be the oldest known book to appear in either of the Americas.

As early as 1534 Bishop Zumárraga, returning to Mexico from a trip to Spain, reportedly brought with him a printer named Esteban Martín, who set up a small press with a limited amount of type and produced two books of which no known copies exist: the *Escala Espiritual* and the *Catecismo Mexicano.* As proof of the existence of Martín's press, a letter exists in which the bishop wrote to the king, stating: "Little progress can be made with our printing because of the scarcity of paper." Additionally, Esteban Martín, printer, is reported as having received citizenship by the council of the city of Mexico. The requirements for such acceptance included five years of residence.

In 1539 the printing office of Juan Cromberger in Seville, Spain, sent to Mexico an Italian printer named Juan Pablos, along with a pressman, Gil Barbero, with instructions to open a branch office. Pablos arrived in Mexico City in September and quickly set up his press, producing his first book, *Breve y Mas Compendiosa Doctrina Cristiana en Lengua Mexicana y Castellana,* a quarto containing twelve leaves, by December, 1539. This volume has been described, but the only known copy has since disappeared.

During the next two years two other books were printed, of which only fragments are presently in existence. It is known that in 1543 still another volume was produced, but that volume also has been lost. Thus, the reputation of Pablos as the first New World printer must rest with the Zumárraga work of 1544, of which there are nine copies extant.

By 1559 the monopoly enjoyed by Pablos was broken when his assistant, Antonio Espinosa, who also has the distinction of being the first to cut a type and cast it in the Americas, secured permission to set up a press. Within the next forty years there were nine presses in operation in Mexico.

Some of the New World "firsts" include the initial printing of a dictionary in 1555, the first ecclesiastical treatise in 1549, and the premier production of literary essays, *Comentaria in Ludovici Vives Exercitationes Linguae Latinae,* by Francisco Cervantes de Salazar, in 1554. In the same year were published the first college textbooks.

The first book on physics, *Phisica Speculatio,* written by Fray Alonso de la Veracruz, was printed in 1557, and Pedro de Ocharte printed the first psalter in 1584. Dominating early Mexican printing of course were the works on Christian doctrine and religious instruction, followed by grammars, vocabularies, and dictionaries of the Indian languages, although the incunabula also includes song books, histories, medical books, law books, and scientific works.

June 15

On this day in 1903 a young man named Dard Hunter, just nineteen years old, awoke in the sleeping car of a railroad train to find himself in the Buffalo, New York station. The son of the publisher of the *Gazette* in Steubenville, Ohio, Hunter had been introduced to the typesetter's case at eight years of age. His interest in printing had continued to grow. While attending Ohio State University he came across books from the Kelmscott and Doves presses which so inspired him that he desired nothing else but to travel to Europe to visit the English private presses. This being impossible at the time, he elected instead to go to East Aurora, New York to call upon Elbert Hubbard, proprietor of the Roycrofters, one of the unique figures in American printing and publishing history.

Hunter spent the summer in Aurora, making furniture, doing some wood-carving and designing iron and copper objects to be manufactured in the blacksmith's shop. He enjoyed the easy atmosphere and the friendliness of Hubbard and his wife so much that he decided to remain with the Roycrofters instead of returning to college.

Hunter, with some experience as a printer, became the designer of a number of the Roycroft books and commercial printing. Except for a year spent in Mexico, he remained with Hubbard until 1908. In that year he married and went to Europe with his wife, who was a pianist and wished to study in Vienna. Here Hunter continued his own studies in typography and design. In 1911 he went to England to work, and in the Victoria and Albert Museum in London he viewed some hand molds for making paper, which so interested him that he determined to learn more about the craft of papermaking. This chance discovery eventually led to his career as one of the world's outstanding authorities on the subject. He became author of numerous books and monographs on papermaking and in addition founded the famous Dard Hunter Museum.

It is interesting to note the comments of this enlightened man on Elbert Hubbard, whom he knew at first hand. In his autobiography, *My Life With Paper* published in 1958 by Alfred A. Knopf, he wrote:

"Elbert Hubbard would be out of place in the present-day world, although he no doubt had a marked influence upon his own time. Even though the books produced at the Roycraft Shop were bizarre and lacked taste and refinement, they were, nevertheless, a step in the right direction. These books were better made than most of the work done in this country at the time, and people who had never before thought of collecting books began assembling the Roycroft issues. Mr. Hubbard probably had more influence in the development of book-collecting than any other person of his generation."

June 16

Mr. Porter Garnett, associate professor of graphic arts at Carnegie Institute of Technology, received a letter, dated this day in 1925, from Mr. Henry L. Bullen, curator of the Typographic Library and Museum of the American Type Founders Company, at Jersey City. This correspondence stated in part:

"The Library has just received specimens Nos. 17 to 26, inclusive, of the work of your students. These are welcome additions to our collection of fine printing of all periods. I find that, during my long absence, preceding specimens of this series were received. These are very acceptable gifts. From time to time we have asked a group of printers whose standards of excellence are high to send us specimens of any printing they may have done 'which they believe will be admired a century hence.' We never get many specimens under this test. I think it is the ultimate test. Your Specimens I feel sure will be admired centuries hence as they deserve to be admired today. This library has assumed the duty of transmitting them to posterity."

Porter Garnett was naturally delighted to have on the record Bullen's opinion of the work of his students. Just three years previously he had established in the School of Printing at Carnegie Institute of Technol-

ogy a course in the principles of fine printing. The practical work of the students was to be produced in a printing office equipped with the finest types and was to be printed upon a hand press. The name given to this printing office was The Laboratory Press.

The prospectus announcing the new course was widely praised by many of the first-rate typographers and printers, both from the viewpoint of its effect as a piece of printing and as representative of an idea in graphic arts education. It was as roundly damned by a number of the practical printers, who felt that the only college course in printing should be concerned primarily with the requirements of the industry. This could be readily interpreted to mean that the industry needed more executives who could produce printing cheaper and faster and at a greater profit to all concerned.

The pages of the trade periodicals carried some of the criticism directed at the new program. J. Horace McFarland, one of the most successful printers of the time, wrote an article in *The Printing Art,* under the title "What is Fine Printing?" in which he stated that in his opinion it did not fulfill the primary function of printing—to convey thought. "The boys who are to be taught printing at Carnegie, splendid institution that it is, ought to be directed toward the best possible selling effort through the printed page, an ideal considerably higher than the ideal contemplated by the course in fine printing."

But criticism or not, the work of The Laboratory Press went forward, and a generation of students received an opportunity to conceive and produce printing which met every requirement inherent in the term, fine printing. These young men were inspired to carry into their careers the enriched spirit of a great craft, and there is not much question but that the industry benefited greatly from their exposure to such high standards.

The student projects produced at the press are still much sought after as examples of the printer's art, and with the current emphasis towards photo-mechanical printing, they may indeed fulfill Bullen's "ultimate test." Oddly enough, the present administrators of the school are no longer aware of the Garnett contributions. When the type designer, Hermann Zapf, visited the campus in 1961 he had to visit a private library in order to examine the work of The Laboratory Press.

June 17

It was on this day in 1965 that the writer received from Don Canfield, the Utica, New York typesetter, a most welcome gift in the form of a copy of *Typographical Printing Surfaces* by Lucien Alphonse Legros and John Cameron Grant, a book which is long out of print and without which no technical library on printing is complete. In 1900 Legros, a mechanical engineer acting as a consultant in the development of the Wicks Rotary Typecaster, was astonished to learn that there existed no technical treatise on the manufacture of printing type and typesetting machines. In the precise no-nonsense approach of an engineer, he thereupon researched his subject and with the help of a popular English writer, published such a book in 1916.

At the price of $17.00 the 732-page work sold not at all, so little interest existed in the technical aspects of the craft. In 1932 the book was remaindered at $4.00 and again found but few takers. During the post-war period, however, with the technological advances taking place in typesetting procedures, the demand for the volume has greatly increased. When available, it now fetches a handsome price, depending upon how much the purchaser wishes to have it. This recent popularity has no doubt been engendered by the remarkable increase in the number of collectors who are specializing in printing books, particularly those devoted to the technical aspects of the craft.

Typographical Printing Surfaces, notwithstanding its formidable title, is the most informative volume ever put together on the subject of typsetting machines. It is well documented and well illustrated, and has absolutely no rivals in the encyclopedic coverage of its subject matter.

Many readers of the book have been intrigued by the paragraphs of quotations which precede each chapter, most of which contain the credit line "Mirrour of Printing." Operators of private presses, a group always searching for an item out of copyright with which to exhibit their prowess as printers, have spent many an hour pouring over bibliographies looking for this book, but with no luck, simply because it doesn't exist outside of the imaginations of Legros and Grant.

Under the heading of the first chapter, "Printing-Surfaces," is the quote: "Raised work of Metal engraved and eke of Wood, wherefrom Impressions may be wrought before Men's Eyes, outshooteth the Art of him that Prynteth Books; For they be Many and of Diverse wise, and out of their knowledge and by us not to be treated. The Prynter hath Woes of his own enow: God knoweth!"

The quotation accompanying the chapter on type design was: "God hath given us Eyes, but herein is Mystery, for the Devil of his Malice hath them marred that they see not at all Times aright." The quote for the chapter on type faces represented a quizzical viewpoint indeed: "He that readeth a Face at Sight hath the Gift of Kings; And verily for him that is of the Craft it is a Dower-Royal so to tell Face from Face, for some be Right-Rogues and offend in any Forme."

As a final sampling, here is the authors' viewpoint on the obtuse subject of legibility (Chapter XI): "He that laboureth in the Craft laboureth in vain be not that which he Setteth up plainly to be observed and understood of all Men's Eyes; Nay, even of him whose Sight is somewhat marred by Smoke and Sin God us Forgive and the Setting of ale-jug to ale-jug, albeit it be done without ill Intent and in all clerkly Fellowship and Learning."

June 18

On or about this date in 1788 a retired printer, statesman, and flyer of kites wrote to William Caslon III:

"I yesterday received your favour of April 2, informing me that the Types I ordered by mine of Feby 17, would be shipt in about a Fortnight which I am glad to hear. I promised to make you good Pay, and accordingly on the 31st of March I wrote & sent a Bill for 150 £ to Messrs. Smith, Wright & Gray my former Bankers in London, with Directions to pay your Bill. So that I doubt not your having received the Money within a few Weeks after you had shipt the Goods. I have set up my Grandson B. Franklin Bache in a Printing-House here, and what further Founts he may want from you, he will send Bills to pay for. I approve much of your Resolution not to send your Types abroad upon Credit. Their Excellence will secure a sufficient Demand without it. Some other British Founders have been so extravagantly liberal in that Way, and thereby created such a Number of Master-Printers more than the Business of the Country can maintain, as may probably in the End be hurtful to both the Debtors and Creditors.

"Your Friend W. T. Franklin is well at his Plantation 16 Miles from this City. I am glad to hear of the Welfare of you & yours, being with sincere Esteem, Dear Sir, Your Friend & Servant, B. Franklin."

It was to be another dozen years or so before American typefounders would be able to even begin to meet the demands of the burgeoning printing industry of the new American republic. The renowned Caslon firm was thus happy to continue sending type across the Atlantic as it had for many years. Most of the colonial printers had been weaned on the sturdy Caslon letters. It was therefore natural that many of the historic documents by which the colonists protested their continuing subservience to the Mother Country were composed in Caslon types.

The broadsides issued by the Maryland Sons of Liberty, in 1766, were set in Caslon, as was the notice to the members of the Association of the Sons of Liberty of New York to assemble about the Liberty Pole on the Common. The famous New York broadside of May 20, 1766, announcing the repeal of the Stamp Act, was composed in the type, along with the Proclamation of General Washington concerning the impending attack by the British, the first printing of the Declaration of Independence, and the proclamation informing the public of Washington's arrival in New York for his inauguration.

By the time of the first American type specimen book, that of Binny & Ronaldson printed in 1812, Caslon type had lost its ninety-year popularity. It succumbed to the newer fashions in type which had been inaugurated by John Baskerville in England, along with the Didots and Giambattista Bodoni on the Continent. There was no need for American founders to produce copies of Caslon until after the middle of the century. Possibly because of their knowledge of the revival of Caslon in England with the 1843 publication of *The Diary of Lady Willoughby* by Charles Whittingham of the Chiswick Press, the Johnson Type Foundry of Phila-

delphia purchased fonts of the type. From these originals, electrotype matrices were manufactured and the first announcement of this undertaking appeared in the pages of the company's house organ, the *Typographic Advertiser,* in January, 1859. By July of the same year, thirteen sizes had been produced. The revival proved to be popular, as the 1865 specimen book of the firm listed the entire series, Pearl (4½-point) to four-line Pica (48-point), under the name of Old Style No. 1. By the last decade of the century, the type had become exceedingly popular. It was selected for the new fashion magazine *Vogue,* and the Inland Type Foundry went so far as to purchase matrices from the English firm so that they could offer the "Genuine Face, reproduced by permission." When the typesetting machines were introduced, it didn't take long to make Caslon available for them also, and today the fine old type has also been adapted to the phototypesettting machines which are becoming increasingly important in typographic production.

June 19

John W. Gardner, President of the Carnegie Corporation, in an address before the annual meeting of American school board members on this day in 1962, said: "A school board member . . . should understand, for example, that there is a lot that no one knows for sure about the teaching of reading. Beware of the individual who knows all the answers. He's a fraud."

Gardner, now Secretary of Health and Welfare, was reviewing some recent research into the reading habits of schoolchildren, and of course his words were used on both sides of the fence in one controversial bit of research then being undertaken by educators in England and in the United States. This was the augmented roman alphabet invented by Sir James Pitman, grandson of the inventor of shorthand, under the name of Initial Teaching Alphabet.

Basically, the augmented alphabet contains forty-three characters, each of which represents a sound in the English language. Since standard English ordinarily requires about 2,000 different ways to spell these forty-three sounds, it would appear that the augmented alphabet is at the very least a step in the right direction. Of the conventional alphabetical characters, the augmented roman alphabet uses all but *q* and *x* and adds nineteen symbols of its own.

The whole idea is based upon the concept that the logical mind of a child cannot comprehend the quixotically illogical structure of English spelling, with the result that most of the reading difficulties of the developing years are seeded at this point. Pitman, in explaining his method, is careful not to pronounce it as a panacea for all the problems of illiteracy. He says, "The main point to be borne in mind is that this alphabet is intended for use during the first two years only of the young child's school career, after which the transition will be made to traditional orthography. It was, therefore, essential to arrive at a compromise between maximum resemblance to the existing alphabet and spelling system (if it can be dignified by the name of system) and a maximum phonetic consistency. It must be emphasized that the augmented roman alphabet and spelling system is not intended as a permanent spelling reform."

From the results of the preliminary experiments it would appear that the augmented alphabet is doing the job, with a number of teachers expressing their enthusiasm. At present no type designer, however, has attempted to bring great beauty to the new characters, which are available only in a workaday and readable type named Erhardt, a product of the Monotype Corporation of London. Adults may be comforted with the knowledge that the new alphabet will continue to be restricted to five and six-year olds, because the prosaic characters do not seem to be capable of presenting English prose splendidly.

June 20

Robert Estienne, the Paris printer, published on June 20, 1536 *Seminarium,* written by his brother Charles, a professor of Greek. This volume was but one of thirteen edited and printed by Estienne between the end of April and the end of September of that year. During a twenty-five year period the great scholar-printer printed some 465 editions of which thirty-nine were in folio, making up

to fifty-two volumes. Estienne was not only concerned with the printing of learned data, but he served also as editor and publisher, securing a well-deserved reputation for the authenticity of his texts.

The poet John Dorat composed in 1538 a pseudo-Horatian poem describing Estienne's methods of working:

> I then, in hopes my business next to do,
> Admir'd the town, admir'd its sages too,
> Then swift to Robert at his house repair'd,
> To speak with him concerning it prepar'd.
> Once at his door, my suit knew no delay,
> His ready servants brought me in
>   straight way,
> There, amid volumes open lying round
> (A portly flock) the man himself I found,
> Intent (to further wholesome
>   learning's state)
> Errors to purge and lines to punctuate;
> Pallas the while, his judgment to inspire,
> (As to Tydides in his combats dire)
> Behind him stood his counsellor to be
> And all his works with her did well agree;
> The footnote to supply with ease and skill,
> The great lacuna learnedly to fill,
> Some matter from the proof-sheet
>   to delete,
> Or what was else for the occasion meet.
> Me, when he saw that I
>   towards him came,
> He greeted, ask'd my business
>   and my name.
> Speechless I stood, quite seiz'd
>   with awe to see
> The sage companions of his industry,
> Noted for civil learning—all their care
> The copy for the presses to prepare. . . .
> More favor added, for he offer'd straight
> To take me in his house, in company
> With men of learning and authority;
> And more the liberal printer will'd
>   to give—
> Upon his substance, in his home, to live:
> What fair resort! O Jove,
>   what noble sphere,
> And most to the devoted scholar dear:
> What does he hear along the
>   cheerful board?
> Among the foaming cups, with
>   one accord? . . .
> What, but the purity of Latin speech
> In rev'rend elegance pronounc'd by each?
> His wife, his handmaids, and his
>   clients too,

His children (lively band) hold speech
with you
Habitually in no other way
Than Terence or than Plautus in a play.

June 21

The Fann Street Foundry of London was this day in 1820 auctioned to William Thorowgood, manager of a business called Patent Roller Pump. "This gentleman was previously unconnected with the typographical profession," wrote Talbot Baines Reed, somewhat disparagingly, in his *History of the Old English Letter Foundries*. In point of fact, Mr. Thorowgood was taking a flyer, "with the proceeds, it is said, of a fortunate draw in one of the State Lotteries." His luck apparently continued unabated in his new endeavor, as just a year later he was appointed Letter-Founder to His Majesty King George IV.

Thorowgood learned the typefoundry business rapidly. In his specimen book, issued in 1821, the embryo typefounder wrote: "I cannot omit the opportunity offered in presenting my first specimen to your notice, to return my most sincere thanks to the profession for that portion of their patronage which I have received since my succession to Mr. Thorne. Although some difficulties presented themselves in redeeming the pledge I made of renovating my small founts and casting them of metal more durable than those in common use, yet I flatter myself that those friends who relied upon my professions will bear ample testimony that they have not been disappointed, and that the superior facilities of manufacturing types possessed by myself in common with other founders of the metropolis has been used to their advantage."

As the Royal Letter-Founder, Thorowgood necessarily had to offer scholarly types, issuing a well-cut Greek, a Fraktur, a Hebrew, and several Russian types. In 1828 he enlarged this collection with the purchase of the well-known foundry operated by Dr. Edmund Fry. It was in the "jobbing" types, however, that the Fann Street Foundry was most successful. The middle years of the 19th century witnessed the unparalleled promotion of display types, and the English foundries were most responsible for nurturing this movement. Ornamental types of every description were in great demand—Tuscans, Fat Faces, Egyptians, Outlines, Inlines, Shadeds, and many more. The fat face named Thorowgood, issued in 1821 and still available, is one of the well-known types to be cast by the Fann Street Foundry. Contemporary types in this style are attributed to Bodoni, here in the United States, bearing such titles as Ultra Bodoni, Bodoni Black, Poster Bodoni, etc. These types, however, are much more mechanical in form than Thorowgood.

In 1838 Thorowgood took on as a partner Robert Besely, who later became Lord Mayor of London and who created the best known of the types called Clarendons, these being the Egyptian or square-serifed types with the addition of bracketed serifs. In the middle 1950's such a style experienced a strong revival which is still running its course. In 1849 Thorowgood retired, the firm being renamed Robert Besely & Co. In 1861 the firm became Reed & Fox, and in 1877 Sir Charles Reed & Co. Talbot Baines Reed, younger son of Sir Charles, managed the foundry until his premature death in 1893 when it was taken over by A. W. Tillie. Finally it was acquired by Stephenson, Blake & Company, which remains the principal English typefoundry.

June 22

In Augsburg, Germany on June 22, 1484 was published the first book to be printed by a woman. The book was *Sachsenspiegel* by Eike von Repgow and the printer was Anna Rügerin.

Frau Rügerin was the widow of a printer. In taking over her late husband's printing office, she began a tradition in the craft, from this time on there being numerous instances of women continuing to operate printing establishments following the deaths of their husbands. The widow of an employing printer was also less likely to remain in that status for any length of time, frequently marrying one of the journeymen printers. There is, in fact, some logical reasoning behind the explanation sometimes suggested as the origin of the term widow line—a line of less than complete width that begins a page. A printer's widow rarely remained alone, hence the short line should follow the pattern.

While it was all very well for a widow to take over as a proprietor, printers had different feelings about women working as printers, and there has been a great deal of strife, particularly concerning women compositors who would work for less wages than their male counterparts. In the days of the hand presses, of course, there was little competition from women, but when power presses were introduced they were often employed as feeders. Traditionally the bindery has always been the department in which women have been able to establish themselves, since the male of the species no doubt felt that less skill was necessary for the task of folding and sewing.

In a little book published by Harper & Brothers in 1845 describing the methods of bookmaking in the firm's printing plant, an illustration shows women feeding the power presses. There were thirty machines in the pressroom and all were fed by female help. The typefoundry attached to the plant also employed women in a number of the finishing operations in producing type.

There remained, however, a great deal of opposition to women working at the trade. In 1893 a printing trade publication commented editorially upon a story which appeared in the New York *Sun* about a woman who had worked for thirty years as a printer and had made a success of it. The lady was quoted as saying, "The girl who is thinking about an occupation, with a view to making it support her, might do a great deal worse than to learn the printer's trade."

The magazine stated, "Let us tell our women that the girl who is thinking about an occupation with a view to making it support her might do a *great deal better* than to learn the printer's trade."

Most of the arguments against the female printer were based upon economics. The *Sun* article went on to say, "Her pay is $18 a week, which is a very good salary indeed, as women's wages run," and here the trade magazine italicised the remainder of the quote, *"though it may be remarked in passing that she replaced a man at $22."*

"Just merely in passing!" exclaimed the periodical, which enjoyed an exclusively male readership, no doubt. With lightly veiled sarcasm, the editorial continued, "Women would be more valuable, of course, if they didn't require so much waiting on. If an office employs five or six women, it has to employ a boy to do odd things for them, or they will bother the men employees so much asking to have things lifted or carried that men won't work in the office."

June 23

Non amo te, Sabidi, nec possum
    dicere quare,
  Hoc tantum possum dicere, non amo te.
Or rather freely paraphrased from the Epigrams of Martial, as it appeared in the widely read *Tom Brown's Schooldays:*
  I do not love thee, Doctor Fell
  The reason why I cannot tell,
  But this alone I know full well,
  I do not love thee, Doctor Fell.
The object of this apparent lack of affection on the part of Tom Brown was his teacher, John Fell, Bishop of Oxford, who was born June 23, 1625. One of the great names in the history of Oxford University and its Press, Doctor Fell no doubt crossed up schoolboy Brown in the performance of his Latin and has hence been immortalized. But even without Master Tom, the good Bishop would have earned his place in the heavens for his typographic contributions.

Shortly after becoming Dean of Christ Church, John Fell became a Delegate to Oxford University Press in 1662. He acquired for the Press a great font of type which bears his name; he aided in the acquisition of the paper mill at Wolvercote, where the paper for the Press is still made, and he initiated the printing of bibles and prayer books, another activity in progress to the present time.

Shortly before his tenure as a Delegate, the Press had gone through a difficult period, resulting in the statute from the Archbishop of Canterbury that an architypographus be appointed from the ranks of the scholars to oversee the work of the Press. Dr. Fell formed a committee to take charge of the full management of the printing office, and by efficient organization left his stamp upon every department of the Press.

Among the details in which Fell interested himself was the question of orthography. He set up a system of rules for spelling in which such words as editour, colour, humour, etc., were divested of their letter "u." He left out the ending "e" in calme, some, have, presse, etc. Being some three centuries ahead of his time, this practice brought round criticism upon his head from readers, booksellers, and printers, naturally enough.

It is to the credit of Bishop Fell that Oxford University Press owns the oldest type punches and matrices surviving in England. These types were originally the personal property of Dr. Fell and were bequeathed by him to the University. In his travels to the Continent, Fell purchased the types and brought them home to Oxford. The letters have been described as being Dutch in origin, probably designed by Christoffel van Dijk. This is undoubtedly true in some of the romans, but Stanley Morison, in his paper on the Fell types, attributes certain sizes of italic to the hand of the great French punch-cutter, Robert Granjon. In the cutting of italic type, Granjon had no peer, and the 10-, 11-, and 12-point sizes at Oxford are definitely considered to be Granjon letters.

June 24

To Crochallan came
The old cock'd hat, the grey surtout,
    the same;
His bristling beard just rising in
    its might,
'Twas four long nights and days
    to shaving night;
His uncurl'd grizzly locks, wild
    staring, thatch'd
A head, for thought profound and
    clear, unmatch'd;
Yet though his caustic wit was
    biting, rude,
His heart was warm, benevolent,
    and good.

This poetical sketch was written by the poet Robert Burns about his friend, compositor William Smellie, who died this day in Edinburgh, Scotland in 1795. Noted for his learning even in a city that was then beginning its reputation as an intellectual center, Smellie is known to have written almost all of the entire first edition of the *Encyclopedia Britannica*.

Born about 1740, William Smellie had been apprenticed at twelve years of age to a maker of whalebone stays for women's corsets, but the boy had different ideas and bound himself to a printer instead. He was most fortunate in selecting the establishment of Hamilton, Balfour, and Neal, then printers to Edinburgh University. This official connection allowed the boy to attend certain courses at the University, a privilege of which he immediately took advantage, spending all of his free time in studies. Within five years he had so progressed that he was made corrector of the press, an exceedingly responsible position for such a young man, particularly in an office engaged in scholarly printing for a university.

At eighteen years of age Smellie produced an edition of *Terence*, entirely set and corrected by himself. It won for his master a prize offered by the Edinburgh Philosophical Society for the best edition of a Latin classic. At nineteen he completed his apprenticeship and went to work as proofreader to the firm of Murray and Cochrane, editing for that firm the *Scots Magazine*. At the same period he edited a Hebrew grammar, instructing himself in that language in order that he might take on the responsibility.

In 1868 Smellie was approached by Andrew Bell, known in Edinburgh primarily for an ability to engrave dogs' collars, and Colin Macfarquhar, a printer, with an idea of writing and printing an encyclopedia. The three men reached an agreement which was substantiated by a letter which Bell wrote to Smellie:

"Sir, as we are engaged in publishing a Dictionary of the Arts and Sciences; and as you have informed us that there are fifteen capital sciences which you will undertake for, and write up the subdivisions and detached parts of these to conform to your plan, and likewise to prepare the whole work for the press etc. etc; we hereby agree to allow you £200 for your trouble."

The work was published over the next three years in 2,659 pages, most of which were probably written by Smellie. He subsequently refused to edit a second edition of *the Britannica* because of a disagreement with the sponsors.

June 25

The *Journal of the Printing-Office at Strawberry Hill* contains in its first entry, upon this day in 1757 the simple statement, "The Press was erected. Wm. Robinson, printer." The proprietor of the press was the English essayist Horace Walpole, younger son of the great prime minister, Sir Robert Walpole.

Walpole's attitude to printing may be noted from a letter which he wrote to Sir Horace Mann, saying, "In short, I am turned printer, and have converted a little cottage here into a printing-office. My abbey is a perfect college or academy; I kept a painter in the house, and a printer." Such a *grand seigneur* viewpoint no doubt accounted for his inability to hold on to his printers who "had not even an aide-de-camp or devil" to assist them. "I am plagued with a succession of bad printers," he finally wrote in 1860. The third printer he employed annoyed him so much that he wrote to a friend: "At present my press is at a stop; my printer, who was a foolish Irishman, and who took himself for a genius, and who grew angry when I thought him extremely the former and not the least of the latter, has left me. I have not yet fixed upon another."

The fourth printer, Thomas Kirkgate, was a fine craftsman who also became Walpole's secretary, and served him until his master's death in 1797. The types of the press were cast by William Caslon, whose ledger records the sale on August 13, 1768 of 282 lbs. of "English" (a size of type approximately 14-point) for the sum of fourteen pounds and two shillings.

Walpole had built himself a gothic castle at Twickenham which became a showplace. The press was part of this idea, and represented a dilettante's approach to the craft. Disraeli wrote of Walpole that he was "conscious of possessing the talent of amusement, yet feeling his deficient energies, he resolved to provide various substitutes for genius itsself, and to acquire reputation, if he could not grasp at celebrity. He raised a printing-press at his castle, by which means he rendered small editions of his works valuable from their rarity, and much talked of because of seldom seen."

A criticism of Walpole's printing was the frequent appearance of typographical errors, which he attributed to "the knavery of his printer." His disdain for such matters is obvious from his remark, "I hope that future edition-mongers will say of those at Strawberry Hill, 'They have all the beautiful negligence of a gentleman."

Walpole's interest in fine printing was not limited to his own work. The literary world of his own time was becoming excited about typography through the influence of such great printers as Baskerville and Bodoni, from whom Walpole commissioned printing. The output of the Press at Strawberry Hill was therefore part of, and a contributor to the lively interest in fine printing. The books printed there were of better quality than the commercial printing of the times and are so remembered.

June 26

The benevolent Patent Office of the United States issued on June 26, 1860 a patent to Henry Harger of Delhi, Iowa for an invention which "consists in the arrangement of machinery in connection with the type case by which the types are fed to the composing-stick, and of an arrangement of fingers and levers in connection with the composing-stick, by which the types may be taken from the case and set in line."

There appears to be no further mention of the Harger device in the public prints, as to whether it was ever marketed or even used commercially in any way. We can be assured that this composing stick is not of the kind that will comfortably fit in the back pocket of a compositor—a common repository for that simple tool. During the 19th century there were numerous typesetting machines evolved from the dreams and mechanical aptitudes of horny-handed compositors, who were also afflicted, presumably, with corns and bunions from long hours of standing at the case.

By 1900 the transition had taken place, and the compositor had become automated, with the aid of Watchmaker Mergenthaler's linotype machine and by the monotype of Accountant Lanston. The cycle was completed when the operator of the typesetting machines found that he had merely switched the anatomical location of his bunions, and he became just as anxious to get back to the case as originally he had been to learn to operate the machine.

Many of the original ideas concerning the mechanization of typesetting evolved upon the principle of handling single types, in one way or another. Between 1840 and 1870 there were 34 patents granted in the United States for typesetting and distributing machines and the same number in England, testifying to the ever-increasing need for such equipment. Presses had been automated early in the century. The resulting increase in the production capabilities of the printing office, particularly in newspaper and book printing, had been so astonishing that there was unquestionably fame and fortune awaiting the inventor of a successful typesetting machine.

Most of the early machines foundered on the difficulty of justification of the line of type, which the compositor accomplished by a rather laborious selection of spaces after the line had been composed. Spaces made of compressible material were tried, and even congealable fluids were attempted, along with plaster of Paris and gelatin substances, but with no practical results. By the time the most complicated of all these typesetters, the Paige Compositor, was finally perfected during the last decade of the century, the concept of assembling cast printer's types in a machine had already been bypassed with the successful demonstration of the Mergenthaler mechanism in which the type was actually cast in the machine. At one stroke every other idea was antiquated, and no matter how unique the approach, the machine in which it was represented was headed not for the print shop, but for the museum, to serve as another example of American mechanical genius.

June 27

The proof that a pugnacious Irishman named Joseph Charless was the first printer in the trans-Mississippi West is more or less taken from the records of a Dr. B. G. Farrar of St. Louis whose journal lists the printer as being dosed with calomel on this date in 1818. No doubt he needed it to rectify a malfunction brought about by a rapid and hazardous trip from Louisville, Kentucky at the insistence of the Governor of the Missouri Territory, Meriwether Lewis, whose administration was chafing at the lack of a press in the territory.

Charless had left Ireland for Philadelphia in 1796 and had worked in that town as a printer for several years prior to going West to Lexington, Kentucky, where he set up shop, becoming part owner in 1803 of the *Independent Gazette.* In 1807 he founded the *Gazette* in Lexington, Kentucky, selling out a year later in order to go to St. Louis.

Once settled, Charless issued a prospectus for a forthcoming newspaper to be called the *Missouri Gazette and Louisiana Advertiser.* In it he wrote in the richly colored terms expected of pioneer editors: "It is self evident that in every country where the rays of the press are not clouded by despotic power, that the people have arrived to the highest grade of civilization, there science holds her head erect, and bids her sons to call into action those talents which lie in a good soil inviting cultivation. The inviolation of the Press is co-existent with the liberties of the people, they live or die together, it is the vestal fire upon the preservation of which, the fate of nations depends; and the most pure hands officiating for the whole community, should be incessantly employed in keeping it alive. For the reasons above stated, we conceive it unnecessary to offer any thing like professions to the public, but rather let the columns of the GAZETTE speak for themselves, and the print let to live or die by the character it may acquire, but its intended patrons have a right to be acquainted with the grounds upon which their approbation is solicited."

During the following years Charless suffered all the vicissitudes of the newspaper publisher in an unsettled territory. From time to time mail service was so undependable that he waited for several weeks for news of the outside world, resorting to sending riders East to the Indiana Territory. Indian raids and inclement weather delayed the arrival of both news and supplies. Several times it was necessary to discontinue publishing when the supply of paper ran out. And of course there was the perennial problem of collecting from subscribers. In 1816 Charless penned an impassioned plea for payment that could serve as a classic of the genre:

"Could a printer strike sustenance from his head, as Vulcan struck Pallas from the head of Jove, then, indeed, it would be folly in him to complain; but such miracles are not to be worked now-a-days. Or could his look convert stones into flesh, as the head of Medusa did flesh into stone, he might do tolerably well. But printers unfortunately for themselves, are no magicians, altho' they deal in an *art* which has charmed mankind. They have much headwork to perform; but their teeth require to be occupied also. Indeed,

129

with some, the occupation with the teeth is the major subject. And, to confess the truth, it forms a part of our ambition also, otherwise we should not now be writing this paragraph."

June 28

The bibliophile William Blades tells of a letter written by the Rev. C. F. Newmarsh, Rector of Pelham, to the Rev. S. R. Maitland, Librarian to the Archbishop of Canterbury, concerning a copy of the *Boke of St. Albans,* printed by Wynkyn de Worde in 1496. This early English imprint, probably the most celebrated of all English sporting books, is titled, *Book of Hawking, Hunting & Blasing of Arms,* and was written by Dame Juliana Berner. In 1935, A. S. W. Rosenbach sold a copy of the same book for $24,200. The Rev. Newmarsh wrote:

"On June 28, 1844, a pedlar called at a cottage in Blyton and asked an old widow, named Naylor, whether she had any rags to sell. She answered, No! but offered him some old paper, and took from a shelf the *Boke of St. Albans* and others, weighing 9 lbs., for which she received ninepence. The pedlar carried them through Gainsborough tied up in string, past a chemist's shop, who, being used to buy up old paper to wrap his drugs in, called the man in, and struck by the appearance of the *Boke,* gave him three shillings for the lot. Not being able to read the Colophon, he took it to an equally ignorant stationer, and offered it to him for a guinea, at which price he declined it, but proposed that it should be exposed in his window as a means of eliciting some information about it. It was accordingly placed there with this label, 'Very old curious work.' A collector of books went in and offered half a crown for it, which excited the suspicion of the vendor. Soon after Mr. Bird, Vicar of Gainsborough, went in and asked the price, wishing to possess a very early specimen of printing but not knowing the value of the book. While he was examining it, Stark, a very intelligent bookseller, came in, to whom Mr. Bird at once ceded the right of pre-emption. Stark betrayed such visible anxiety that the vendor, Smith, declined setting a price. Soon after Sir C. Anderson, of Lea (author of Ancient Models), came in and took away the book to collate, but brought it back in the morning having found it imperfect in the middle, and offered five pounds for it. Sir Charles had no book of reference to guide him to its value. But in the meantime, Stark had employed a friend to obtain for him the refusal of it, and had undertaken to give for it a little more than any sum Sir Charles might offer. On finding that at least five pounds could be got for it, Smith went to the chemist and gave him two guineas, and then sold it to Stark's agent for seven guineas. Stark took it to London, and sold it at once to the Rt. Hon. Thos. Grenville for seventy pounds or guineas."

Evidently the same methods of purchasing the volume held over to the present century, as Rosenbach's biographer stated that when a customer looked at it and enquired of its price, the Doctor shouted, "$24,200 and I wouldn't sell it to another person for less than $40,000. My God, I'll never see another copy for sale in my lifetime."

June 29

Compositor William A. Hunter, of Bryan, Ohio no doubt wearying of his continued purchasing of soap, received a patent this day in 1858 which offered some promise of alleviating the problem. The nature of Hunter's contribution to the history of American ingenuity evolved the construction of a type case with a metallic screen bottom. In this way the case might constantly be kept free of dust, which was to collect on a shelf or drawer underneath the case—to be emptied in all probability by the printer's devil, already grimy beyond all redemption.

Comp Hunter might better have paid serious attention to the re-design of the entire case, which had changed but little in four centuries, and which over one hundred years later is not at all improved. It was just a year after Hunter's brainstorm that another typographic originator, one Tom Rooker of New York, was granted a patent for arranging a type case by placing "at the side of the lower-case its corresponding upper-case, so that the movements of the body and travel of the hand of the compositor may be greatly reduced."

The Rooker case is the model now universally used, although there are several variants such as the French case, introduced in the 19th century, in which the capital letters were placed in the same case with the lowercase but along the top. In the United States such an arrangement is called a Yankee Job Case, no credit being given to French talent.

Rooker's type case is undoubtedly the one now called California Job Case. Possibly the idea appeared to be eminently practical to those printers who heard of the discovery of gold in that state and joined the migration to the West Coast but preferred to hold on to their own trade if the nuggets were not immediately forthcoming. Shipping a few fonts of type was a great deal simpler in one case than in two, and of course there were certain features attractive to employing printers who were anxious to reduce their typesetting hour costs.

The fresh young engineers now being attracted to the printing industry in its present state of automation by computer are honestly aghast when they contemplate the type case and learn that it has received so little up-grading in over five hundred years. They find particularly appalling the cap case in which the letters J and U are placed after the Z, simply because these letters had not been devised when the case was invented. Possibly their viewpoint of the technology of printing becomes quite slanted when they are told that the J has been in use since the 17th century and that the U became commonly used prior to 1800.

June 30

On this day in 1948 occurred the death of the most prolific of all American type designers, Morris Fuller Benton. We have grown accustomed to considering Frederic W. Goudy as the type designer who contributed the widest variety of types to America's composing rooms. But when comparing the output of the almost forgotten Morris Benton to that of his contemporaries, there is little question that he is in first place among American designers for sheer volume.

Benton began his career in the shadow of another Benton—his father. Linn Boyd Benton was the inventor who revolutionized typefounding with the punch cutter, which he invented in 1886. The elder Benton also worked with Theodore L. De Vinne in the design the type called Century Expanded.

When the younger Benton received his engineering degree from Cornell in 1896, he became his father's assistant at American Type Founders Company. In the beginning he helped to design equipment for the foundry. In 1906 he became fully engaged in type design, later becoming the head of that department of ATF, a post which he held until his retirement in 1937.

Benton's first type was Roycroft, produced about 1898. This effort was followed by planning variants of Century, an activity which was not completed for two decades. Within the next three or four years several other types still in wide use were produced—Wedding Text in 1901, Alternate Gothic and Franklin Gothic in 1903, along with Typo Script and Cloister Black.

Following this activity Benton became engaged in work which might have engulfed a lesser man. He began with the original 11-point size of a private type which had been designed by the architect Bertram Goodhue, and which was called Cheltenham. By 1908 Benton had produced eighteen variations of "Chelt" and in the process made it the most widely used type of the period.

Benton evinced a positive clairvoyance in producing types which a half century later are among the top current styles. Alternate Gothic and Franklin Gothic have stood the test of time, along with News Gothic, first offered in 1908 and still extremely popular.

The first of the Benton historic adaptations was Bodoni, cut in 1909, followed by Cloister Oldstyle in 1913. Garamond followed in 1914, with the collaboration of Thomas M. Cleland. In 1928 he produced a fine copy of the type originally cut for the famed Shakspeare Press of William Bulmer, by the punchcutter Robert Martin. This type was named Bulmer.

Of Benton's entire output of some 178 designs and variations, there was but one type which bore his name. In 1934 he cut a classic roman letter and named it Benton, but when the type was marketed it was called Whitehall. This decision was made by the foundry for a practical reason. The type in inventory is stacked alphabetically on the shelves, making it necessary to move a great many fonts when a new type is brought out with a name beginning with "B." Whitehall therefore saved some time but lost its designer an opportunity to perpetuate his name.

July

July 1

On this day in 1589 in Antwerp a man died of whom Thomas Frognall Dibdin wrote in his *Bibliographical Decameron:* "Of all the printers whose works have ever adorned the literary republic, none, I think, stand upon so broad and lofty a pedestal as Christopher Plantin. Jenson and Robert Stephen had equal elegance, and Aldus and Froben equal zeal and learning; but take his smaller and his larger works together, his pocket Latin Bible and his Polyglot Bible, and you will hardly find anything to approach, certainly none to excel them."

Plantin was born in Saint-Avertin, near Tours, in France, probably in 1520. As he lost his mother in early childhood, he was raised by the canon obedientiary of the Church of St. Just, who was his father's employer. Thus Plantin received the beginnings of a classical education. At fifteen he was apprenticed to a bookbinder in Caen. Upon the completion of his indentures he went to Paris where he remained some three years, apparently learning the craft of printing, as by 1549 he was in Antwerp setting up a printing office. None of Plantin's biographers have been able to determine exactly why he left Paris, where he had evidently made a number of friendships with the scholars, booksellers, and printers of the university quarter in which he lived and worked. Plantin, in a letter to Pope Gregory XIII, stated that he was drawn to Antwerp by the opportunities for his trade and by its proximity to Louvain University.

This would seem to be a reasonable explanation, but in actuality the atmosphere of Paris was not conducive to the freedom of the press. King Henry II was then making a vigorous attempt to eliminate heresy, and no printer felt really secure from the accusations of the clergy concerning the printing of supposedly subversive material. It was in 1546 that Etienne Dolet, the printer of Lyons, was burned at the stake with his books. Plantin was therefore not alone in leaving France, as many printers moved their businesses to other countries to escape the pressures against reform.

Plantin, once he had established himself in Antwerp, prospered, even though he again was confronted with the religious problems of his times. In 1555 the Netherlands came under the rule of the Spanish king, Philip II, who prohibited Protestant worship and set up the Office of the Inquisition. Plantin, who was mildly sympathetic to the Calvinists, lost his printing office, but by that time he had made many friends, with the result that his loss was not so severe as it might have been. He returned the following year and reestablished himself. Even under such trying conditions, Plantin became one of the great printers, producing scholarly books upon a variety of subjects. Measured against the establishments of his contemporaries, the Plantin printing office was a giant of its kind. It was not until the 19th century that any other printing offices became larger than that of the Antwerp printer. In 1563 he added a typefoundry for which he purchased punches from the widow of Claude Garamond and from the great punchcutters—Le Bé of Paris and Granjon of Lyons.

132

July 2

One of the earliest experiments in the creation of a roman alphabet which could satisfactorily lend itself to the more economic aspects of typesetting was granted the approbation of a patent on or about this day to Philip Rusher in 1802 by the British Patent Office. Rusher's patent (No. 2620) reads as follows :

"Various Improvements and Alterations in the Form of Printing Types, and the Manner in which Printing is to be performed therewith, so as to Diminish the Trouble and Expence of Printing, and to render it much more Uniform and Beautiful. . . .

"Each capital letter, with few exceptions, should be comprized in the compass of an oval, or made to occupy the space that might in printing be filled by an oval, in which form they will occupy less room than usual, and be much more uniform. Each small letter is to be without any tail piece or descender, and the metal of the type (usually forming the shoulder) in its whole length, both in the small and capitals, is to extend no lower than the body of the letter, consequently the letters will occupy less room . . . in printing, without being less legible. Those of the small letters, whose heads or ascending points rise above the body of the character, should have their heads shortened or lowered about one third, which will make them appear more uniform with the other letters, and will likewise allow room for a greater space between the lines in printing; or the type may be placed closer.

"In printing, each line may be placed immediately under the body of the preceding line, and thus a great part of the paper heretofore occupied by the type will be saved; or spaces may be placed between the lines to extend them to the usual distances asunder."

Rusher's place in English typefounding was set for all time by Talbot Baines Reed in his classic history of the art, *A History of the English Letterfounders*. In a footnote Reed described him as "a misguided reformer." Rusher found it necessary to finance personally the first use of the type by commissioning a printer to produce an edition of Samuel Johnson's novel, *Rasselas, Prince of Abyssinia*. The type was a modification of Caslon with the lower-case characters changed to conform to Rusher's system. Two editions were actually printed, but the venture was not successful. The idea therefore expired with the first experiment.

July 3

Andrew Marvell, essayist, wit, controversialist, and Member of Parliament, received upon this day in 1796 a letter which read, "If thou darest to print any lie or libel against Doctor Parker, by the eternal God, I will cut thy throat."

The correspondent, who merely signed himself J. G., was a partisan favoring Parker, the Bishop of Oxford, with whom Marvell had been engaged in a long controversy. As an assistant to the poet Milton and Latin secretary to Oliver Cromwell, Marvell was at the center of events during the entire Restoration. He wrote numerous satires concerning the immorality and corruption of the period, much of which he published anonymously. His satire on the fear of the press as expressed by the monarch, Charles I, is an interesting bit of ironic prose:

"The Press (that *villanous* Engine) invented much about the same time with the Reformation, that hath done more mischief to the Dicipline of our Church, than all the Doctrine can make amends for. 'Twas an happy time when all Learning was in Manuscript, and some little Officer, like our Author, did keep the Keys of the Library. When the clergy needed no more knowledge than to read the Liturgy, and the Laity no more Clerkship than to save them from hanging. But now since Printing came into the World, such is the mischief that a Man cannot write a Book but presently he is answered. Could the Press but one be conjured to obey only an *Imprimatur,* our Author might not disdain *perhaps* to be one of the most zealous Patrons. There have been wayes found out to banish Ministers, to fine not only the People, but even the Grounds and Fields where they assembled in Conventicles, But no Art yet could prevent these seditious meetings of Letters. Two or three brawny Fellows in a Corner, with meer Ink and Elbow-Grease, do more harm than an *hundred Systematical Divines* with their *sweaty Preaching*. And, which is a strange thing, the very Spunges, which one would think should rather deface and block out the whole Book, and were anciently used to that purpose, are become now the Instruments to make things legible. Their ugly Printing-Letters, that look like so many rotten Teeth. How oft have they been pull'd out by B. and L. the Publick-Tooth-drawers! and yet these rascally Operators of the Press have got a trick to fasten them in a few minutes that they have grown as firm a Set, and as biting and as talkative as ever. O *Printing!* how has thou disturb'd the Peace of Mankind! that Lead, when moulded into Bullets, is not so mortal as when founded into Letters."

July 4

"In Congress, July 4, 1776. A Declaration by the Representatives of the United States of America, in General Congress Assembled." Thus reads the heading of the first printed copy of America's most famous document. The engrossed copy of the Declaration of Independence, signed by most of the members of Congress, is the one most readily recognized as the official "first edition," but actually it was not written and signed until August 2nd. The printed copy became the official copy as it was inserted into the Minutes of Congress.

The printer to whom the Declaration was entrusted was John Dunlap, who had come from Ireland as a boy and had learned the printer's craft in the office of his uncle, William Dunlap. He established his own business in Philadelphia in 1765. In 1771 he founded a weekly newspaper, the *Pennsylvania Packett; and the General Advertiser,* which in 1784 with a slight change of name became one of the earliest daily newspapers to be published in the United States.

When printer Dunlap received the manuscript of the Declaration to put it into type, he obviously had a "rush job" on his hands, as he was ordered to complete the job with the utmost dispatch. He has been roundly criticized for his typographical errors, about which it was said that the capitalization and punctuation followed "neither previous copies, nor reason, nor the custom of any age known to man." As Dunlap in all probability had to set his type by candlelight, from copy which may have been rapidly written, there are doubtless many reasons for the errors.

There is certainly no chance of checking the copy, as it no longer exists. Dunlap had no way of knowing that he had produced a great historical document, and was therefore not at all concerned with the manuscript which he received from Congress.

For his broadside, the printer used a sheet of paper which measured fifteen by eighteen inches, the type form being twelve by seventeen inches. The type was Caslon Oldstyle, in the English casting which was commonly used by the Colonial printers. The main body was set in the size then called English, which is about 14-point. There are no signatures on this printed copy, but the name of John Hancock appears as President of the Congress, as does that of Charles Thomson, the Secretary. The only other name on the document is that of the printer. There is no record of the number of copies printed, but Congress had ordered that copies be sent to all the assemblies and conventions, to the various councils and committees of safety, and to the commanding officers of the continental troops. All of this took some time. One writer has stated that if horses ran any faster in 1776 than they did in the time of the Roman emperors, the American roads were worse. The resulting celebrations throughout the Colonies were therefore dated upon the receipt of the broadsides.

July 5

George Bruce, one of the best of the American typefounders, died on July 5, 1886, just four years after the printing of what is considered to be one of the finest type specimen books produced in the United States—the 1882 catalog of the Bruce Type Foundry.

Coming to these shores from his native Scotland in 1795, when he was just fourteen years of age, George Bruce apprenticed himself to a Philadelphia printer. In 1806 he combined with his elder brother, David, in establishing a printing firm in New York. David, a pressman, became extremely interested in the new craft of stereotyping. He returned to Great Britain to discuss the subject with Earl Stanhope who was at the time the leading authority on stereotyping. When he found Stanhope unwilling to divulge any information, he returned to New York and began his own experiments, resulting in the successful establishment of the process in the United States.

At that time there was very little consistency among typefounders concerning the size of the types which they produced. Consequently printers were annoyed with the variations between the size of one founder's product and that of another. George Bruce attempted, about 1822, to bring some order to this problem and devised a system of sizes which covered every type size from Pearl (5-point) to Canon (48-point). Bruce's system, the first practical endeavor made by an American typefounder, has since been superseded by the method finally adopted by all American foundries in 1886, and later ratified by founders in Great Britain in 1898.

Bruce took the sizes of 7-point to 12-point, and made them the standard. All other sizes were to be determined by the multiplication or division of these standard six sizes, using the rule of geometrical progression. The 11-point was made as much larger than 10-point as 9-point was made larger than 8-point. Each size increased .122462", which when increased six times in a series, doubles on the seventh progression the size of the first body. While it was an attempt to apply scientific reasoning to the size of type, it was quite unwieldy, and the Bruce firm could not interest any other founder in adopting the practice.

July 6

William A. Dwiggins chose this date for the first illustration in his whimsical essay, *Towards a Reform of the Paper Currency, Particularly in Point of its Design*, published in 1932. The illustration bears the caption, "Infuriated Artists demolishing the Bureau of Engraving and Printing at Washington. Morning of the 6th of July, 1951. First phase of the Communist Revolution."

That the artists of this fair land had cause to be infuriated is aptly explained by WAD in his satire. Indeed, since there has been no significant improvement in the design of our currency since the Hingham typographer first brought the matter to our attention, there is some reason to believe that these same artists are still infuriated.

Thinking about money as something which has to be designed is, as Dwiggins carefully points out, foreign to the ordinary citizen of the republic who grows up "to take dollar bills as a matter of course, as part of the phenomenon of nature, unexplained acts of God."

The Bureau of Engraving and Printing scarcely could have sanctified Dwiggins' remarks, and most certainly, having celebrated in 1962 the one hundredth year of its existence, it will not care to be reminded that certain discerning users of its product are less than happy with its design. Dwiggins believed that a sort of osmosis had set in at the Bureau in its earliest days, a not uncommon malady in government circles.

"The present currency," he writes, "is the last of a series of copies—copies of copies of copies of copies, along a weary sequence back to the Louis-Philippe original. Changes do happen in such a sequence—a gradual blunting of the original intention. It is an astonishing fact that the present design is many degrees *worse* than the original!"

In an accompanying footnote, Dwiggins claimed that he had discovered a theory to explain the quality of art in Washington. "This explanation proceeds on the simple assumption that the Washington brand isn't art—that it is never set up to be art—that no one in the bureaus claims it is art, or ever thinks of it in that way. It is another kind of stuff altogether. It sours easily because it isn't intended to stay fresh—it is meant to last only for the short time during which it is being manipulated. The proponents of the theory maintain that the whole affair, in fact, is simply *manipulation*—a civil-service process for filling in the time. You are given a piece of paper and instructed to cover it with lines copied from a pattern sheet; you go on putting the lines on the paper until the space is full and then you are through and it is time to go and play golf."

July 7

Richard Brinsley Sheridan, Member of Parliament, dramatist, orator, and distinguished defender of the Press, died in London this day in 1816. Just three years previously his constituents of the town of Stafford had presented him with a "vase cup" which bore the following engraving:

To the Right Hon. R. B. Sheridan
the eloquent, intrepid, and incorruptible
Guardian of that Palladium
of all the Civil, Religious, and Political
Rights of Freeman,
The Liberty of the Press.
This Cup is presented
by his *friends of Stafford,*
as a small Tribute of their unbounded
Admiration,
irrevocable Esteem and eternal Gratitude.

During his career, Sheridan spoke frequently upon the issues stated upon that inscription. He was active as a member of the Society for the Freedom of the Press, and in the grandiloquent style of the times he paid tribute to its ideals. "Give them," he states, "a corrupt House of Lords, give them a venal House of Commons, give them a tyrannical prince, give them a truckling court, and let me but have an unfettered press, and I will defy them to encroach a hair's breadth on the liberty of England."

July 8

"Towne was not deficient in intellect and was a decent workman. He was a *bon vivant,* but he did not possess the art of accumulating and retaining wealth." So wrote Isaiah Thomas, the American printing historian, of Benjamin Towne, who died on July 8, 1793.

That statement is practically the only decent remark concerning printer Towne that can be found in the record. But he must necessarily be a part of the history of the American newspaper, as he happened to be the publisher of the first daily newspaper to appear on this continent, even if it was, as Mott has written, "from first to last a sorry-looking, poverty-stricken sheet—shabby forerunner of the great American daily newspaper." And of course, Mott was thinking about the *New York Times* rather than, say, the late *New York Graphic.*

Towne had learned the printer's trade in his native England, and his first work in the Colonies was with the well-known printer-publisher, William Goddard. In 1769 he became a partner with Goddard in the publication of the *Pennsylvania Chronicle,* but the two men within a short time were in violent disagreement. In 1774 Towne began his own paper in Philadelphia, the *Evening Post,* as an organ representing the patriot's interests. This newspaper was the first to put into print the Declaration of Independence in its issue of July 6, 1776. During the British occupation of Philadelphia, Editor Towne changed his colors and became a Royalist. When the occupation ceased it apparently bothered Towne very little as he again changed hats and returned to his "patriotic" views. Although he was not particularly popular, he managed to continue his paper until 1784.

It was on May 30, 1783 that Towne published the *Evening Post* as a daily. It was printed on a half sheet of paper and contained four two-column pages. Ben Towne probably did all the printing himself, setting the type and pulling the impressions. He also found it necessary to peddle it in the streets. He was for long remembered in Philadelphia for crying in the streets, "All the news for two coppers." For the seventeen months of its existence as a daily the *Evening Post* was not very consistent in its publication schedule, sometimes appearing five or less times a week. Advertising revenue was very low, as was the list of subscribers. This situation was not surprising considering the "turncoat" policies of its publisher.

In order to boost his circulation, Towne asked the influential Dr. John Witherspoon, President of Princeton College and member of Congress, to write for his sheet. Witherspoon agreed if Towne would print "a Confession, Recantation and Apology," which he, Witherspoon, would write. But Towne refused. Possibly his reason was that the statement had him say, "Instead of being suffered to print, I ought to be hanged as a traitor to my country." The "confession" was widely published in other papers, to the discomfiture of the printer, but he should have known better than to lock horns with a man like Witherspoon, who was so ardent a patriot that he had coined the term "Americanism."

July 9

E. W. G. Kircher, a printer of Goslar, a city located just a few miles inside the eastern border of West Germany, petitioned the City Council on this day in 1796 as follows:

"I, the undersigned, transfer to the engraver, Herr Walbaum of this town, and his wife the privilege graciously granted me by the Most Honourable Council of the Free and Imperial City of Goslar for the establishment of a typefoundry in that city; in such a manner that I completely renounce any claim to it and leave it to Herr Walbaum, if he should wish to petition the Most Honorable Council to have it transferred to himself, to make this supplication without further reference to myself. However, I make the proviso that Herr Walbaum, if he do not remain in Goslar all his life, shall not pass this privilege to a third person but shall return it to myself. Moreover, he shall fulfill exactly the promise, given by me to the Most Honorable Council, namely to establish the typefoundry this year. Everything else I forego of my own free will and waive any further claim."

This is the first record of Justin Erich Walbaum as a typefounder. He was then twenty-eight years of age and ready to begin his career in a field far removed from that to which he had been apprenticed—that of baker. However, when Walbaum received his journeyman's certificate as a baker, he did not have sufficient funds with which to acquire the necessary moulds needed by a confectioner. This lack evidently gave the young man sufficient incentive to supply what was needed by his own efforts. He used old swordblades which he fashioned into chisels and began to learn how to engrave wooden moulds. He acquired such proficiency that he was soon engraving in steel. His reputation in this art grew until he found that he was earning more money in engraving than he possibly could as an assistant baker, and thus he became a professional engraver.

He next applied for a position with a music printer as an engraver of music sheets. From this point it was a simple step for Walbaum to become interested in the cutting of punches for printer's types and consequently to establish himself as a typefounder. As Goslar was at that period in economic straits, the Town Council was pleased to have an attractive new business located there and it extended tax-free privileges to Walbaum. However, he soon found that his location was too restricting to his rising talents, and therefore petitioned the Duke of Saxe-Weimar for similar privileges. As Weimar was then the literary and intellectual center of Germany, Walbaum found himself immersed in an atmosphere which was most conducive to his work.

The Walbaum types which have been revived in our own time follow the pattern of the letters of Didot in France and Bodoni in Italy, contemporaries of the Weimar founder. They have however a warmth the latter types lack, and it is this feature which has resulted in their present revival and popularity.

July 10

Born this day in the city of Boston in 1868 was a man whose career spanned the most important typographical trends of the last hundred years, and who lived long enough to be called the "dean" of American typographers, art directors, and designers.

Will Bradley first handled type in his sixth year when his father, a newspaper cartoonist, brought home a font for his son to use with the small press the boy had purchased with money earned as a delivery boy. After the loss of his father, young Bradley was taken to Ishpeming, a small mining town in northern Michigan. He completed his formal education at the age of twelve when the teacher sent him home and told him to remain until he had the correct answer to a problem in division. Not caring for arithmetic, Bradley asked his mother for permission to "go to work and earn money so I can learn to be an artist."

Almost immediately he found himself serving as a "devil" for three dollars a week, in the office of the *Iron Agitator,* owned and edited by George Newett. His first job was the wash-up of a Gordon press. Bradley later told of the practice of the country shop in using local help for straight-matter typesetting, but relying upon the tramp printers for display composition and presswork. He therefore listened carefully to the itinerant job printer employed in the office and when that individual finally moved on to another town, Bradley took over his duties, receiving an increase of wages to six dollars a week while a new devil was taken on in his place.

Before he was thirteen, Bradley received and accepted an offer to go to work for a four-page tabloid, the *Peninsula Record,* for eight dollars a week. A few months later his former employer hired him back at ten

137

dollars a week and the title of job printer. When he was fourteen this wage was increased to twelve dollars, and at fifteen he was made foreman at fifteen dollars a week, a man's wages for the period.

At sixteen the urge to be an artist was so strong that Bradley, having saved fifty dollars, journeyed to Chicago and went to work for Rand & McNally. Here he learned to engrave tints on woodblocks. As he was "learning" a new skill, he received no salary. After several weeks his money ran out and he returned home to the print shop. Rand & McNally wrote to him stating that if he returned and worked an extra hour each day, sweeping and dusting, he would be paid three dollars a week.

Just as soon as he had saved more money, he returned to Chicago and took the job. However the following year he again left the firm and went to work as a compositor for Knight & Leonard, Chicago's leading fine printers. There his fine work was immediately noticed and he was made a designer at $21 dollars per week. Within two years he was free-lancing, had received recognition for the design of covers for *Harper's Magazine,* and was on his way to one of the great careers in American design.

<hr>

July 11

John Bell, the English publisher, typefounder, and bookseller, in his anxiety to produce the most splendid printing of his times, inserted into the columns of his own newspaper, *The World,* upon this day in 1787 the following advertisement:

"Press-men for Book-work—Wanted, Four Complete Press-men, who can execute Book-work in the most perfect manner, and who can be warranted for their regularity and sobriety. They may depend on constant employment so long as they execute their business perfectly; they will be paid by the piece or by the week, as may be most conducive to their own interest, and the satisfaction of their employer. For particulars enquire at the Commercial-Office of this Paper, corner of Exeter Exchange in the Strand. None need apply but the very best workmen; as none of an inferior description will be continued."

Apparently this request for paragons of their kind struck a warm note among the printing fraternity, as somewhat later another advertisement appeared, this time asking for a compositor who would doubtless be fit company for his strong-backed brethren in the pressroom:

"Wanted: A Compositor for a Daily Newspaper. He must be a perfect good hand, sober, steady, attentive to business and of creditable appearance. It is needless for any other to apply than those who possess the above requisites, and the most scrupulous enquiry will be made into their ability. Apply at the office of the Paper, Exeter 'Change, in the Strand."

Since Bell's printing office contained such a unique group of printers, at once both industrious and sober, the proprietor next attempted to locate a man who could not only live with such qualities but make them productive. He placed another advertisement asking for:

"An intelligent Person of liberal Education who possesses a Taste for Printing—and who can devote the whole of his time to the superintendence of a Daily Publication, may hear of an eligible situation, by applying to the Printer of the Paper, at the corner of Exeter 'Change, in the Strand."

It is possible to detect in the first two advertisements the reputation acquired by the craft printers of the times. It is difficult to pin down exactly when printers as a group began to be accused of intemperate habits. Possibly it was the length of the working day under which men of better than average intelligence found it necessary to labor. Compositors learned in several languages were not at all uncommon, and such craftsmen, no doubt chafing under the restrictions placed upon them, found release in the less confining atmosphere of the ale-room.

Until fairly recent times, when the era of the tramp printer became a thing of the past, a printer was naturally assumed to be a toper. Up to the turn of the century small town hotels and boarding houses as often as not posted notices that printers would not be accepted. Nowadays the printer tends to be an industrious and sober individual who works his shift and goes home to spend his evenings with his family. It may be noted also that there has been a certain loss of the romance formerly associated with the craft. Moralists may observe this to their satisfaction.

July 12

On this day in 1403, "the reputable men of the Craft of Writers of Text Letters those commonly called scriveners and other good folks citizens of London who were wont to bind and sell books" appeared before the Lord Mayor requesting him to form them into a guild. Permission to organize was granted the following year by the Lord Mayor and the Aldermen of the City of London. The stationers thereupon elected a master and two wardens, and found a building in Milk Street from which to run their affairs.

The title of *stacionarius* was applied during the Middle Ages to university librarians, but by the 14th century stationers were illuminators and "courthand" writers. The actual derivation of the name is lost in obscurity, but by the time the guild was formed stationers probably were the craftsmen who dealt with the work of the scriveners.

By 1542 the group had acquired sufficient prestige to request from the Crown a Charter and from the City of London permission to become an official guild or a Livery Company. In 1557 this petition received the royal favor, Queen Mary giving the group the authority to organize the printing and book trades in England under the name of the Company of Stationers. The members were to consist of the booksellers, printers, and bookbinders. By 1560 the Stationers became a Livery Company also. Thus began its centuries' long domination of the printer's craft in England, the Charter having forbade any person from practising "the art and mystery of printing" unless he was either a member of the Company or had permission to do so under Royal Letters Patent.

Until almost the close of the 18th century, the Worshipful Company exercised almost complete control over printers of the country. The Charter made it obligatory to register with the Company every book or piece of printing before it would be allowed to leave the press, in effect making the Company rather than its author the copyright holder of a work. The members of the Company were instrumental in the formation of the Decree of the Star Chamber in 1586 which controlled the number of presses, master printers, and apprentices in London, Oxford, and Cambridge (the only allowable locations for printing).

Offenders against these rules suffered the wrecking of their printing presses, fines, and imprisonment, or all three penalties. Although the Court of Star Chamber was discontinued in 1641, the Company continued the old rules and was responsible for a new decree passed in 1643. Within the Company also, complete control was exercised. Members were fined for such minor offences as working on Sunday, using bad language, or binding primers in parchment. It also set itself up as censor of what it thought to be lewd printing. During the 17th century the Company reached its most prosperous period. In 1603 James I granted in perpetuity the right to publish almanacs and prognostications, which presented the Company with the means of obtaining rich returns. At the present time, while this right still exists, the decline of interest in such books has resulted in the publication of but a pocket diary each year by the company.

July 13

An almanac published in 1780 by the printer Isaiah Thomas in Worcester, Massachusetts, gained a unique distinction and greatly increased its printer's reputation and subsequent business in almanacs with an accidental prognostication for this day. When the apprentice who was composing the page for this date inquired of Thomas what should be placed against the date, the printer, engaged in another task, put the boy off with the remark, "Anything, anything!"

The apprentice, no doubt feeling his oats as an editor, set the words, "rain, hail, and snow." Nobody checked the proof of the page, so into the book it went. Naturally enough the purchasers of the almanac were surprised to find such an entry for a summer date, but they were astounded when on July 13th it actually did rain, hail, and snow.

Almanacs were for centuries a basic item of trade for printers, when there were weekly newspapers and virtually no other means of disseminating information. They served in the capacity of newspapers, by carrying advertisements particularly for nostrums and patent medicines. Their use had become so widespread by the 16th century that Henry

III of France decreed that they could not be utilized for making prophecies against parties and individuals. In England James I granted a monopoly in the printing of almanacs to the Universities and to the Stationers' Company, which was subject to censorship by the Archbishop of Canterbury.

In the American colonies, the almanac published by Benjamin Franklin under the title *Poor Richard's Almanac* helped to establish its printer's reputation as a sage.

Isaiah Thomas, whose reputation was enhanced by the amazing prognostication of his 1780 almanac, became the best known printer of his generation. He established printing offices in various locations, such as Boston, Albany, Baltimore, and Newburyport. He also became well established as a book printer, producing in his career over four hundred titles, including prayer books, children's books, and textbooks in a variety of subjects. He published the first novel to be written by a native American—*The Power of Sympathy,* by William H. Brown. In common with other printers of his time, he was not averse to making a profit in what today would be under-the-counter literature.

Thomas' biographer mentions two of these titles, *The Amours and Adventures of Two English Gentlemen in Italy,* and *Aristotle's Complete Master Piece, in three parts; Displaying the Secrets of Nature in the Generation of Man,* both of which were "standard hayloft reading for curious boys in that generation."

Encouraged by the success of these books, Thomas wrote to England in 1786 for a copy of the infamous *Fanny Hill, or the Memoirs of a Woman of Pleasure.* He received a letter from the English bookseller: "The Memoirs of a W. of P. which if you must have, must beg you will apply to some of the Ship Captains coming here, as it is an article I do not send to my Customers if I can possibly help it."

July 14

When John Henry Nash, the distinguished San Francisco printer, wrote to Bruce Rogers expressing an interest in acquiring the original matrices of Centaur type, he mentioned that their value was no doubt decreased due to their recutting as a monotype face. Rogers replied, in part, in a letter dated on this day, 1930:

"As to the sale of the original Centaur matrices, I'm afraid, from the paragraph in your letter (in which you say that they are probably less valuable, now that the same name is used for the monotype series, than they were before) that we can hardly come to any agreement on it. Because my opinion is that since a version of the design is now obtainable by almost any printer, the real *original* is worth just as much or even more, than before. Not, perhaps, to the ordinary printer. I have never thought it of any value whatever to *him*—and for him the monotype face is quite good enough. But the real *Centaur,* (thanks largely to our mutual friend Henry L. Bullen, who gave it such praise in the beginning and who tried to get the American Type Founders to buy it before they cut the Cloister Roman) might now almost be considered a historical type—whatever its merits as a design might be. I still think it would be better to send out a circular letter—but after consultation with Fred Goudy, who is in London at present, and who has probably had more experience in making and selling type-designs, I have decided to fix the price at $2500. And at that figure I doubt if you will be further interested in it. I suspect that someone like Kittredge, who has a large establishment backing his efforts, would be more likely to consider its purchase—even with the restriction that I mentioned in my earlier letter—i.e. that H. W. Kent should have the privilege of having type cast for his Museum Press, if they ever required any more of it. But that, as I said, is a remote contingency, as he now has it on the monotype. . . ."

July 15

That the century old House of Elsevier was no longer in existence became obvious when the printer-publisher Joseph Athias advertised in the Haarlemsche *Courant* on this day in 1683 that he had purchased from Madame Elsevier, widow of Daniel Elsevier, the typefoundry attached to the House, and was ready for business in the City of Amsterdam.

It was in 1583 that the founder of the House, Louis Elsevier, with the aid of a lavish loan from the great printer, Christopher

Plantin, established himself in Leyden as a book broker, bookseller, and publisher. The city was in the midst of both a commercial and intellectual revival, with the famed University as its hub, attracting scholars of repute from all over Europe. As at present, the reputation of a professor rested upon his publications, so Louis Elsevier made it his business to cultivate the distinguished faculty of Leyden, and thus became their publisher.

Such men as Thomas Erpennius, the orientalist, whose Arabic grammar was in print for well over two centuries, and the greatest scientist of his time, Joseph Scaliger, were published by Elsevier, as were the statesman-historian, Grotius, and the mathematician, Snellius.

It was not until 1616 that the Elseviers established their own printing facilities. Prior to this time, their books were printed by a number of Dutch printing offices. At no time is it apparent that the family ever considered the typography of their books to be of primary consideration. They were content to have their printing readable and competently produced. Since they catered to a scholarly clientele they were concerned about keeping their list nominal in price, and naturally enough adopted the format of the small pocket-size books made popular by Aldus Manutius in Venice. This *format elsevierien* is considered by modern authorities on printing and the art of the book to be run-of-the-mill Dutch printing of the 16th century.

During the 18th and 19th centuries, however, bibliophiles and book collectors set up the Elsevier editions as being far superior to the products of the other printers of the 16th century, and touted the Elseviers as being the finest printers of their time. For example, Timperley in his *Encyclopedia* published in 1842, writes: "The Elsevier editions have long and deservedly been esteemed for the clearness, delicacy, and perfect quality of the characters, for their close position together on a solid and very white paper, and the excellence of the presswork. Their Virgil, Terence, and Greek Testament have been reckoned their masterpieces; and are indeed so very fine, that they have justly gained them the reputation of being the first printers in Europe. Their types were so elegant, that their name has been given to all the beautiful letters ever since."

"At the beginning of this undertaking I made up my mind to copy nothing from the work of others, but to stick to nature as closely as I could; and for this purpose, being invited by Mr. Constable, the then owner of Wycliffe, I visited the extensive museum there, collected by the late Marmaduke Tunstal, Esq., to make drawings of the birds. I set off from Newcastle on the 16th July, 1791, and remained at the above beautiful place nearly two months, drawing from stuffed specimens."

So wrote Thomas Bewick, the great English wood engraver, who so revived that art in his time, at the moment of setting to work on the illustrations for the two volume work, *History of British Birds,* which with the earlier published work, *The General History of Quadrupeds* represent landmarks in the history of wood engravings. When Bewick returned to his shop to prepare the engravings from the drawings he had made at Wycliffe, he was disappointed with the results. He found, as did the American artist-naturalist John James Audubon—some thirty years later—that stuffed birds on museum shelves were dull specimens in comparison to those in the field or recently shot. Bewick thereupon depended for his engravings on birds sent to him from all over Britain. As a result his magnificent blocks are a great deal more authentic than they might otherwise have been.

Bewick was apprenticed to Ralph Beilby, a metal-engraver of Newcastle-upon-Tyne, when he was fourteen years of age. Beilby, while he was a fine artisan in ornamental silver, undertook a great deal of work which did not require much craft skill. However the wide variety of his output allowed Bewick to obtain experience that would not have been possible in an establishment with higher standards.

Upon occasion printers would come to Beilby to commission the cutting of wood blocks. As the engraver was not skilled in this work, young Bewick was entrusted with it. The boy became very proficient. It was at this time that he met William Bulmer, then an apprentice of one of Beilby's printer customers. Bulmer later founded the Shakspeare Press and became the best English printer of his time, producing the books which made Bewick's wood engravings world famous.

Since the skill of the printer was an important factor in the best reproduction of the wood engravings, Bewick was always careful to have his blocks printed by the most competent craftsmen. His method of work was to draw his picture upon the block and to outline with a fine steel point the details which were to appear the darkest. The lines which were to print lighter to give the effect of perspective he then gouged out in varying depths, whereupon the detailed drawing was completed and the actual engraving started. Straight gravers were utilized for the unlowered surface, and curved for the lower parts. Under the hands of Bewick the finished result was meticulously detailed and a true work of art. At the present time the original blocks fetch a fancy price whenever they become available.

July 17

On this summer day in 1903 in a Park Ridge, Illinois barn there was struck the first proof to come from the Village Press under the watchful eyes of its enthusiastic proprietors, Frederic W. Goudy, Bertha Goudy, and Will Ransom.

Whereas most private presses consider type to be but one of the appurtenances of a printing office, this press began because there already existed a type, and an excuse to use it was all that was necessary. Goudy had been commissioned by the firm of Kuppenheimer & Co., of Chicago, to design a type which could be used for advertising. When the drawings were completed and a price obtained from Robert Weibking to engrave the matrices, the firm decided that it was too costly a project for them, so they paid Goudy for his time and returned the drawings.

At this juncture the type designer was approached by Will Ransom, a friendly and engaging young man from Snohomish, Washington, then studying at the Art Institute of Chicago. He wished to work with Goudy in his shop in the Fine Arts Building. As Ransom had already engaged in amateur book printing and was anxious to continue, it was decided that the two men would work together. At about the same time Goudy be-

came entranced with Longfellow's poem, *The Village Blacksmith,* utilizing its setting for the name of his press. Goudy later admitted that in the first announcement of the Village Press he had stretched a point about the origin of the type. The announcement read:

"The Village type was designed for the exclusive use of the Press. . . . The design seems based upon an early Italian model, but Mr. Goudy disclaims any conscious intention of imitation, rather having evolved it letter by letter as ideas came, taking some of the best modern private faces—the Golden of Morris, the Montaigne of Bruce Rogers, the Merrymount of B. G. Goodhue, the Doves of Emery Walker, with critical and careful consideration of selecting and adopting those points in each which appealed to him, making changes, and with one idea finally in mind throughout, that of considering each letter as a pen-letter reduced to type with all limitations of material and use as type."

The first book to come from the Village Press was *Printing, An Essay,* by William Morris and Emery Walker. It was printed in an edition of 231 copies on Alton Mill paper. This book along with a copy of the third book from the press, *The Blessed Damozel,* was exhibited at the Louisiana Purchase Exposition in St. Louis in 1914. Both volumes were awarded a bronze medal.

Shortly thereafter Ransom sold his share in the Village Press. In 1904 the Press was moved to Hingham, Massachusetts. In 1906 it was established in New York City, where its equipment was destroyed by fire in 1909. In 1911 it again became active in the Goudy home in Forest Hills, Long Island. Finally it was removed to Deepdene, as Goudy called his home in Marlborough, New York. Melbert B. Cary, the bibliographer of the Village Press, listed 232 items produced by the end of 1937, when the Press became dormant.

July 18

Addressing the Editor of *The Printer's Register,* a Dublin printer on this day in 1868 wrote about the effect of the Factory Acts Extension Act of 1867, relative to the employment of young people and women:

"None of us can object to the general principles of the Act, or their application to our trade; but I believe that many of its provisions, as they now stand, are quite inapplicable to Letter-press Printers; and I cannot well see how they can be properly carried out.

"Although nominally only 'children, young persons and females' come under it, it really affects every one in employment, as it would be impossible to keep a separate set of hours for the different classes; and machinery could not run without the attendance of those under the age specified.

"The provisions forbidding the employment of children under 13, unless with a portion of the day devoted to school, are admirable, and I am sure will meet the approval of the trade generally.

"It appears to me that the rule allowing persons above 16 to be employed in printing offices as if they were above 18, might be made general, and that it should not require a special permission. Printing is not a very laborious occupation, and it appears to me that at 16 a boy's constitution is sufficiently formed to enable him to bear any of the labors to which he is likely to be placed.

"It is difficult to imagine how printers can be expected to keep the same hard and fast rules as to hours of labor as do other trades. Ours essentially is a 'hand-to-mouth' business. We cannot store up work to prepare for a hurry. Everything must be done offhand, or it cannot be done at all; and if a double demy poster, in solid Double Pica, comes in to us at 5 in the afternoon, 700 copies to be delivered that evening, our customer would scarcely understand the Factory Act standing in the way of our working a few hours overtime, and if we refused to take the job he would very soon find someone else to do it. Imagine our keeping to exact hours in the coming election! But suppose we keep to the legal hours, from 6 to 6, or obtain permission to work from 7 to 7, or from 8 to 7, with only one meal hour, which has been our custom here, and we find much the best plan, causing only one break in the day, I still cannot see how we can get our old 60 hours per week and break off on Saturday with 7½ hours work.

"I believe that every purpose of the Act would be attained, as far as printers are concerned, and much complication avoided, by simply enacting that no young person or female should ordinarily work more than 60 hours a week—on any hours between 6 a.m. and 8 p.m. on five days in the week, and 6 a.m. and 4 p.m. on Saturdays—no interval greater than 5½ hours between each meal. This would leave each employer at liberty to select the hours that would best suit him."

July 19

Joell Munsell, printer, of Albany, New York, recorded in his diary on this day in 1828, "For two years I have been taking much pains in collecting a copy of all the different papers published in the Union, and indeed, the world. The number I have procured already amounts to upwards of 400. It is an unprofitable task."

Munsell, at that point deprecated his newspaper collection, but as he was only twenty years old and had been a printer for only three years, there really had not been much time to accumulate a wide selection of newspapers. Before he was through, however, Munsell had gathered over 10,000 newspapers into one hundred bound volumes. Covering both England and the United States, these newspapers were all either first editions or special historical issues. They were acquired by the New York State Library, although unfortunately many of them were destroyed by fire some years later.

Munsell, the son of a Northfield, Massachusetts wagon builder, first followed his father's trade, but at seventeen he read an advertisement in a Greenfield, Massachusetts newspaper in which the publisher stated:

"Two boys 14 to 16 years of age, who sustain a good reputation for intelligence and sobriety, are wanted as apprentices. Such one will be received on liberal terms."

His father took a dim view of his son being bound to a printer. While agreeing with his father that the parental objection was based upon concern for a large family, young Munsell nevertheless left Northfield for the first time, tramped up to Greenfield, and secured the job in the office of the *Franklin Post*. His decision was to have far-reaching consequences because Munsell became one of the important scholar printers on the American scene during the middle years of the 19th century. Although he had never been in a printing office before, he demonstrated a natural aptitude for the work of the compositor. Just two months after he had started to learn the trade, his fellow employees read about an apprentice in another country office who had set a large amount of type very quickly. They asked young Munsell to try to beat the record. This he did, setting 8,120 ems in a working day, some 600 more than the unknown apprentice.

After two years, when his employer sold his newspaper and decided to go to Albany, New York to open a book shop, Munsell was offered a job there as a clerk. The young man accepted. After a short period, finding the job unsatisfactory, Munsell returned to printing. Within a few months he had established his own newspaper, the Albany *Minerva,* at the same time beginning the correspondence which enlarged his horizons and resulted in the magnificent collection of newspapers. While his newspaper was successful, Munsell soon discontinued it. It was actually a moonlighting operation, being printed in the publisher's spare time. For several years he worked in a number of establishments in Albany and in other cities. Finally he purchased the printing office in 1836 which was to become famous as Munsell's Press, while its proprietor became one of the important printers of his era.

July 20

"It is hoped that this humble attempt to bring to the knowledge of American readers, a quaint and beautiful little treatise upon a subject so interesting, written so many centuries ago, and by a man who played so distinguished a part in his time, as prelate, a statesman, and a scholar, will commend itself to our reading men, and that the faults of the editor may not have so far marred the author, as to preclude the former from at least toleration if not pardon, and the latter from a just appreciation. I shall have accomplished my highest wish in regard to the book, if I in any degree succeed in rescuing from comparative forgetfulness in these modern times, a performance so truly excellent and in its day so wonderful."

So wrote Samuel Hand in his preface to his translation of *Philobiblon* by Richard de Bury, in its first American edition, printed by Joel Munsell of Albany, New York on this day in 1861. The Hand translation is no longer considered to be a good one, although the fault is not primarily his but the corrupt Latin of his original source.

De Bury, born Richard Aungerville in 1287, had been tutor to the Prince of Wales, who later became Edward III. Noted for his learning, he became Bishop of Durham, and in 1334 was appointed Lord High Chancellor and Treasurer of England. It is said that a purchase of books from the library of the Abbot of St. Alban's so moved him that he wrote a treatise about books in 1344, the year before his death. This work, *Philobiblon, or the Love of Books,* is the earliest known essay on the subject, making its author the first bibliomaniac of record.

Philobiblon received its initial printing in Cologne in 1473 and has subsequently gone through numerous editions. The premier English translation was made by Thomas James, Bodley's first librarian at Oxford University in 1509 and printed by Joseph Barnes, who was the first Oxford printer to have the title of University Printer.

"In libras mortuos quasi vivos invenio: in libris futura praevideo," wrote de Bury. "In books we find the dead as it were living: in books we foresee things to come. . . . Towers are razed to the earth, cities overthrown, triumphal arches mouldered to dust; nor can the king or pope be found, upon whom the privilege of a lasting name can be conferred more easily than by books."

Munsell's edition contains the original Latin, printed on verso pages, with the translation on recto pages. It is quite typical of 19th century bookmaking, composed in a modern roman cleanly and neatly printed.

July 21

"Dear RR," wrote a distinguished designer of printer's typefaces on this day in 1937 to an equally distinguished graphic artist who was then working upon his first type design: "the way I work at present is to draw an alphabet 10 times 12-point size, with a pen or brush, the letters carefully finished."

The type designer was William Addison Dwiggins, long-time resident of Hingham, Massachusetts, one of America's finest craftsmen in all aspects of the production of print. RR was Rudolph Ruzicka, then pondering the design which resulted two years later in the splendid book type known as Fairfield. WAD was, as always, friendly and completely undogmatic concerning his own approach to the problems of creating a new type. Unlike many type designers who necessarily have to work closely with the technicians who are concerned with the purely mechanical problems of transfer from drawing to matrix, Dwiggins was always ready to redraw his letters to conform to the standards set up by the manufacturer. He was a practical man in all things.

The designer of a new type which is to be primarily useful for the printing of books must of course submerge any desire he might have to create a distinctively different roman letter. His task is not unlike that of the composer of music to accompany a motion picture; it must set the mood for the photoplay, and anything else is interference. Dwiggins' realization—and acceptance—of the type designer's role in this endeavor is evident in a paragraph of his letter to Ruzicka:

"Fitting is the process of working out the exactly right amount of space to go between letters. Each type-letter, wherever it goes, carries along with it two *fixed* blank spaces, one on each side. And of course, each of the 26 is likely to be placed alongside any of the other 25 with *their* fixed blank spaces. So the odds against you in the fitting game would seem to be 2704 to 1. (Would it be that, or 2500 to 1?)"

Never jealous of his artistic prerogatives, Dwiggins had no complaints to offer concerning the French curves and straight edges used by Linotype's staff. "They do a surprisingly careful job," he said. The inherent rightness of the Dwiggins' method is discernible in his achievement in the design of Electra and Caledonia, both of them currently among the most widely used book types. His dictum of sublimating his own personality to that of his designs is readily apparent in both of these types. There are no tricks or unusual characteristics. Indeed, the embryo typographer who relies on such features has a great deal of trouble in trying to remember either type and must learn to recognize them by the effect they have when combined into words upon the printed page. There could really be no more fitting tribute to pay to a type with the necessary qualifications for subtly transferring an author's mind to that of the reader.

Born into a family of clothiers in Rochester, New York on this day in 1884, Elmer Adler proceeded slowly to the printer's craft, taking thirty-six years to become involved in a printing office. But at his death in San Juan, Puerto Rico in 1962, he was counted among a small group of men who have made a singular contribution to that craft during the present century.

Adler was unmotivated by a succession of schools during his youth, and failing to receive the formal recognition of a diploma from any of them, he found himself in the family business, handling advertising and promotion. From this exposure to the world of print he developed an interest in books and with an inherent sense of good taste gravitated toward those volumes which were most representative of the art of the printer.

In 1922 he abandoned the apparel business and established in New York City a unique printing firm, the Pynson Printers. This company for a period of eighteen years produced a wide range of distinguished printing, encompassing books, promotional pieces, announcements, and all the ephemera of the commercial printer, with one basic difference from that of the competitive firms in New York. And that was the fact that Adler was more than simply a printer—in fact, he had a horror of becoming merely a manufacturer of the printed word.

During this period Adler also became the guiding spirit behind the publication of the bibliographic quarterly, *The Colophon,* a periodical more in demand today for both its content and fine printing than it was during its palmiest days. In 1940 both the periodical and the Pynson Printers were terminated, and Adler began a third career—one that was probably closest to his heart, that of teaching.

From 1940 to 1952 Elmer Adler was the central figure in an extracurricular study group at Princeton University which was primarily concerned with the graphic arts. The seminars he conducted during this period became a notable feature of campus life and attracted many students who later became connected with publishing and printing.

Three years after his retirement from Princeton he accepted an invitation to visit

Puerto Rico to help upgrade book design and printing on that island. With his usual enthusiasm Adler established a museum in a dilapidated building which he completely restored and named Casa del Libro. Under his guidance this museum became the foremost library specializing in the art of the book to exist in this hemisphere outside of the United States and has become a suitable memorial to a man who throughout a long life insisted that good taste be the governing factor, no matter what career he followed.

July 23

Here lyes the Daye that darkness
    could no blind
When Papish fogges had overcaste
    the sunne,
This Daye the cruelle nighte did
    leave behind
To view, and show what blodi actes
    were donne
He set a Fox to wright how martyrs runne
By Death to lyfe. Fox ventured
    paynes and health
To give them light: Day spent in
    print his wealth,
But God with gayne returned his
    wealth agayne
And gave to him as he gave to the poore.
Two wyves he had, partakers of
    his payne,
Each wyf twelve babes and each of
    them one more:
Als [Alice] was the last increaser
    of his store
Who mourning long for being left alone,
Set up his tombe, herself turn'd
    to a stone.
            Obit July 23, 1584

As prolific out of bed as in, John Day was the great English printer of his time. Born in 1522 he was apprenticed to Thomas Reynolds and by 1546 was operating a printing office in St. Sepulchre's parish of London with William Seres. Fortunately he enjoyed the patronage of Matthew Parker, Archbishop of Canterbury, for whom he produced a number of books. In 1472 he printed on His Grace's own press *De Antiquitate Britaniccae Ecclisae,* written by Parker, believed to be the earliest privately printed book produced in England.

July 24

On this day in 1520 Henri Estienne, the elder, died. It is not known when he was first established as a printer, but about 1496, just twenty-six years after the first press came to France, his name begins to appear on scholarly books. During his lifetime, he published over one hundred of these, all of them in Latin, none being printed in the vernacular. Thus was begun one of the great houses of printing, to remain in one family for almost one hundred and fifty years. The name Estienne has frequently been latinized to Stephanus and even more to the plain English Stephens.

The founder of the house is reputed to have been a man of noble birth who became alienated from his parents when he became excited about the new art of printing. The difficulties encountered by printers in the early years were innumerable, particularly in France, where the Faculty of the Sorbonne dominated the printing of books. The family of Estienne was for many years to suffer persecution at the hands of this body which questioned what it thought to be heretical tendencies. Possibly the elder Estienne incurred doubts when he asked Jacques Le Fevre to act as one of the press correctors. Le Fevre is known as the teacher of Calvin, and while his intellectual merits were recognized, his faith was open to question. But for François I, who interceded for him, his life would have been in jeopardy. The king was increasingly involved in such controversies, as his liberal views brought him into conflict with the Theological Doctors who with the influence of the Papacy eventually prevailed over the royal opinions.

However Estienne's obvious talents as a scholarly printer brought him a great deal of work from the University of Paris, whose coat of arms he used as a device. The famous Estienne press mark of the olive tree was not to be used until his son Robert became proprietor of the press after his father's death. Henri's standards built his reputation, but they were sometimes beyond the capabilities of even the brilliant men he used to read his texts. The celebrated German humanist, Beatus Rhenanus, friend and biographer of Erasmus, was discharged by Estienne for permitting errors to pass his eye. The printer argued that his imprint should be a guarantee for a trustworthy text and that any typographical error would discredit him as a publisher.

Upon the death of the founder of the firm, his foreman Simon de Colines became the guardian of his children and his executor. Colines, who was a fine printer, married the widow and to use the expression of Estienne's biographer, Mark Pattison, *"afin de s'eviter l'embarras d'une liquidation."* Robert Estienne, who was seventeen years of age when his father died and who was to become the most celebrated printer of his family, received his early training from his father. He was immeasurably helped by Colines who had the scholarly attributes so necessary in classical printing.

July 25

The first issue of a periodical called *Humors of a Coffee House* appeared upon this date in London in 1707, published "for the benefit of a black coffee man called Bohee."

The "coffee break" is thus of ancient lineage, as proved by this publication and others similar to it during the 18th century. Prior to the days of regularly published newspapers, the London coffee houses were the centers of informed opinions on the happenings of the times. All of them subscribed to the current newsletters, which they in turn made available to their patrons, and in addition they frequently housed very adequate libraries of books.

In 1728 the foremost coffee house engaged in a protracted quarrel with the proprietors of the newspapers concerning the pirating of news supplied by the coffee houses. There was even a threat on the part of the coffee men to publish their own newspapers. They stated that it was their responsibility to supply London with news "from the stores of intelligence" in their own hands.

They further accused the newspaper owners of employing men "to haunt coffee houses and thrust themselves into companies" where they were not known so that they could eavesdrop on the conversation. These persons, it was stated, loitered about "like housebreakers, waiting for an interview with some little clerk, or a conference with a doorkeeper in order to come at a little news or

an account of transactions; for which the fee is a shilling or a pint of wine."

The scouts were also charged with "neglecting business all day by playing cribbage in an ale house, and having no news, had recourse to fiction, drawing up treaties, hanging for love, and drowning for despair, telling of deaths, robberies and revolutions, and turning the world upside down." In all, a slate of crimes for which every succeeding generation of newsmen has been indicted.

Since advertisements were becoming commonplace in the newspapers, the coffee men took further umbrage against this source of profit to the papers. One of them disparaged this practice in print by stating, "Another complaint the coffee men have against the proprietors of the present newspapers is that they are made tools and properties of in the business of advertising. They stipulate for news, not advertisements. Yet the papers are ordinarily half-full of them. The *Daily Post,* for example, is often equipped with thirty, which yield three pounds fifteen shillings that day to the proprietors for the least. And sometimes that paper has more. Well, may they divide *twelve hundred pounds a year and upwards!* They are paid on both hands—paid by the advertisers for taking in Advertisements and paid by the coffee men for delivering them out; which (to make use of a homely comparison) is to have a good dinner every day and be paid for eating it. Here's luck, my lads. Never was there so fortunate a business."

The coffee house in later years took two directions. It either raised itself to the elegance of a club, or it deteriorated to what American newspapermen would call the gin-mill. Certainly it is to the tune of clinking ice that a great deal of contemporary news is gathered, with the coffee being ordered only when it's time to meet the deadline.

July 26

On his day in 1775 the Second Continental Congress took action upon the report of a "Committee to consider the best means of establishing Posts for conveying Letters and Intelligence through this Continent." Thus was the first publicly-owned American postal system set up in opposition to that of the

British government. However, the role of the colonial printers in the formation of the postal system seems to have been relegated to the footnotes in many standard histories.

During the colonial period the printer in each locality was a man of affairs, particularly if he held the title of "Publick Printer." As publishers of newspapers these men invariably frequented the sessions of the various colonial governments, and of course gathered at first hand news of all the important events taking place. With thirteen different local governing bodies enacting legislation, there was a great deal of printing to be done in order to acquaint the public with the debates, votes, and proceedings stemming from each session. The printer thus became involved in all of the important decisions being made in his locality. In addition to carrying out the responsibility of printing the proceedings, he also interpreted them through the columns of his newspaper.

Many of the colonial printers also found it most advantageous to be postmaster for their localities. This office gave them at first hand access to all the important correspondence coming into their areas, which naturally enough provided newsworthy material for their journals. Then, the post office was a busy meeting-place in any town, which simplified the problems of newspaper distribution. And possibly most important of all, the postmaster/publisher was enabled to send out his sheet without cost via the post riders and to deny this service to all of his competitors.

The first American newspaper to be regularly published, the *Boston News-Letter,* was produced by John Campbell, who was both "Publick Printer" and postmaster. It is recorded that succeeding postmasters actually believed that the newspaper went along with the office. In 1734 *The Boston Weekly Post-Boy* bore the imprint:

"Boston: Printed for Ellis Huske, Post-Master: Advertisements taken in at the Post-Office in King's Street, over against the North-Door of the Town-House, where all Persons in Town or Country may be supplied with this Paper."

When Benjamin Franklin became the Philadelphia Postmaster in 1734 there were no established regulations for carrying newspapers by mail. He admitted the advantages: "It facilitated the correspondence that improv'd my newspaper, increas'd the num- ber demanded, as well as the advertisements to be inserted, so that it came to afford me a considerable income. My old competitor's newspaper declin'd proportionably."

July 27

A rested and refreshed crew reported back to the San Francisco printing office of John Henry Nash on the morning of this day in 1926. Nash's customers were informed in a notice sent out some weeks previously that, "Everybody in the shop wanted to go fishing & they all wanted to go at the same time, so I've decided to shut up shop until they all get back. The place will be closed from the *tenth of July* to the *twenty-sixth.* This is not the usual way of arranging vacations but what else can you do when the folks you work with through the year develop decided notions about the proper time to go fishing? If it seems unbusinesslike to shut up shop for two weeks, I can only say that business is not everything. But having a certain amount of native caution, I do hope that Herbert Fleishhacker will not hold this thing against me if I ever ask him for a big loan.—John Henry Nash, Printer, San Francisco."

In 8-point italic along the bottom of the notice was printed, "I myself am not going, I'll be in the library every day from nine till four."

The footnote perhaps explains the position of Nash as one of the fine printers of his time, one to whom time in a library was more fun than just fishing.

Born near Toronto, Canada in 1871, John Henry Nash left high school to become a printer's apprentice when he was sixteen years old and remained in Canada until his twenty-third year. At that time he went to Denver for a year before finally establishing himself in San Francisco, where he remained for most of his life. Nash became associated with the bookseller Paul Elder, who had established a small publishing business and needed a printer to take charge of it.

In 1916 he organized his own firm, and since he was a complete individualist, this move was undoubtedly in his own best interest. He was then most fortunate in becoming involved in printing a catalogue of the library of Charles W. Clark, the wealthy son of Senator William Andrew Clark, the Montana copper king. From this point Nash's career prospered and within a dozen years he was styled the "Aldus of San Francisco," not at all an apt title, as his best books were all large quartos and folios whereas the Aldine books were smaller in format. Perhaps the title of "San Francisco Bodoni" would have been more appropriate, as Nash was served by Clark as the Italian printer by the Duke of Parma.

Probably the best of the Nash books was the four volume Dante, which took four years to complete and has been called one of the great American books. Nash preferred to dispense with illustration, allowing the pure typography to set the pattern, in the manner of Cobden-Sanderson in England whom he greatly admired. Many of his books have an austerity which makes them rather cold, but they are splendid examples of the printer's art. Nash was strictly a compositor, the presswork being performed by another printer under Nash's strict control. His books had none of the warmth which designers such as Bruce Rogers and W. A. Dwiggins managed to instill in their work. Nevertheless Nash must be considered one of the fine printers this country has produced.

July 28

In the office of the Washington *Republican,* a typesetting contest was held on this day in 1874. The first prize was a gold composing stick, with a silver stick to be presented for second. It is to be doubted, however, that the successful type stickers actually put their gold and silver sticks to actual use, probably preferring to prop them up proudly in the family dining room china closet.

The composing stick has a long history as a primary printer's tool, but that history is not very well documented. The writers of many of the earlier manuals apparently took the stick for granted and rarely mentioned it other than in a description of typesetting procedures.

Johann Gutenberg must have had to devise such a tool, just as he had to conceive the press with which to impress his types, but there is no mention of the composing stick in the accounts of his printing office. The earliest known illustration of a stick was printed in Lyons, France in 1499 in the *Dance of Death.* The stick shown appears to be approximately the same length as its contemporary model—about ten inches—and was constructed of wood, from which, no doubt, came the name of the tool.

During the next two centuries there were other illustrations of compositors at work, but until the publication of the *Mechanick Exercises* of Joseph Moxon in 1683, there was no actual description of the composing stick. Moxon states that the sticks of his period were made of iron plate, ten inches long, and were perforated with several holes in order to adjust them to various measures. It is not known when the adjustable stick was adopted. The earliest sticks were cut to accommodate but one single measure. Until the 20th century such sticks were still available.

A good compositor insists that his composing stick be accurate. Two hundred years ago the comp was also concerned about this factor. Moxon notes: "Compositors commonly examine the Truth of the Stick by applying the head of the Sliding-Measure to the inside of the Head of the Stick; and if they comply, they think they are square and true made." The stick described by Moxon was in use with few variations until the 19th century. One of the modifications was a slot along the side of the stick for adjustment in place of the holes. Another innovation was the substitution of a thumb screw for the slotted screw which required a screw driver for adjustment.

The year 1810 saw the introduction of the first known steel stick, fitted with a slotted side and a thumb screw for adjustment. In 1855 Oliver Grover, of Middleton, Connecticut, patented the first stick with a knee-action clamp which became extremely popular with the swifts of the period and which is still the most widely used style of composing stick. In 1860 a Syracuse, New York printer named Steve Brown invented a stick which was marketed by the A. and B. Newbury Company and which was called the Newbury. When the firm went out of business the stick was adopted by English printers and was no longer available in the United States. About thirty years later a comp traveling in Europe saw a Newbury, and so admired it that he brought it home. With a few changes he had it patented under the name of Buckeye stick. It is still in fairly common use.

July 29

The typographical equivalent of the one-armed paper hanger is undoubtedly the left-handed compositor, and for five centuries the term has been one of derision. "How many readers of *The Inland Printer*," asked Sam G. Sloane in 1888, "ever saw a left-handed typesetter? By this I mean a typesetter who picks up the types, places them in the composing stick and spaces out the lines, all with his 'sinister paw'?"

Apparently the idea was so novel that Sam went out of his way to look for such a person, and reported that he had found one. Born on this day in 1856 on a farm in Coles County, Illinois, was C. S. Glassco, who was to achieve national recognition as a left-handed comp. Glassco lost his right hand in a farm accident when but five years of age. After attending college in Greencastle, Indiana and Ann Arbor, Michigan, he became an apprentice compositor in the office of the Journal in Tuscola, Illinois in 1874. After employment in a number of mid-western weekly newspapers, he returned to Tuscola as the foreman of the *Saturday Journal* office.

Glassco had developed the ability to set type at an average speed of 7,000 ems per day and had accomplished as much as 13,-500 ems in a ten-hour period, which was above average production for even the right-handed swifts of the period. Most modern compositors would find it beyond their ability to maintain such a speed.

Lacking a good right hand, Glassco held the composing stick in the crook of his right arm and notwithstanding his handicap, managed to compose justified lines of type with apparent ease. He was equally skilled in distribution, holding several lines in his elbow in the same manner as the composing stick. He was particularly proud of the fact that he could handle any length of line as well as a two-handed comp.

Apparently the idea of a left-handed compositor was anathema to most employing printers, as at no time has there been any demand for composing sticks suitable for the lefty, although individuals may have constructed their own. Certainly manufacturers of printer's tools have never offered such an item for sale. Compositor Glassco managed to get along with the standard stick, and so have—by necessity—all the rest of the port-handers. The left-handed composing stick thus remains an elusive article, which almost every composing room apprentice has learned to his chagrin when, during his first days on the job, he was sent to fetch one, along with a paper stretcher and the box of dots for the lowercase "i."

July 30

In 1894 a letter bearing this date was written by an English gentlemen named William Morris, using as his address, Kelmscott House:

My Dear Cockerell

I have to be at court to-morrow before 10 in order to be the first witness examined; so I shall probably miss you, and I shall probably not be back here till next Monday: so I leave these instructions.

Open all letters and send on those that *need* immediate answer or which might please me.

Let me know how the sales are going on Thursday. Kindly take the Huntingfield to Quaritch in a day or two. I have told him that I am not going to buy it.

I got three hours off the dangling this morning and called on Quaritch and told him about the Chaucer and that I was going to publish it myself: he was not surprised, but on my asking him how much he had sold produced a list of 43 sold to private persons, remarking, as was true, that the trade would probably transfer their orders to us. Finally he ordered 50 at 25 per cent discount, which I agreed to. Please write and acknowledge this order.

The number of the Chaucer is to be 325 paper, and 13 (or 14?) vellum. The price £20, done up in boards like *The Golden Legend*. Having gone over the number of lines with Ellis, I find it will not make more than 600 pages, which will go into one volume.

When I come back I shall bring the corrected hymn book sheets. I want Bowden to have everything ready to begin the Chaucer on *Monday:* I shall be disappointed if he cannot do this.

If Bowden wants anything settled you must settle it, please, on your own responsibility. Send me on James if he writes.

This is all I can think of.

Yours ever
W.M.

The Chaucer, the fortieth book printed at the Kelmscott Press, became in the words of one writer, "not only William Morris's monument, [but] it can stand, with the Albert Memorial and the Forth Bridge, as a memorial of the virility of the Victorians."

The book, of which 425 copies on paper were printed, was in the making one year and nine months. As a representation of the art and craft of printing it is a magnificent work. As a readable book it is of course something else again, but this is neither here nor there. It is almost inconceivable that any printer could examine a Kelmscott Chaucer and not be beside himself with admiration for the quality of the printing and be enthused enough to attempt to emulate it.

The £20 price was a splendid bargain, too. Currently a paper copy "done up in boards" would cost a collector $1250 to $1600. The vellum of which fourteen copies were printed at one hundred and twenty guineas could also be considered reasonable in price as it is now offered at $6,500 to $10,000, although the price has gone as high as $12,500.

July 31

In the Prologue to the edition of Malory's *Morte d'Arthur*, completed upon this last day of July in 1485, its printer, William Caxton wrote:

"After I had accomplysshed & Fynsshed dyvers hystoryes as wel of contemplacyon as of other hystorycal and worldly actes of grete conquerors & prynces, And also certeyn bookes of ensaumples and doctryne, Many noble and dyvers gentylmen of thys royame of England camen and demaunded me many and aftymes, wherfore that I have not do made & enprynte the noble hystorye of the saynt greal, and of the mosst renomed crysten Kyng . . . Kyng Arthur . . . ."

William Caxton, the first English printer, was a well-to-do merchant who had spent almost thirty years abroad, most of this time in the Low Countries. He was also a man of letters who found recreation in the translation of classics into English. He became interested in the young art of printing during a visit to Cologne, where he actually became involved in the production of a book. Upon his return to his home in Bruges, he completed a translation of a French work, *Recuyell of the Historyes of Troy,* in order that the English-born Duchess of Burgundy could read it. The translation, in manuscript, was so popular at the Burgundian court that Caxton set up a press with which to supply copies.

This book, produced with the aid of the Bruges printer Colard Mansion, became the first book to be printed in English. It is set in a blackletter type, probably of Flemish origin. It has been stated that the style is based upon the handwriting of Mansion who had been a calligrapher prior to taking up printing. William Blades, the authority on Caxton, has mentioned that there were so many ligatures that only five letters in the font had but one matrix. When Caxton returned to England in 1476, the type was not brought with him.

The first press in England was set up at Westminster. For many years it was believed that the first book to be printed was *The Dictes or Sayengis of the Philosophres,* which was completed in 1477, but an indulgence was discovered in 1928 which has been authoritatively ascribed to Caxton. The date on this indulgence, of which but a single copy is known, is December 13, 1476, making it the first English imprint.

The type of many of the Caxton books is a *lettre batarde,* derived from a Burgundian copy of the French national hand of the period. Used by Caxton, it is not at all distinguished, as the Westminster printer was much more concerned with the contents of his books than in their printing. His press used eight different types, all of them being of the form which in Europe is called gothic, but which in the United States is termed blackletter or textletter. Three of these are pointed blackletter, familiar in Northern Europe as the *lettre de forme,* or Textura. The books printed in these types are much superior to those in which the earlier letters were used.

Probably the best known book produced by Caxton is *The Canterbury Tales* of Goeffrey Chaucer, the first printing of which took place in 1478. It is fitting indeed that one of the great English classics also became a renowned addition to English incunabula in its first printing.

August

In the self-deprecating manner of the 19th century writer, one Thomas Hodgson wrote in the introductory chapter of *An Essay on the Origin and Progress of Stereotype Printing,* published this day in 1820:

"The Writer of the following pages can lay claim to little merit beyond that of collecting, into one publication, a variety of information, which either lay scattered in different works, or was unknown to the generality of English readers. Whilst pursuing some enquiries nearly connected with this subject, it struck him as singular, that whilst almost every other branch of the typographic art had been the subject of so much curious research and minute description, Stereotype Printing, notwithstanding the public curiosity it has of late years excited, should never yet have been fully and accurately described,—and that so great a want of information, with respect to its history, and to the nature of its processes, should prevail, not only amongst the generality of the public, but also amongst those writers, who have spoken of it incidentally, or treated it more professedly."

Stereotyping, now as solidly respectable in the printing industry as type itself, was at that period in the position of computer typesetting in the 1960's—accepted by a few, questioned by many, and condemned by everyone else.

Hodgson, in his fair and balanced treatise, was not quite willing to accept the findings of the promoters of the new process. "Having traced," he wrote, "the progress of stereotype printing from its first origin to the present time, when it appears to have attained so great a degree of perfection, it only remains to enquire, whether these advantages, with which the practice of the art was so confidently expected to be attended, have been derived from it. . . . Experience, however, I am afraid, has shewn that these advantages have at least been greatly overrated."

The opinionated J. Johnson, in his very popular two-volume *Typographia* of 1824, not only didn't approve of the new process, but he was willing to shout the fact from the house-tops: "It appears that the invention of Stereotype, like that of Printing, is somewhat involved in mystery; . . . but, we conceive that its author is not worth the pains of our tracing; and more particularly when we reflect, that so many of our brethen who well deserve (from their ability) a comfortable subsistence, and who ought to be enabled (from their profession) to move in a respectable sphere of life, are now, through this process, reduced to a very humble pittance, thereby bringing the first Art in the world down to a level with the lowest; and, at one season of the year, nearly one half of the valuable body of men alluded to may be considered as totally destitute of employ, on account of the standard works, which was the summer's stock work, having been Stereotyped."

As late as 1838 here in the United States Thomas Adams, in his manual, *Typographia,* echoes some of Johnson's sentiments, but in the third edition of his work, published in 1845, he says, "In all cases of book work where a small edition only will be required, it is best to print from types, and then distribute them: but in most cases of standard works or books published in parts, or numbers, stereotyping becomes absolutely necessary."

August 2

"Bibliotheca Moresiana: A Catalogue of the Large and Valuable Library of Printed Books, Rare old Tracts, Manuscripts, Prints and Drawings, Copper Plates, sundry Antiquities, Philosophical Instruments, and other Curiosities, of that eminent British Antiquary the late Rev. and learned Edward Rowe Mores, F.A.S., deceased."

Thus began the title page of Catalogue No. 17 of Auctioneer Paterson, describing the sale to be held at his Great Room, No. 6, King Street, Covent-Garden, London on this day in 1779. There were some 3,000 items catalogued, with a strong emphasis upon antiquities. The surprising thing about Mores' library was that it contained relatively few books about printing, although he was the owner of a typefoundry and had done a considerable amount of research into that art. Auctioned with the library was the entire edition (eighty copies) of the unpublished *A Dissertation upon English Typographical Founders and Founderies,* written by Mores and completed just before his death in 1779.

Talbot Baines Reed in his work on English typefounding called Mores "a learned and eccentric antiquary and scholar," a viewpoint which has been echoed by Daniel B. Updike in his Notes to the first reprint of the *Dissertation,* published in 1924 for the Grolier Club. Both of these opinions have been further substantiated in the excellent and scholarly introduction to the edition edited in 1961 by Harry Carter and Christopher Ricks for the Oxford University Press.

The important contribution to our knowledge of early English types made by Mores came through his purchase of the typefoundry of John James at the latter's death in 1772. The punches and matrices of the James Foundry, some of them dating back to the days of Wynkyn de Worde and John Day in the 16th century, were completely unorganized. It may be that this factor alone excited the interest of Mores who had been investigating, with a true antiquarian's ardor, the history of English printing for some years. The fulfillment of these desires came about with the opportunity to catalogue the materials of the James Foundry. Mores threw himself into the task, producing a work which has been criticized for its many imperfections but which must be recognized as an important contribution in its field.

August 3

A Belfast Orangeman named Hugh Gaine on this day in 1752 published the first issue of *The New York Mercury,* a newspaper which established a unique first in American journalism by simultaneously publishing in two locations, each with its own political philosophy. When he arrived in New York in 1745, upon the completion of his apprenticeship in Belfast, Gaine was just eighteen years of age. He was employed by James Parker for $1.25 a week. Later his bed and board was added, prompting him to remain with Parker until 1752. Then he left to establish his own printing office. The fifth number of the *Mercury* contained a statement in which its editor said: "By Hugh Gaine at his Printing-Office on Hunter's Key, next Door to Mr. Walton's Storehouse, where all persons may be supplied with the paper at Twelve Shillings per annum, and Advertisements of a moderate Length inserted at Five Shillings each; Also, Printing done at a reasonable Rate, with care and Expedition."

The success of the sheet was immediate. Within four months Gaine was announcing that subscriptions were being taken in such distant locations as Lime, Connecticut, Philadelphia, and Elizabeth-Town, New Jersey. While the paper prospered, Gaine was not content to be merely the publisher of a weekly news sheet. He added such items as almanacs and bibles and other books in such variety and volume as to become the most prolific printer of his time. Among American first editions printed by Gaine were *Robinson Crusoe* and the initial New York printing of the New Testament. Apparently finding that even this activity was not sufficient to keep him busy, he took on the sale of military supplies, such as broadswords, musical instruments, clothing, furniture, and all the goods which accompany the operation of a general store. And as a sideline he sold the always profitable patent medicines.

When the notorious Stamp Act was passed, Gaine suspended the *Mercury,* publishing an occasional paper which he named *A Patriotic Advertisement.* Politically he leaned toward the Colonial cause but in print hewed to the neutral line. In September, 1775 when the British occupation of New York appeared imminent, he had one of his presses and a quantity of types hauled to Newark, where he began publication of a paper, *The New York Gazette and the Weekly Mercury.* In it he ardently supported the Whig persuasion, while at the same time remaining neutral in the New York paper. In such fashion he straddled the fence until November, 1776 when, following the Battle of Long Island, he became convinced that the British would suppress the American rebellion. Ceasing the printing of the Whig sheet, he confined his activities to New York and espoused the loyalist beliefs.

It was during this same year that Gaine published a book which became notorious. *Military Collections and Remarks* was written by a British Army major named Robert Donkin and contained a passage which has subsequently been cut out of all known copies but one. Donkin wrote, in reference to instruction in the use of the Indian bows and arrows, "Dip arrows in matter of small pox, and twang them at the American rebels, in order to innoculate them; This would sooner disband these stubborn, ignorant, enthusiastic savages, than any other compulsive measures. Such is their dread and fear of that disorder!"

August 4

The United States Patent Office granted this day in 1845 to Thomas W. Starr of Philadelphia a patent upon "an improved formation of the matrix for casting the face of type, borders, and cuts therein, by means of a type, or cut, and a metallic plate, with an opening in the matrix with slanting sides. Thus prepared, it is placed in a solution of copper, and connected with the pole of a galvanic battery, in the same manner as practiced in electrotyping, and after receiving a sufficient deposit of copper is fitted up for use."

Starr's patent was directed to the New York typefoundry of James Conner, one-time stereotyper and Grand Sachem of Tammany Hall. Until the development of the electrolysis in matrix manufacture, it had been necessary to cut each type character in a steel punch which drives the matrix. This entailed laborious work requiring great skill. The basic idea behind Starr's invention was to cut a character in soft type metal and then use the electrotype shell of this letter as a matrix with which to cast type duplicates.

It didn't take the two dozen existing American typefounders very long to realize that it would be just as simple to duplicate each other's types, particularly those which were in popular demand. Very quickly "similar" types began to appear in the various specimen books. And of course the European typefounders were fair game. As the 19th century witnessed the birth and development of the book and job printer, the founders had not been slow in meeting the demand for an ever widening variety of type styles. The period is looked back upon today as being one of excess in the development of new letter forms. Starr's patent simplified the printing of designs and significantly stifled individual contributions to purer letter forms.

Prior to 1870 the European type designers set the pattern. Such types as the sans serif of William Caslon IV, first shown in 1816, and the slab serifed faces which were called Clarendons and Egyptians, were extremely popular and widely copied in the United States. During the last thirty years of the last century the American type designers came into their own, producing types of kaleidoscopic variety.

During the 1960's the display types of the previous century have received a revival in advertising typography. The metal types themselves have not been re-introduced but have been made available as film alphabets. Doubtless the revival will be simply a fad and the circus types will again become the property of the specialized collectors.

August 5

An edition of two thousand copies of the L'Estrange translation of *Seneca's Morals* was delivered on August 5, 1817 to the New York bookseller, Evert Duyckinck. At the foot of the title page of this volume was the imprint, "J. & J. Harper, printers," representing the first use in any book of one of the famous names in American publishing.

Just seven years previously a sixteen year old Long Island farm boy named James Harper completed his reading of the *Autobiography of Benjamin Franklin* and at once informed his parents that he wished to be a printer. Agreeing with his youthful decision, the senior Harper made arrangements with a New York printer, Abraham Paul, to take the boy as an apprentice. Thus on a wintry December day in 1810, the Harpers, father and son, climbed on the farm wagon and journeyed via the Post Road to Brooklyn Heights, at which point they were rowed across the East River to Manhattan. Here James began his notable career as printer and publisher.

New York City at that time had a population of 96,000 living in an area which stretched from Battery Park to Chambers Street, north of which were swamps and farmland. Thirty-four years later the fledgling printer was mayor of the city, which had expanded northward as far as Fourteenth Street and had grown to a city of 350,000 people. In the first years of his indentures, James Harper, fresh off the farm, was subject to a great deal of ridicule from the city-bred apprentices, his mode of dressing being a particular source of fun. Eugene Exman, the biographer of the Harper Brothers, recounts an early incident relating to Harper's problems during his apprentice days. One of his tormentors made a sardonic remark in praise of James's trousers and asked him for the card of his tailor. "That's my card," Harper replied as he implanted a flat-soled kick on the seat of the other's pants. "Take good care of it! When I am out of my time, and set up for myself, and you need employment, as you will, come to me, bring the card, and I will give you work." Forty-one years later a man claiming to have received this unique "card" called at the Harper establishment and asked James to redeem it, which he did, immediately.

Within the next few years, John and Wesley Harper, the younger brothers of James, also apprenticed themselves as printers. When James became a journeyman, he and John discussed starting their own business and began to save their money toward that goal. Early in 1817 they had accumulated $500. With the assistance of their father, who had mortgaged his farm, they rented the second floor of a small frame house at Front and Dover streets. Even as an apprentice James had a single-purposed ambition, which was to see his name at the foot of the title page of a book.

By 1825, a fourth brother, Fletcher, became a partner. By then the firm was employing fifty persons and was operating ten presses, making it the largest printing office in New York. By 1830 J. & J. Harper was the largest book printing establishment in the United States. In 1833 the firm became known as Harper & Brothers, a name which was retained until 1962 when a merger made it Harper & Rowe.

August 6

That the craft of printing in the California of 1849 was every bit as bounteous as prospecting for gold is obvious from the account of the establishment of the *Pacific News* which appeared in *The Pacific Printer, Stationer and Lithographer* in 1884:

"Thirty-five years ago on the 6th of August, there arrived in the harbor of San Francisco the good ship *Prescott*—good ship metaphorically or poetically, for the ship *Prescott* was anything but a good ship, the best proof of which being she had taken 195 days to make the passage from the port of Mystic, Connecticut to San Francisco. The ship had been at anchor but a few hours before it was well known that included in its freight was a complete printing establishment—in short, all that had been necessary to publish a newspaper in the town of Norwich, Connecticut. The press was a No. 3 Washington. In connection with the material was the lumber for a two-story building, already framed, large and conveniently arranged. Twenty reams of 24 x 36 news paper had been brought, supposing that would last until supplies could be had.

"The owner of the office, who had exhausted his money in paying passage for himself and his two sons, and necessary freight, landed the next day with but a few dimes; but soon after landing he was eagerly sought after. At that time the *Alta California,* a foolscap sheet, and the only periodical, was being published. Another paper was much desired, and soon the owner of the press was met by parties who immediately offered $10,000 for the old hand press and stock of type. He had sufficient sagacity to see that if the parties could give this for his office, that perhaps he could soon make it and more, so declined to sell. They then offered, if he would publish a paper in the interests that they wished, they would loan him $10,000 and give a lot on which to put the building. As the interests to be advocated exactly coincided with his ideas, he accepted this offer, and the money was placed in the bank, material landed, building erected on Kearney street, between Jackson and Pacific, and the first week in September, 1849, appeared the *Pacific News,* a tri-weekly 24 x 36.

"A steamer paper was published each month, and on the day of publication a line of people, reaching from Washington street to the counter, would eagerly buy the paper at one dollar a copy. The supply of paper was soon exhausted. Every vessel was boarded as soon as she came in to look for supplies. One edition was printed on manila paper, and another by laying four sheets of foolscap on the form. The first month the $10,000 borrowed was returned. Jobbing was done to the capacity of the office, and Wm. Dunn made for the owner a foolscap hand press, for which he was paid $500.

"Chas. Eames, Ferdinand Ewer, Bayard Taylor, and others composed the staff of editors. Warren Leland, who had become a partner, was a business man, although he sold out his interest the first of January 1850, and off what he had made was enabled to start the Metropolitan Hotel in New York. Printers received in those days $100 and $150 per week, and had bunks in the office."

August 7

Printers have ever been quick to dissent from prevailing acceptance of unsophisticated promotion; thus typo Charles H. Gard of Chicago followed tradition when he took pen in hand and placed tongue in cheek on this day in 1890 to write to the editor of a printer's trade publication:

"I clip the following from the *Printer's Album and Electrotyper,* May, 1890, issue, page 18: 'One of our western agents writes us as follows: One of our town customers has had a peculiar accident, which I must tell you. Belt came down to the press from the ceiling of second story and was caught on set screw, and wound up and drew the whole press up and through the second floor before the belt broke, and down came the machine with a crash. Inside of thirty minutes after the accident happened we had the parts on the cars, on the way to replace those broken, having had one of your presses in stock from which we took these parts to ship to our customer. The next mail brought the following: "Every part fitted just to a dot," which speaks well for the interchangeableness of your presses.'

"Very queer! Did the customer or the press have the accident? The writer does not inform us that 'belt which came down' ever went up again, nor does he tell whether the press boy went up with the machine, or not. He forgets to tell us how many nicely colored cards were printed during the ascent and descent, and he forgets to tell us just how many splinters the press made of the upper floor going up or the lower floor coming down. We know of no comparison to such an accident on record, save Jules Verne's vehicle that took him to the moon and return. The writer should inform the waiting typographic multitude whether the press boy threw out the press dog or the monkey-wrench when the anti-gravitation point was reached, and if due astronomical observations were made enroute. Pending the arrival of above explanations, must we not doubt the accuracy of this last rise in printing machinery, without the usual thirty-and five off for cash?"

August 8

"To the Right Reverend Father in GOD, JOHN Lord Bishop of *Oxford,* and Dean of *Christ-Church;* And to the Right Honourable Sir LEOLINE JENKINS Knight, and Principal Secretary of State; And to the Right Honourable Sir JOSEPH WILLIAMSON Knight; and one of his Majesties most Honourable Privy-Council." Thus began a book about printing, written by Joseph

Moxon, Member of the Royal Society, and Hydrographer to the King's Most Excellent Majesty, who was born this day in 1627.

The book, entitled *Mechanick Exercises: Or, the Doctrine of Handy Works. Applied to the Art of Printing,* was in two volumes and was published in 1683. It was the first book ever written on the subject, some two hundred and twenty years after the invention of the art.

Moxon was a maker of mathematical instruments who also for a short period was a typefounder. This experience, in addition to the fact that his brother was a printer, no doubt acquainted him with the craft. In 1677 he set about to write and publish a series of monthly pamphlets on "the doctrine of handi-works," beginning with the "Smiths, the joyners, the carpenters, and the turner's trades," and finally the craft of the printer.

As the first printer's manual, Moxon's book naturally set the pace, and for two hundred years every other manual to be written was patterned upon his treatise. Some of them were actually copied verbatim, and others simply by rewording. The later writers sometimes acknowledged their debt to Moxon, but several did not. The fact that Moxon's material was as pertinent to the 19th century printers as to those of the 17th century is indicative of the progress, or rather the lack of it, made by the industry in the ensuing years.

The original two-volume edition is naturally enough one of the most desirable books for printers to own should they also happen to be book collectors. Of the three hundred printed, only fifty-three are now known to exist. Thirty-two of these are in the United States and one in Canada, the balance being in Europe.

The first reprint was that of Theodore L. De Vinne who produced an edition for the Grolier Club in 1896, following the original exactly. In 1958 Herbert Davis and Henry Carter edited a much needed reprint, published by Oxford University Press. This edition, authoritatively annotated, is a splendid piece of work which was much desired by all students of typography.

Oddly enough, the publisher of this edition limited the printing in the belief that the work would not sell rapidly, but the current interest in Moxon was sufficient to exhaust the edition in three years, necessitating a reprint, with added data.

"The fact that Sam Nowell of the Class of August 9, 1653 had his 'study in the printing roome' indicates that the press had very little business; . . ." This statement by Samuel Eliot Morison in *The Founding of Harvard College* concerns the establishment which is generally termed the Cambridge Press, the first printing office to be set up in the English Colonies.

Some historic accounts call the print shop the Stephen Day Press, but there remains considerable controversy about the exact responsibility Stephen Day had in the operation of the Press. Day and his son Matthew were brought from England, along with a printing press and supply of types and paper, by the Reverend Jose Glover, who unfortunately died during the passage, in the summer of 1638. The elder Day was by trade a locksmith, and the only evidence of his activities in printing is the information that he was frequently called upon to repair the printing press when it got out of order.

Another factor which casts doubt on Day as a printer is that while he could write his name, he was not at all adept in his command of English, as a letter to John Winthrop, the younger, attests: "After my deutie and sarves remembred to youer worshep and mestres Wantrop, thaes ar to in tret that you will be plased to acomodat Mr. Homan withith a lott. . . ."

On the other hand, Matthew Day was not yet eighteen years of age when he left England and it does not seem reasonable that he would have been hired by Glover for the responsibilities of setting up the press. Most authorities, however, agree that it was Matthew who set the type for the first piece of printing to be produced in Colonial America, the *Freeman's Oath* of 1638, no copy of which is known to have survived. The first name to appear on an imprint of the Cambridge Press was that of Matthew Day, but this was not until 1647, on the title page of an almanac for that year. Matthew was in full charge of the shop when he died on May 10, 1649.

Samuel Green took over upon Day's death, and managed the printing office for the next forty-three years. Writing in 1675, he stated: "Printing was the employment I was called unto when there was none in the country to carry it along after the death of him that was brought ovr for that work by Mr. Jose Glover, and although I was not before used unto it yett being urged thereunto by one and another of place did what by my own endeavors and help that I gott from some others that was procured, I undertook the work."

Those historians who recognize Stephen Day as the full-time printer point out that on December 10, 1641, the General Court of the Colony voted that: "Stephen Daye, being the first that set upon printing, is granted 300 acres of land where it may be convenient, without prejudice to any towne."

George Parker Winship in his detailed study, *The Cambridge Press, 1638-1692,* remarks that it certainly should have been simple for the legislators to know, at that date, who had performed the printing of the *Bay Psalm Book,* which was completed in 1640.

August 10

Rarely mentioned among the hazards of life experienced by the itinerant printer as he tramped from job to job was the abuse he had to suffer intellectually, by having to set type for a variety of periodicals with whose opinions he did not necessarily agree. Concerning the vulnerability of the ubiquitous compositor to editorial suggestion, an anonymous printer wrote to a friend on this day in 1885:

"The reason why I have been astonished at the interest of the printers in this paper of the new crusade, is because the sons of Faust are apt to be a cynical, skeptical crew. They see so many sides of life, and see so far into them all, that they are in danger of assuming a fixed attitude of incredulity or mockery, and of losing all their enthusiasm.

"Look how they 'box the compass' as they pass from office to office. Take, for example, Pop Rednose, who is now turning forty. He got his first job as an apprentice on the *Evangelist,* and set up so many sermons urging him to repent that he determined to become a saint. He had just reached that point when he got the sack. His next job was on Abbe McMaster's *Catholic Register,* which soon led him to doubt the truth of

Protestantism, and brought him to the very edge of the ancient Roman Church. He had just about made up his mind in favor of auricular confession, when a dirty proof of one of the Abbe's illegible editorials landed him on the sidewalk. His next sit was on the *Truth Seeker,* which soon brought him to a total unbelief in all sorts of religion. He became a sub on the *Times,* which made him a Republican and sent him to the war, but came back to a case on Manton Marble's *World,* and soon turned up as a really solid Democrat.

"He soon left the dailies, got a job on a teetotal weekly, found out the horrors of drinking, and resolved to quit liquor; but in two months got a fatter job on the *Wine and Spirit Merchant,* where he set up the praises of the 'ruby,' and saw it was necessary to his health. He soon got a weekly job on a moral reform paper, spent his time over copy against the tobacco habit, and determined to throw away his pipe; but he got a still fatter thing on the *Tobacco Leaf,* where he read every day of the charms of the Virginia weed, to which he soon returned. From an allopathic weekly, which led him to take calomel with his regular diet, he went to a homeopathic monthly, which taught him never to go beyond the millionth trituration of a speck. After a while Freemasonry was the thing, as he put in type an article on the thirty-ninth degree, and latterly has been disposed in favor of civil service reform, as he tinkers up the leaded brevier of Mr. Ford's Brooklyn *Union.* But, after all his experiences, here and there, Pop Rednose has become a thorough skeptic and cynic, with a sneer for every new philosopher, and a firm faith only in printers' 'fat.' And this is not much of an exaggeration of the history of many typos, who pay their dues regularly into Union No. 6.

"They are apt to become case-hardened ere their hair is gray, and to lose their freshness while yet their salad days are unspent."

August 11

"I sit in meditation on the matrices and punches of the Doves Press fount of type, and revolve in my mind whether I should destroy them in my lifetime, dedicate them to the purpose of the Press, and to the River upon whose shore the Press has lived and worked."

Thus reads the entry for August 11, 1912 in the *Journal* of T. J. Cobden-Sanderson. The decision of the distinguished private press printer to destroy the matrices and punches was eventually carried out, inciting a public quarrel between Cobden-Sanderson and Emery Walker, his partner in the operation of the Doves Press. It had been a legal agreement between the two men that the types should go to the partner who survived the other, but Cobden-Sanderson, whose eccentricities were remarkable, apparently could not stand the thought of his types being used by any other hand but his own. In 1911 he had written his will into his *Journal:*

"To the bed of the River Thames, the river on whose banks I have printed all my books, I bequeath The Doves Press Fount of Type —the punches, the matrices, and the type in use at the time of my death, and may the river in its tides and flow pass over them to and from the great sea for ever and for ever, or until its tides and flow for ever cease; then may they share the fate of all the world, and pass from change to change for ever upon the Tides of Time, untouched of other use and all else."

Will Ransom in his sympathetic work on the famous private presses, *Kelmscott, Doves, and Ashendene,* writes that the destruction of the Doves Press type "was the most dramatic and intensely emotional event in the private press movement." It certainly was most controversial, with the friends of both principals taking sides and relieving their feelings in letters to the editor of *The Times,* none of which deterred Cobden-Sanderson from what he believed to be his duty.

Writing in his *Journal* at midnight on August 31, 1916, he stated: "The Doves Press type was designed after that of Jenson; this evening I began its destruction. I threw three pages into the Thames from Hammersmith Bridge. I had gone for a stroll on the Mall, when it occurred to me that it was a suitable night and time; so I went indoors, and taking first one page and then two, succeeded in destroying three. I will go on until I have destroyed the whole of it."

The entries in the *Journal* throughout the balance of the year became increasingly incoherent. At one time Cobden-Sanderson

misjudged his aim and the type landed upon a ledge of the bridge. "The tide is ebbing," he wrote that evening, "and there it will remain all the night. Will the flow of the tide lift it off? I doubt it. But there it *is,* and now out of my reach. I aimed, and missed the bed. My idea was magnificent; the act ridiculous."

August 12

Thomas MacKellar, printer, typefounder, author, and poet, was born this day in New York City in the year 1812. He is remembered today primarily as the author of *The American Printer: A Manual of Typography,* first published in 1866 and so popular that it went into eighteen editions. At $1.50 the text was a real bargain, and there was scarcely a journeyman printer on the continent by 1900 who wasn't familiar with it.

MacKellar admitted in his preface that the work was intended to be more useful than original, and in this statement he was following the tradition of the printer's manual. Since Joseph Moxon published his famous *Mechanick Exercises* in 1683, each succeeding manual had borrowed from all the rest. The first American manual issued in 1818 was *The Printer's Guide* by C. S. Van Winkle. It is most informative in its description of the equipment and procedures of the printing offices of the period. The only other American text prior to that of MacKellar was *Typographia* by Thomas F. Adams, published in three editions—1837, 1845, and 1866. Adams was almost completely dependent upon the English books of the same title published by Johnson and by Hansard in 1824 and 1825 respectively.

The more sophisticated apprentices now serving their time would of course laugh their heads off at mid-19th century MacKellar when he says in the chapter on composition, "Experience proves that the apprentice foreshadows the workman, just as surely as the bend of the twig foretells the inclination of the tree. The upright, obedient, industrious lad will become a steady, skillful, and capable man, as unmistakably as the perverse, idling, careless boy will ripen into a lazy, dissolute, and worthless fellow. . . .

"When a lad who possesses these qualities proposes to learn the art and mystery of printing, it should be inquired of him, Has he had a fair common-school education? Is he a perfect speller? Has he a turn for reading? A true affirmative answer to all these queries will entitle him to a position of reading and errand-boy. He is told the hours at which he is to come and go, and a strict punctuality is enjoined upon him. He sweeps the room,—he sorts out the pi,—he learns the position of the various letters in the case. A year spent in this way is an excellent preparative for 'going to case,' or learning the art of composing type."

MacKellar was read and admired because such statements typified the simple virtues expected of teenagers during the period. At times, though, MacKellar's constant attempts to inject humor into his text result in his being too "cute," for modern readers. Since there is so little accurate information concerning the procedures of American typefounding during the last century, it would have been most valuable to have had from one of the best founders of his time a straightforward account of how type was made. MacKellar's chapter on that subject begins, "Mr. Typograph, how are you, sir? Glad to see you. How is business with you? Plenty to do, and customers paying up? . . ." The tone is thus set, and it is with difficulty that the contemporary reader maintains his interest in what really went on in the foundry.

August 13

William Morris, in a letter written on this day in 1884, mentions a Socialist meeting during which he held the chair. Quite possibly this was the meeting at which he met Emery Walker, as his daughter May Morris later wrote that the two men had met first at a Socialist meeting during 1884. The first letter written by Morris in which he mentions Walker's name was written in December of that same year. While the two men became known to one another at that meeting, Walker was actually already known to the entire Morris family as a familiar figure who passed their home each day on his way to business. By 1888, however, Walker had become a motivating force in the life of William Morris.

Emery Walker was twenty-two years of age in 1873 when he joined with the firm operated by Alfred Dawson. This was the first photographic reproduction establishment in England. It presented Walker with the opportunity to become the most knowledgeable process engraver of his time. He gained the friendship and esteem of printers, publishers, and artists through the medium of his work, gradually acquiring a notable breadth of understanding of the graphic arts in both its technical and historical factors.

It was during the period following his meeting with Morris that the latter became thoroughly engrossed in the study of the work of the earliest printer. When Walker presented an illustrated lecture on Letterpress Printing in 1888, Morris attended. Here the spark was ignited. As the two men walked home from the lecture, Morris suddenly said, "Let's make a new fount of type." Thus the famous Kelmscott Press was born. Walker refused a partnership with Morris in the operation of the press, but he supplied the technical advice which Morris needed so badly.

Following the death of William Morris in 1896, Walker came to the aid of T. J. Cobden-Sanderson in the formation of the Doves Press, assisting in the selection of the types, based upon a 15th century font of Nicolas Jenson. Walker also suggested the equipment to be purchased and aided in the actual production of the books which were printed. In Walker's long service to the printing craft, his association with the Doves Press was the only instance in which he became involved in the actual printing of books, the format of which he helped to plan. It is unfortunate that the increasing neuroticism of Cobden-Sanderson eventually led to a break between the partners, but Walker's advice and counsel had already been a prime factor in the direction of the Doves Press. The establishing of two out of three great English private presses therefore may be credited to Emery Walker.

Walker's good friend, Sir Sidney Cockerell, wrote of him in the obituary which appeared in the *Dictionary of National Biography:* "It is scarcely too much to say that his influence, direct or indirect, can be discerned in nearly every well-designed page of type that now appears, and that to him more than any other man this century's great improvement in book production has been due."

August 14

The *Cincinnati Advertiser,* in its issue of this date in 1833, carried an announcement concerning the publication of what might well have been the first comic book to be produced in the trans-Allegheny west. The publisher was a Yale man, Nathan Guilford (Class of 1812), in company with his brother, George. The title of this book was *Western Comic Almanac for 1834,* and it featured anecdotes about the currently popular comic types, Irishmen and Quakers, illustrated with grotesque woodcuts.

Nathan Guilford was no newcomer to the publishing of almanacs, that staple of the American printing trade since the erection of the first press in the Bay Colony almost two hundred years before. Early in the 19th century the acceptance of the educational almanac was beginning to wear thin, hence the recourse to a more diverting approach. In 1822 Guilford, a lawyer turned bookseller-publisher-printer-typefounder, had written and published *The Freeman's Almanack,* which purported to contain "a great variety of useful selections, with the maxims and advice of Solomon Thrifty."

Under the pseudonym of Thrifty, entrepreneur Guilford earnestly endeavored to spread the word for universal education, a cause for which he was to devote much of his life. In his very first effort as an almanac editor, he wrote in a "Solomon Thrifty says" vein: "The first and most important advice which he can give, is, *to send your children to school.* He says it is a disgrace to a freeman to let his children grow up without being able to read, write, and transact business. He thinks it a shame for a man to go to the polls, who cannot write his vote.— Education, says he, is the soul of a republic; and every American, who neglects to educate his children, he considers not only a bad father, but a traitor to his country."

While no doubt honest in his convictions as Solomon Thrifty, Guilford was not exactly selfless in his eagerness to spread the word —by the medium of print. As a book publisher and the silent partner of the first typefoundry to be set up in the west, the Cincinnati Type Foundry, he had much to gain. The printing office of Oliver and William Farnsworth, containing but three hand presses, produced in a six-month period in the late 1820's, 9,000 spelling books, 7,000 of *Murray's Introduction and English Reader,* 6,000 English grammars, 2,000 arithmetics, 1,500 primers and chap books for children, and 60,000 almanacs, "all of which have a ready and rapid sale."

By the close of 1826, Cincinnati, with a population of sixteen thousand citizens, was served by nine printers, who produced over 200,000 copies of a variety of books, most of which could be called educational. Could it be wondered then, that Solomon Thrifty urged: "If you have no school in your neighborhood, *let it be your first care to establish one.*—It will be a great blessing to your children, and a lasting benefit to society."

August 15

A Presbyterian dominie who made solid contributions to the history of American invention was born this day in 1838 near Rochester, New York. Merritt Gally lost his father, also a minister of the Presbyterian persuasion, and found it necessary at the age of eleven to earn his own living. He apprenticed himself to a printer and quickly learned the trade, editing and printing a newspaper before he was out of his teens. When he became twenty-one years of age he decided that he needed a liberal education and thereupon enrolled in the University of Rochester, from which he graduated in 1863.

Deciding to follow his father's profession, Gally next attended the Theological Seminary at Auburn, New York. He was ordained as a minister and received a call to a small church in upstate Lyons. Here he served for three years. Then he succumbed to the blandishments of a career as an inventor, to which his facile mind was inexorably drawing him. Naturally enough his earlier interest in printing was responsible for his first important development, that of a platen press, which he called the Universal Printing Press.

Gally received a patent for this machine in 1869, and his new career was off to a most auspicious beginning, as the principle of the new machine endeared it to several generations of printers. Prior to the Universal, platen presses operated at a disadvantage when compared to hand presses in which the platen was at all times parallel to the bed of the press. In the platen press either the bed or the platen was hinged, so that the meeting of bed and platen was somewhat out of parallel, a difficulty which could be partially surmounted by the adjustment of the platen.

Gally's press had a solid fixed vertical bed. The platen was not hinged, and it rolled up from its feeding position, becoming parallel to the bed about one inch from the form, then being pulled directly toward the bed, allowing an even impression all over the form at maximum pressure. Unlike other platen presses, the Universal had no ink disc, but a fountain immediately above the form for the supply of ink. The combination of parallel impression and even inking contributed to the ability of the press to produce superior printing.

The Universal was at first manufactured in Rochester by Hamilton & McNeil, who produced five hundred presses in a year and a half. Gally transferred the manufacturing rights to a firm in New York City, who subleased it to the plant of the Colt's Patent Firearms Manufacuring Company. After building some 2,400 machines, Gally's basic patents expired, and the Colt Company made a number of modifications in the design and manufactured the press under a name which became quite famous—the Colt's Armory. This model has endeared itself to countless printers and now represents the most desirable item in the equipment of a serious private press operator.

Some five hundred patents were granted to Gally during his lifetime, the most widely known one probably being that of the player piano and the mechanical organ. He also patented in 1872 a device for the assembling of matrices, automatically spaced with wedges, which in 1884 was sold to the interests which were backing Ottmar Mergenthaler.

August 16

"Dear Doctor: A moment of historical importance, not only for our monastery but for the whole civilized and literary world, has come on: the moment in which we are about to put into your hands the most precious jewel of our archives, one of the oldest books of the world, a copy of the parchment-bible,

printed by Johann zu Gutenberg himself, the world-renowned German inventor of the art of printing."

And so saying, Pater Dr. Herman Peissl, O.S.B. of the Benedictine Monastery St. Paul, in Carinthia (Austria) handed over to Dr. Otto H. F. Vollbehr this day in 1930 the finest copy extant of the Gutenberg Bible, for delivery to the United States Library of Congress.

Continuing, Dr. Peissl said: "In this memorable moment, we are thankfully looking back upon our dear ancestors and brethren, who were the true wardens of this treasure for centuries and centuries. In this moment we state in the face of the world, that the alienation of the famous work was a need-sale, brought about by the downfall of the financial state of our monastery after and in consequence of the Great War.

"A special thank you are deserving for preserving the book, sacred by age and contents, from the sort of getting an object of commerce, as you intend to incorporate the work bought by you into the Congress-Library of the United States, whereby it will be accessible for the publicity in much higher a degree than it was possible hitherto."

This great Bible, the only one of the forty-seven known copies to be bound in three volumes, and from which the monastery realized $250,000, has fulfilled one of Dr. Peissl's predictions. In the Library of Congress it has been viewed by more people than any other copy of the Gutenberg Bible.

August 17

From the press established in Lima, Peru by the Italian printer Antonio Ricardo, there issued on August 17, 1584 the first piece of printing known to have been produced on the South American continent. Ricardo, a native of Turin, had originally traveled to Mexico City about the year 1570, where he worked occasionally with the printer Pedro Ocharte. From Ocharte he received equipment for the establishment of his own printing office in 1579.

While there was at the time sufficient work to keep several printers busy in Mexico City, there was no press in Lima. This city was already endowed with a university and a Spanish civilization of considerable wealth.

ALOIS SENEFELDER
See February 26 for his story.

Ricardo arrived in the City of Kings in 1580, but he had to wait for a period of four years before the Real Audiencia received permission from the Spanish king to set up a press. The Jesuits were exceedingly anxious to provide devotional books needed in the native languages. Even with this pressure the king required a great deal of information, necessitating involved explanations carried on across vast distances.

The first work which Ricardo undertook when the royal permission was finally granted was a catechism in the Spanish and Quichua and Aymara languages. While this volume was in progress, a royal decree was sent from Spain, requiring prompt action from the Peruvian Real Audiencia. The decree required the dissemination of the papal order of Gregory XIII reforming the Julian calendar. The change had taken place in Europe during October 5 and 15, 1582, but it was April, 1584 before Lima received notification. The decree contained a paragraph which stated: "And because in certain parts of our said Indies, by reason of so great distance, it has not been possible before this to receive the aforementioned order of His Holiness by which ten days are to be dropped from the month of October of the present year, I hereby command and ordain that the change be made in the following year of 1584, or in the first one in which notice of the foregoing be received, and that this decree embodying the commands of His Holiness be published in said kingdoms: the which we order you to observe and to comply with and to execute . . . so that the aforementioned may come to the notice of everyone and none may plead ignorance thereof we order that this our letter be publicly proclaimed in those cities wherein reside our royal courts and chanceries of the said Indies, and that printed copies of it be distributed in other localities, so that all may be informed and may know what His Holiness has proclaimed."

The Real Audiencia quickly authorized the printing of the King's *Pragmatica*, as it is called. A manuscript annotation which appears on the only known copy of this document, now at the John Carter Brown Library in Providence, Rhode Island, affirms that the decree was published on August 17, 1584. The catechism, which was in the press when the decree was ordered, was issued at a later date, although there still remains some controversy about which one may be considered to be the first item from the press in South America.

August 18

Harold Curwen, proprietor of the distinguished English printing office, the Curwen Press, wrote under this date in 1920 to Oliver Simon, a recently demobilized young officer of the 53rd (Welsh) Divisional Cyclist Company:

"I think I shall get this through all right but I'll have to speak to the whole of the Combined Chapel before you can start. They are a little shy of it till I've had a chance to explain that I don't intend having a continuous string of pupils nor is there any prospect of my clearing out any of the staff as a consequence of any insight you might gain as to their qualities . . . ."

A few months earlier, when Simon, the son of a retired Manchester cotton merchant, had gone to London to seek employment he had, according to his autobiography, *Printer and Playground*, ". . . happened to pass Sotheran's bookshop, then in Picadilly, where an astonishing window display of sumptuous, dazzling, richly decorated books caught my eye and arrested my steps. I felt compelled to enter and make inquiries and was told, for the first time in my life, about William Morris and the Kelmscott Press, and of the Kelmscott *Chaucer* in particular, which held a place of honour in the window. As I left, I knew I could abandon my vague and unenthusiastic plans to enter the cotton trade, forestry or bank: it was plain to me that I *must* become a printer."

Through a chain of fortunate friendships Simon ended up at the door of the Curwen Press with the request to learn the business of printing. Curwen was successful in persuading his employees to accept the young man for a year of training. Simon was entranced with his new life as a printer. Fortunate, too, were both the Press and the cause of good printing everywhere, as Simon became a leading figure in English typography for the next forty years. Within three years Simon was a founding editor of the fine journal of typography, *The Fleuron*, which was a contributing force in the flowering of historical research in printing which took place between the two World Wars. In 1924 he helped to organize the Double Crown Club, the distinguished dining club composed of people intimately concerned with the arts of the book.

Simon's next important contribution was the founding and editing of *Signature,* a quadrimestrial journal of typography and the graphic arts, which continued on a somewhat smaller scale the idea behind *The Fleuron.* First published in 1935, it ceased publication in 1940. A bomb struck the Curwen Press on October 7th, smashing all of the windows in the roof of the pressroom. Fortunately the weather was fair, as the last forms were printed under the sky. *Signature* for these five years set a standard which has never been surpassed by any printing periodical.

August 19

In the city of Antwerp the house in the Vrijdagmarkt (the Friday Market) was opened to the public on this day in 1877. This building was named the Three Compasses by the printer Christopher Plantin when he first occupied it in 1576, and for exactly three centuries a printing office was maintained on the premises by Plantin and his descendants.

Known today as the Plantin-Moretus Museum, the building now houses the finest collection of historic punches and matrices in existence. Most of them are of 16th century origin and represent the work of such masters as Claude Garamond, Robert Granjon, and Guillaume Le Bé. The collection numbers 4,443 punches, 15,825 justified matrices, and 4,681 strikes (unjustified matrices).

It was not until the period following the second World War that it was recognized that the real value of the museum to typographic scholars rested upon the punches and matrices. Mr. Harry Carter, Archivist to the University Press at Oxford, had visited the museum in 1924 and found that this collection was in great disorder, many of the punches being rusted and the fonts mixed up. While Carter impressed the museum officials with the need to catalogue the punches and matrices, this work was not attempted seriously until after the war.

By 1956 the first inventory of the great collection was drawn up, and since that time great strides have been made in the proper fonting and identification of the punches. An American, Mike Parker, went to the museum on a scholarship and developed a system of photographing the punches which was of great value in furthering the work of cataloguing. The value of bringing order to this splendid collection is already apparent. For example, it was widely believed that most of the types were of Dutch origin, but thanks to the research of the group working in Antwerp, it has been learned that many of the punches were the work of such masters as Garamond and Granjon.

The ancient typefoundry connected with Plantin's printing office has also been partially revived and some casting of type from the early punches has taken place, although as yet on a limited basis, due to the depth of drive differences in many of the matrices. Without question the Plantin-Moretus Museum will become increasingly important to scholars, particularly those engaged in studies relating to 16th and 17th century type design. In addition it remains a fascinating place to visit for printers who will be happy merely to walk about and observe—to feel themselves, for a few moments, part of a great and honorable tradition.

August 20

In a letter addressed to the typefounder George Bruce on this day in 1855 Joel Munsell, the Albany printer and typographic historian, asked for precise information concerning the construction of the Ramage printing press, probably the most widely used press in America during the first thirty years of the 19th century. Nearly every account of the establishment of a printing office in that period mentions the Ramage, and during the westward expansion up to the Civil War the Ramage was the major piece of equipment of the pioneer printers in many of the western states.

Adam Ramage was a Scotsman who arrived in Philadelphia in 1795 and began to construct wooden printing presses there, being the first to engage in such a business as a professional in the United States. Presses based upon European models had been constructed in America by carpenters, but in most cases merely to supply local demand. Ramage successfully met the needs of the expanding printing industry for presses just as his fellow Scotsmen, Archibald Binny and James Ronaldson, did for type at the same time when they started the first successful typefoundry.

A description of this popular press and its operation was written by Edwin Scrantom of Rochester, New York and appeared in the *Rochester Democrat & Chronicle* in 1871:

"The press was formed by two heavy upright pieces of timber, standing about seven feet high, called the 'cheeks,' which stood three or four feet apart, and were held together by a cross piece at top and bottom. Running through the center of the cheeks was a carriage way, or 'ribs,' resting on another crosspiece called the 'winter piece.' These rib pieces, conveniently set apart one from the other, extended out each side of the press of sufficient length to accommodate the 'bed' to run backward and forward when the printer was working off the form he was engaged in, whether of book, handbill, or newspaper. Next is the 'bed' of the press, which ran out and in on the ribs, and which received the form of the type that was made up to be printed. This bed ran on straight, polished ribs of steel, the ribs being the same, and both were oiled. To the bed were attached two frames with joints—the larger one that folded down on the form, and on which the unprinted sheet was laid, was the 'tympan,' and the upper one, that folded down on the tympan, and held the sheet while it was being printed was the 'frisket.' Now to make the impression, a large screw with a coarse thread was placed in a box and that box was fastened into a crosspiece between the cheeks, called the 'summer piece.' The screw, which worked in the box, had a long point and worked in the center of a square follower, which was kept in its place by springs, and was called the 'platen.' Fixed to the screw immediately under the 'winter piece' [summer piece] was a lever of iron, crooked in a half circle at the eye where it was attached to the screw, and had a long bar, the end of which was supplied with a large, round, wood handle. This bar swung transversely across the press from side to side, so as to give the power of the screw, and when the press was in repose its place was against the back of the press, where it was held by a 'stop.' "

August 21

In Milwaukee, Wisconsin on this day in 1840 was born Nelson C. Hawks, who was to become—to borrow a journalistic expression—the "father" of the American Point System of type measurement. At sixteen years of age Hawks was apprenticed to a printer, but a month after he had gone to work, his employers sold the business, leaving the boy without a job. However, he was presented with several fonts of type which he brought home to use as the nucleus of a very small newspaper office. Hawks published a 9 x 11 inch paper called *Young America* for two years. Then he established the *Free Press* in Oconomowoc.

In 1865 Hawks returned to Milwaukee where he opened a job printing office. It was at this time that he became concerned about the lack of precision in the types then being manufactured by typefounders in the United States. There were no standards of type size, or in height-to-paper, a fact which naturally contributed to the frustration of printers who attempted to combine in a single job the types of more than one founder. In discussions with his fellow printers Hawks urged that they get together and demand of the founders that types be produced to a standard size.

The Great Chicago fire of 1871 which destroyed 17,000 buildings, wiped out the two typefoundries then located in the city. Hawks made every effort at that time to persuade Marder, Luse & Company, the larger of the two and the most important of the Western typefounders, to change over to a systematic method of casting type when the foundry was rebuilt. He met with no immediate success, so he next approached the Cincinnati Type Foundry with a similar proposition, and was again rebuffed.

At about the same time he accepted the offer of Marder, Luse & Company to establish a branch office of the firm in San Francisco, as the Pacific coast printing industry was then experiencing very rapid growth. Out of this association was the forming of a new firm, the Pacific Type

Foundry. John Marder of the Chicago company went out to California in May, 1874 to visit Hawks and to discuss the problems to be encountered in the new venture. Again Hawks used this opportunity to promote his cause. He advocated as a standard the pica type cast by the Philadelphia foundry, Mac-Kellar, Smiths & Jordan, since the type of that concern was the most widely used by American printers and because it was the smallest of the pica ems in general use, making a new changeover by other foundries less expensive.

Marder, convinced by Hawks' enthusiasm that one large founder must eventually restore order to a chaotic situation, returned to Chicago. In 1879 Marder, Luse & Company announced to the trade that they were instituting what they called the American System of Interchangeable Bodies. From this moment the idea spread rapidly. In 1886 the American Type Founders Association, a trade group of the nation's foundries, met and agreed to make official the American Point System, based upon the idea that Hawks had impressed upon Marder.

August 22

"It has been my endeavor to combine the agreeable with the useful; and should this, a first attempt, meet with the approbation of the 'Gentlemen of the Press,' to whom it is most respectfully inscribed, the aim of the Compiler will be attained, his warmest wishes realized, and a debt of heartfelt gratitude be owing to them from C. H. T. a brother typo."

With this paragraph, written and dated this day in 1833, a wounded veteran of Waterloo and journeyman printer named C. H. Timperley ended his preface to *Songs of the Press*, which was subtitled, "and other Poems Relative to the Art of Printing." In this compilation, the first of its kind to be printed in English, appeared poems written by Leigh Hunt, Benjamin Franklin, Dean Swift, and Coleridge, in addition to the anthologist himself and a score of anonymous versifiers.

Readers of the periodical press devoted to "the art preservative" for long expected to be entertained with poetry, and it is only during the last fifty years or so that the print-er poets were deprived of space in which to indulge their minstrelsy. Naturally enough, most of their rhyming would be consigned to the hell box by serious critics as "editorial page" verse.

Probably the earliest appearance of verse in relation to the printer's art was in a book printed by Albert Pfister at Bamberg in the 15th century, in which the colophon read:

> If by it we our lives mend,
> This little book has gained its end
> Which certainly in Bamberg town
> By Albert Pfister's press was done
> In fourteen hundred sixty two
> As men now reckon, that is true.

Frequently the terms used in the printing office were italicized in the poems. An example of this is in the *Song* written for the Nottingham Typographical Society by one J. Thompson. The tune for this one is *Hearts of Oak:*

> When our copy is out, 'tis a
> signal to go,—
> *Short of sorts,* when on tramp is
> a *bad case,* you know;
> Then *lay up,* my lads, and your
> *quoins* will be found
> A treasure, *unlock'd,* in life's
> changeable round.

In the United States the most widely reprinted piece of printer's poesy is *The Song of the Printer,* by Thomas MacKellar, which appeared in the eighteen editions of his famous manual, *The American Printer,* first published in 1866. This widely quoted bit of verse begins:

> Pick and click
> Goes the type in the stick,
> As the printer stands at his case;
> His eyes glance quick, and his
> fingers pick
> The type at a rapid pace; . . .

August 23

An advertisement in the New York *Journal* of this date in 1787 stated: "Mr. John Baine & Grandson, Letter-Founders, Lately from Edinburgh, Having concluded to establish their Type-Foundery at Philadelphia, removed to that city, on the 18th inst. with their founding machinery, leaving, at Mr. David Mitchelson's corner of Fly-Market and Water-street, the following Founts of

Types, For Sale, At the annexed prices, sterling money, viz.

1 Fount of Small Pica	373 lb.	at 1s. 2d.
1 Ditto Long Primer	363 lb.	at 1s. 6d.
1 Ditto Brevier	276 lb.	at 2s. 6d.

Ready Cash or no Purchase."

After observing for a number of years that the business of selling type in the American colonies was most lucrative, a Scotsman named John Baine decided that opportunity beckoned any enterprising typefounder who dared an Atlantic crossing. He was at that time 73 years of age, and had been a founder for most of his life, having established such a business in St. Andrews, Scotland in partnership with Alexander Wilson, considered to be the finest of Scottish typefounders.

The New World venture was productive, as there were at that period no foundries serving the growing printing industry in the young Republic. Although no specimen book was issued it is known that type cast by John Baine and his grandson was used in a number of important books printed in the United States, including Mathew Carey's Bible and the *Encyclopaedia* of Thomas Dobson. The elder Baine died in 1790. His grandson continued to cast type, though reluctantly, as he made several attempts to sell the foundry. He finally did so in 1799 to his fellow Scotsmen, Archibald Binny and James Ronaldson.

William McCulloch, a contemporary Philadelphia printer, in his account to Isaiah Thomas, the printing historian, says of the Baines: "Old Mr. Bayne was an original mechanical genius, and is said to have been the first that communicated any insight into the arcana of type founding to Wilson, of Glasgow. Bayne, in his knowledge of the art, like Fox and Bey, was self-taught. All that he accomplished was by his own genius."

August 24

The copy of the great bible printed by Johann Gutenberg in Mainz, Germany and now in the possession of the Bibliothèque Nationale at Paris, contains a note in the hand of Heinrich Cremer of St. Stephens College, Mainz, dated this day in 1456, that he had completed the illumination, headings, and binding. This is the earliest known date in connection with the printing of this great book. From it can be deduced that the printing had been completed early in that year, if not some time late in 1455.

Professor Aloys Ruppel of the Gutenberg Museum in Mainz, the great authority on Gutenberg's life, has stated that Gutenberg's plan for the production of a bible must have been made by 1450. The project represented a gigantic undertaking for so early a period in the history of the craft of printing. The presses needed to be constructed, the type cast, paper manufactured, printers trained, and of course a great deal of money was necessary to guarantee the successful completion of the monumental task.

Gutenberg used the Latin Vulgate translation of St. Jerome which had been completed early in the 5th century. He planned a two-column page, with 42 lines in each column. The first nine pages contain 40 lines, as do pages 129 to 132. Page 10 has 41 lines, but the rest of the 1,282 pages are composed in 42 lines, a fact which has given this edition its name. The Gutenberg Bible is bound in two volumes.

The edition ran to 150 copies on paper and about 35 on parchment. Each copy required 340 folio sheets of four pages each, or a total of 51,000 sheets for the entire printing. For the parchment copies 6,000 skins were needed, as but two sheets could be cut from one calfskin.

When the composition was begun, four compositors were required and two more were later added. The work was printed on six presses, each operated by a single pressman. The average working day at that period was of 12 hours duration, the printers working 8 hours in the winter and 16 hours in the summer. As there were 85 Sundays and festival days, there were 280 working days in the year. It has been estimated that because Gutenberg wished to simulate manuscript bibles, and had therefore cut into type all of the tied or ligatured letters employed by the scribes (290 different characters), it took a compositor one day to set a single page. Six compositors could therefore have completed the job in 212 working days.

Due, however, to the necessity of distributing each page before another could be set and to the need for taking care of the other work of the printing office such as the printing of grammars, letters of indulgence, and the like, the net working time was probably over 400 days. Since the printing was begun in 1452, it took until 1455 at the very least to complete the composition of the folio volumes.

The presses were large enough to print but one page at a time of each four page signature; thus 185 copies of 1,282 pages added up to 231,170 separate impressions. Two pressmen could produce about ten pages an hour, with six presses turning out about 700 pages a day. It took, then, 340 days to print the entire Bible, but as the presses were also occupied with other printing from time to time, it probably was three years before the whole book was off the press.

Altogether, a magnificent task. Five hundred years later, there are but 47 known copies of the Gutenberg Bible, 12 on parchment and 35 on paper. It is still recognized as the finest achievement of the printer's art.

August 25

This is a memorable date in the history of the republic. The event which made it outstanding was the burning and partial destruction of the capital city of Washington in 1814. The guiding spirit behind this feat of British arms was a rear admiral of the Royal Navy, Sir George Cockburn. Good friend and fighting shipmate of the esteemed Lord Nelson, Sir George enjoyed a long and whimsical career in the service of his King. Actually the incident in Washington was but a minor incident but he was rewarded with a K.C.B. for it.

The entire Chesapeake area had long known the depredations of the swashbuckling admiral who had scarcely known shore duty during his twenty-six years of service. Elevated to flag rank at forty years of age, Cockburn had the seaman's splendid disdain for the landsman and appeared to enjoy every moment of his American service.

Sir George, on that sunny August day, broke into the annals of the printer's craft by virtue of his zeal as a minor conqueror. For the past year he had been reading in the Washington newspaper of the contempt in which he was held. He appeared at the door of the *National Intelligencer* and called for Editor Joseph Gales to come forth and eat his words or "watch his rag go out of business."

Gale was of course some time departed from the premises. The admiral thereby contented himself with ordering the library of the newspaper brought out to the middle of Pennsylvania Avenue and put to the match before a goodly crowd of citizens, declaring the volumes to be traitorous. Cockburn became so enthusiastic at the sight that he forgot the traditions of an officer of His Majesty by actually joining in the destruction of the printing plant, helping to smash the presses with his own hands.

In the matter of the type, Sir George's instructions were more explicit. He told the soldiers to pi the type. "Be sure," he said, "that all the C's in the boxes are destroyed so that the rascals can have no further means of abusing my name!"

Editor Gale exhibited remarkable restraint when he later was able to resume publication of his newspaper. In an editorial he wrote, "Greater respect was certainly paid to private property than has usually been exhibited by the enemy in his marauding parties. No houses were half as much plundered by the enemy as by the knavish wretches of the town who profited by the general distress."

Sir George went from service in the War of 1812 to greater glory, serving as the jailer of Napoleon upon St. Helena, becoming First Naval Lord, and finally retiring as Admiral of the Fleet in 1851. For a period he was also a Tory Member of Parliament, during which time he no doubt was pleased that the English printers were always sufficiently supplied with cap C's.

August 26

Of Christopher Sower, Jr. of Germantown, Pennsylvania, who died upon this day in 1784, the historian Isaiah Thomas said, "No medicines could be esteemed effectual, unless procured at Sower's apothecary shop; no almanac, unless published by him, could be correct in time and weather; no newspaper promulgated truth but Christopher Sower's *German Gazette.*"

Thomas might have added that "no type could be cast as effective for printing as that of Sower," the Germantown printer being famed as the first American typefounder. Sower, born in Germany, was brought to the

American colonies by his father in 1724. The elder Sower was a tailor, but during his early years in America he applied himself to some sixteen different trades, by all of which he could earn his living. He became a printer by accident when the equipment for a printing office was sent from Germany to Pennsylvania for the purpose of printing religious books. No printer was available to operate the press, so Sower took it over and became quite successful as a printer. He also learned how to make his own ink and paper.

Sower the younger became a bookbinder in his father's establishment, taking over the shop at his father's death in 1758. He acquired some of his father's skills. He too could manufacture very fine ink, and he built a paper mill to produce both printing and writing paper in 1773. He even built his own presses. In order to maintain a certain amount of independence, Sower imported from Germany punches for the making of type. As his shop was producing German language printing, he needed a large supply of Fraktur type, obtainable only in Germany, and the cost of importing this type was a drain on his resources.

In the colophon of No. 12 of his religious periodical *Ein Gesitliches Magazien,* undated but probably appearing either late in 1771 or early 1772, appeared the notice, *"Gedruckt mit der ersten Schrift die jemals in America gegossen worden."* (Printed with the first type ever cast in America.) Actually Abel Buell of Connecticut had cast type in 1769, but it received little use, while Sower's was cast in quantity for the German bible which he was then engaged in printing.

Christopher Sower was sympathetic to the British cause and lost practically everything he owned during the long period of the Revolutionary War. He ended his life as a bookbinder and as a preacher of the gospel.

August 27

From Kelmscott House in Hammersmith on this day in 1894 William Morris wrote to his intimate friend, the architect Philip Webb, about the books being produced by his famous Kelmscott Press, at the same time getting in his usual little dig at Americans:

"My dear Fellow

"A traveller once entered a western hotel in America & went up to the clerk in his box (as the custom is in that country) and ordered chicken for his dinner: the clerk, without any trouble in his face, put his hand into his desk, and drew out a derringer, wherewith he covered the new-comer and said in a calm historic voice: Stranger, you will not have chicken; you will have hash.

"This story you seem to have forgotten. So I will apply it and say that you will have the Kelmscott books as they come out. In short you will have hash because it would upset me very much if you did not have a share in my 'larx.'

"As to the Olaf Saga I had forgotten what you had had; chiefly I think because I did not prize the big-paper copies much. They were done in the days of ignorance, before the Kelmscott Press was, though hard on the time when it began.

"You see as to all these matters I do the books mainly for you and one or two others; the public does not really care about them a damn—which is stale. But I tell you I *want* you to have them & finally you *shall.*"

When Philip Webb gave all of his Kelmscott Press presentation copies to Trinity College, Cambridge, a printed copy of this letter was inserted in every volume of the collection.

August 28

To contemporary graphic designers, the name of Theodore Brown Hapgood, Jr., a New England Yankee Gentleman who died on this day in 1938, is quite unknown. Yet a fellow designer said of him at his death: "He was a master designer with a passion for lettering. He believed that lettering on a tablet was as essential to the design of the whole as the ornament. . . . It is probably true that the inscriptions, tablets, altar cards, and testimonials which Mr. Hapgood designed are the finest of this kind in the U.S.A."

Born in 1871, Hapgood took his art training at the School of Drawing and Painting of the Art Museum in Copley Square, Boston. He lived his whole life in the State of Massachusetts, maintaining for many years a studio in a building at 69 Cornhill in Boston, which housed also the Publisher Alfred Bartlett and the studio of William A. Dwiggins. It was here also that Thomas

Maitland Cleland maintained for a short period a small printing office.

Hapgood's work embraced a wide range, far beyond that of the modern designer who seeks to specialize just as soon as he is out of art school. His skills included inscriptions in wood, bronze, stone, and marble, hand-illuminated memorials, architectural monuments, and plaques. He was also adept in producing decorative designs for books, including lettering for book covers and for commercial printing. His book plates, while now somewhat dated, are models of intricate design and meticulous lettering.

A fellow Bostonian, the artist and type designer, George F. Trenholm, said of him, "I cannot recall a man who has designed for such a variety of purposes with such facility and consummate skill. He was as catholic in his taste and accomplishments as he was in his mind."

In an age when lettering is more and more becoming a mechanical art, students of good letterform can look to Hapgood's inscriptions as representing the highest standards of craftsmanship. Without question they can investigate to their advantage the broad range of skills represented in a single person. "He worshipped fine craftsmanship," stated one of his close friends. "Therefore, his greatest delight was to provide master craftsmen with designs worthy of their skill."

August 29

"On the 29th day of August, 1862, I commenced the work with one male assistant and four female operatives." With this short statement by Spencer M. Clark, the chief clerk of the Bureau of Construction of the Treasury Department of the United States, recorded the promulgation of his orders from Salmon P. Chase, Secretary of the Treasury. The Bureau of Printing and Engraving could now be considered an active organ of the government.

With the advent of the Civil War the United States Government found it necessary to float a series of loans, as it was upon the verge of bankruptcy. During a special session of the Congress called by President Lincoln on July 4, 1861, Secretary Chase recommended the procedures to be followed, which included the issuance of non-interest-bearing notes which would circulate as money. In spite of the grave doubts entertained by many members of the Congress concerning the constitutionality of the idea, the legislature did authorize the adoption of Chase's plan, and the United States for the first time issued paper money. Having no facilities for printing, the Treasury Department found it necessary to order the paper notes from the American Bank Note Company and the National Bank Note Company, both of which were located in New York City.

Under existing law it was necessary that all of the notes be individually signed by the First or Second Comptroller, or the Register of the Treasury, and then countersigned by "such other officer or officers of the Treasury as the Secretary may designate." Since these officers could scarcely perform this task and fulfill their other obligations at the same time, it quickly became obvious that new regulations would be necessary. In August, 1861, President Lincoln signed a bill authorizing a change in the signature requirements, designating that they be signed by the Treasurer of the United States and the Register of the Treasury. It was also provided that the Secretary could designate other personnel to sign the notes for these officers.

Within a short time, there were seventy clerks, hired at salaries of $1,200 a year, signing their own names to the notes, a practice which was of questionable security in the authentication of the notes. Spencer Clark then suggested that the notes be imprinted with facsimile signatures, that a Treasury seal also be imprinted, and that this work be done on the Treasury premises.

The notes were delivered to the Treasury in sheets of four, which necessitated the employment of seventy women, equipped with scissors, to cut them apart and to trim them to size, at a monthly salary of $50. Clark, appalled at the tediousness of this task, ordered machinery installed to perform this work. In a letter to Clark from Secretary Chase, the Chief Clerk was instructed to "take charge of the preparation for the issue of the one and two dollar Treasury Notes, in accordance as near as practicable, with your program . . . ."

A week after the receipt of this letter, Clark had installed a steam engine and boiler in the basement of the Treasury Building, along with presses for sealing and trimming the notes. The Bureau of Printing and Engraving could thus be considered to be in operation.

August 30

A broadside printed this day in 1734, setting forth the Rules of the Chapel, has survived to become one of the most important sources of information upon the working conditions in the printing office of the 18th century. Some of the rules to be observed by the compositors follow:

"The Stones, Nest of Drawers, &c. to be clear'd by those who last us'd them, within an Hour after Notice, on Forfeiture of 2d.

"For every Capital or other Thing pick'd out of Matter, without putting in something of like Size, the Person so doing to forfeit 1d.

"The Sweeping of every one's Place to be clear'd within a Day, on Pain of forfeiting for every Day 2d.

"Pye belonging to any Person, to be clear'd within two Day after Notice, on Pain of forfeiting 2d.

"Cases to be put into the Frame or Rack within two Hours after done with (if Room) on Pain of forfeiting for each case 1d.

"Braces, Fac-totums, Head-pieces, Tail-pieces, Slips, two-lin'd Letters, to be put into their proper Places in two Hours after done with, on forfeiture of 1d.

"Proof or Revise to be begun to be corrected within a Quarter of an Hour after requir'd, by the Master, or by the Fellow-Workman, unless it appear to the oldest Freeman Compositor, that the Stone cannot be come at, on Forfeiture of 1d.

"He that lays up an Act or Job for his own Conveniency, to tie up the Pages and Indorsement immediately, if not done with. If done with, he that compos'd the Job, or fill'd up the Banks, to tie them up in Pieces convenient for Papering, in two Days after Notice given of their being laid up, on Forfeiture for every Day's Neglect for every Page or Indorsement, of 2d.

"Every form for Distribution, or Papering up, to be wash'd in the Sink, on Pain of forfeiting for each Form 2d.

"If a Form, after laid up and wash'd by the Compositor, remains in the Sink an Hour, after Notice to take it away, the Compositor to forfeit 1d. and for every Hour after 1d.

"No Mixtures of Founts, especially Lower-Case Letters to be permitted; nor of Capitals, without the Consent of the Master, on Forfeiture, for every Mixture of Lower-Case Sorts of 6d. per Sort; and for every Mixture of Capitals, *per* Sort, of 2d."

August 31

When this day happened to occur on a Saturday during the last three centuries, it is probable that English printers took the opportunity to celebrate with a party which has been given the name of wayzgoose. The first factual account of this festivity appeared in the *Mechanick Exercises* of Joseph Moxon, published in 1683. In the section of this manual devoted to "Customs of the Chappel," Moxon describes this typographic soiree:

"It is also customary for all the Journey-men to make every Year new Paper Windows, whether the old will serve again or no; Because that day they make them, the Master Printer gives them a Waygoose; that is, he makes them a good Feast, and not only entertains them at his own House, but besides, gives them Money to spend at the Ale-house or Tavern at Night; And to this Feast, they invite the *Corrector, Founder, Smith, Joyner,* and *Inck-Maker,* who all of them severally (except the Corrector in his own Civility) open their Purse-strings and add their Benevolence (which Workmen account their duty, because they generally chuse these Workmen) to the Master Printers: But from the *Corrector* they expect nothing, the Master Printer chusing him, the Workman can do him no kindness.

"These *Way-gooses,* are always kept about *Bartholomew-tide.* And till the Master-Printer have given this *Way-goose,* the Journey-men do not use to Work by Candle Light."

The origin of the word is unknown, but since Moxon a number of authorities have attempted to define it, and a few puritanical souls have tried to do away with it. Nathan Bailey, in his *Dictionary* of 1731, stated that *Wayz* represented a bundle of straw, and that *Wayzgoose* was therefore a stubble goose, which was the principal dish at the party. The distinguished compilers of the *Oxford English Dictionary* give short shrift to this orthographical fairy tale, asserting that it is a "figment invented in the interest of an etymological conjecture." However, Mr. Bailey's wayzgoose has been honored by becoming the standard name of the celebration rather than the earlier way-goose of Moxon. But no matter what the affair is called, it has been to printers an excuse to howl and to forget their immediate circumstances, no matter what they happened to be.

Possibly the best account of the revelry of the wayzgoose appears in Charles M. Smith's autobiography, *The Working Man's Way in the World,* written in 1857. He described the celebration as taking place in a tavern, large enough to allow "two or three hundred men and boys to disport themselves with pleasure within doors or without." The participants, all dressed in their best clothes, congregated about noon and began the festivities with outdoor games which continued until four o'clock, when dinner was served. It was during the post-prandial proceedings that the conviviality of the occasion began to be obvious, starting with numberless toasts to the health of the Master Printer. After a speech by that personality, a lesser official would receive the same treatment.

When the audience finally ran out of representatives of the Master to toast, new chairmen were immediately nominated, elected, and toasted, each one with more boisterous enthusiasm until all the sober brothers had departed and the wayzgoose declined into a brawl which inevitably scattered inebriated printers all over the landscape, some of whom just as inevitably, were unable to appear for work for several days.

September

September 1

On the first of September in 1906, the strenuous twenty-sixth President of the United States, Theodore Roosevelt, attempted to add spelling reform to his long list of progressive achievements. In a letter to Charles S. Stillings, Public Printer, made public on this day, he said: "I enclose herewith copies of certain circulars of the Simplified Spelling Board, which can be obtained free from the board at No. 1 Madison avenue, New York City. Please hereafter direct that in all Government publications of the Executive Departments the 300 words enumerated in Circular No. 5 shall be spelled as therein set forth. If any one asks the reason for the action, refer him to Circulars 3, 4 and 6, as issued by the Simplified Spelling Board.

"There is not the slightest intention to do anything revolutionary or indicate any far-reaching policy. The purpose simply is for the Government, instead of lagging behind popular sentiment, to advance abreast of it and at the same time abreast of the views of the ablest and most practical educators of our time as well as the most profound scholars—men of the stamp of Professor Lunsbury and Professor Skeat.

"If the slight changes in the spelling of the 300 words proposed wholly or partially meet popular approval, then the changes will become permanent without any reference to what public officials or individual private citizens may feel; if they do not ultimately meet with popular approval they will be dropped, and that is all there is about it.

"They represent nothing in the world but a very slight extension of the unconscious movement which has made agricultural implement makers and farmers write, 'plow' instead of 'plough,' which has made most Americans write 'honor' without the somewhat superfluous 'u,' and which is even now making people write 'program' without the 'me,' just as all people who speak English now write 'bat,' 'set,' 'dim,' 'sum' and 'fish,' instead of the Elizabethan 'batte,' 'sette,' 'dimme,' 'summe' and 'fyshe'; which makes us write 'public,' 'almanac,' 'era,' 'fantasy' and 'wagon,' instead of 'publick,' 'almanack,' 'aera,' 'phantasy' and 'waggon' of our great-grandfathers.

"It is not an attack on the language of Shakespeare and Milton, because it is in some instances a going back to the forms they used, and in others merely the extension of changes which, as regards other words, have taken place since their time. . . ."

"The Edict of Oyster Bay," as the Chicago *Dial* called it editorially, created almost as much havoc in the land as did that of Roosevelt's cousin Franklin, when he changed the date of Thanksgiving some thirty-three years later. After countless letters had been written to editors, and about as many editorials produced by outraged newspapermen, the Congress, as usual, had the last word about the President of the United States interfering with the nation's spelling habits. A rider to the printing money bill of December, 1906 stated, "No part of the compensation provided by this shall be paid to the Public Printer unless he shall, in printing documents authorized by the law or ordered by Congress or either branch thereof, conform in the

173

spelling thereof to the rules of orthography recognized and used by accepted dictionaries of the English language."

To this date residents of the White House have left spelling reform to the pedagogues.

September 2

The *Troy Budget,* an upstate New York weekly of Jacksonian bent, printed a notice on this day during the presidential campaign of 1828:

"During the month of August just passed, we find on looking over our books, that 63 persons have become subscribers. Three persons have discontinued their papers, one because he was moving from the county, one because he had not the time to read it, and one because he was an Adams man, or rather because we were not."

Thus the weekly newspaper editor discussed a matter that was uppermost in the minds of his fellow small town editors—statistics concerning circulation. There were 54 newspapers in the State of New York in 1806, seven of which were New York City dailies; three were semi-weeklies, and three were issued three times a week. One publisher estimated that the average press run was 700 copies, but some authorities of the period consider this to be rather high.

Actually, if an editor could be sure of 100 subscribers he might take a chance in establishing a new sheet. A "most respectable list" was 200 to 400. Success or failure could be measured with a relatively small change in circulation. However, the actual number was not always considered to be the sign of a successful venture. The editor-publisher-printer might enjoy the esteem of his community, but he required some cash income in order to exist and this was not always forthcoming.

Milton W. Hamilton, in his definitive work, *The Country Printer in New York State,* quotes an English observer who stated with some sarcasm that there "was little difficulty in filling up a list with two or three hundred subscribers' names, for probably in no other country where newspapers exist do the subscribers trouble themselves less about finding the means of paying their newspaper subscriptions than they do in the United States."

September 3

When compositors first became automated, they were anxious to exhibit their prowess in the operation of Mergenthaler's Linotype machine by competing with one another in contests of speed typesetting, much as they had done when the hand type-stickers ruled the composing rooms. The machine-age swifts made appearances at county and state fairs and of course at national expositions. On this day in 1904 at the St. Louis Fair, J. F. O'Sullivan demonstrated his virtuosity by setting 6,800 ems of 12-point type solid to a twenty-one pica measure, in one hour at the keyboard of the "Merg."

In this performance O'Sullivan employed all the fingers of both hands in the fashion of a piano player and modestly stated that he frequently wished that nature had been kind enough to endow him with even more fingers and thumbs so that he could give the lino "a run for its money."

A few years later one Charles A. Nichols, an operator employed by the Salt Lake *Herald,* claimed the world's championship for linotype operators by setting 106,300 ems of nonpareil (6-point) in a period of seven hours and fifty-two minutes. This accomplishment occurred during regular working hours, and the slugs which he produced were used in an edition of the newspaper.

Nichols, in his remarkable feat, corrected his own typos, which were primarily machine errors brought about by the difficulty of running out of sorts when the matrix channels of the machine's magazine could not be refilled quickly enough by the distribution system. The machine used had been in constant operation in the composing room of the *Herald* for thirteen years. During the elapsed time of the nimble-fingered Nichols' redoubtable performance, twenty minutes were consumed in machine repair, ten of which were expended in the replacement of a cam. The machine was speeded to nine revolutions per minute, and the machinist proudly noted that even that pace was exceeded at times.

The matter set by Nichols measured 340 inches. Over 190 pounds of metal were needed to set the 4,088 lines of type. The copy was typewritten Sunday matter, with a few takes of reprint. Operator Nichols labored under one difficulty which presumably interfered with his opportunity to establish even more astonishing feats at the keyboard, and that was an inability to use the index finger of his right hand. This might have embarassed an operator of that period, but in today's composing rooms he could readily have held his "sit" with one hand in his pocket.

September 4

As part of a four or five day visit to the Italian city of Turin on September 4, 1506, Desiderius Erasmus Roterodamus, a few weeks prior to his forty-first birthday, received the degree of Doctor of Theology.

Erasmus had received his bachelor's degree in Paris in 1498 and had hoped to secure the doctorate at Cambridge, but in the manner of scholars then and since, he decided instead that courses in several schools would be better than in one. He took advantage of a trip to Italy as tutor of the sons of Henry VII's physician. The Turin degree of course gave greater authority to his name in his printed works, to which he was then devoting most of his time.

In 1496 while in Paris Erasmus had heard of a book by Robert Gaguin, the historian. In it the printer had had the misfortune to complete the last signature with two blank pages. Erasmus volunteered to fill these pages with a eulogy to the historian, and thus "blooded with the printers" as one biographer has put it, "went steadily on."

When in Italy, he wrote to the great Venetian printer, Aldus Manutius, suggesting a new edition of the dramas of Euripedes. Erasmus was attracted to Aldus both by his fame as a scholarly printer and by his "most magnificent letters." As a true bibliophile, the humanist was in love with the appearance of books and rightly knew that Aldus could print his own works in an eminently readable and artistic style.

The two men worked so well together that Erasmus cancelled his projected trip to Rome and remained in Venice at the residence of Aldus' father-in-law, Andrea Asolani, for a period of eight months. Association with printers was to be the true element for Erasmus, and he made the most of the opportunity. In the confusion of the busy printing office he wrote and edited in com-

plete happiness. As he wrote each page the compositors transferred his manuscript into type so rapidly that he had a difficult time in keeping up with them. The library of Aldus was in every way rich in the Greek and Latin classics, and with the circle of scholars attracted to the printing office formed a combination which the visiting philosopher found to be irresistible. He was of the generation which had grown up with the new art of printing, and he was both implemented by it and served it well. Erasmus was one of the first writers to be made famous by the printing press. In his turn he helped to bring to the printed word the reputation for scholarly exactness so necessary during its first century of existence.

September 5

A great and controversial historical figure was this day born in France in the year 1585. Armand Jean du Plessis de Richelieu lived to be a Prince of the Church and First Statesman of France under Louis XIII. Cast as a sinister character by many novelists and not a few historians, Richelieu thought first of France and was enemy only to those whom he believed interfered with her destiny. "Reason must be the rule and guide of all things," he stated, and as a step towards the full realization of that concept he founded in 1640 *L'Imprimerie Royale,* a national printing office now well into its fourth century of service to the French nation.

Its original dedication, given by Louis XIII, "to the glory of France and the Honour of letters," has been mightily fulfilled during those years. Beginning with the *Grecs du Roi,* of which the punches were cut by Claude Garamond about 1550, the establishment presently owns over 300,000 punches and matrices for the composition of some seventy-four languages, both ancient and modern. After the Revolution, the office was renamed in 1795 the *Imprimerie Nationale,* and then under Napoleon became the *Imprimerie Imperiale.* In 1848 the name was changed to *Imprimerie de la République.* This name was altered during the reign of Napoleon II, again becoming the *Imprimerie Imperiale.* Finally in 1870 the famous printing office assumed its present title, the *Imprimerie Nationale.*

Richelieu's pursuit of heretical Protestant sects resulted in the capture of Sedan in 1642. In this location he acquired the typefounding tools, punches and matrices of a printer named Jean Jannon. These were quickly removed to the new royal printing office in time to be of use in the setting of the dying Richelieu's memoirs, *Principaux de la Foi,* the second book to be printed there. The first book had been a splendid *De Imitatione Christi,* composed in a commonly used Parisian type of the period. The Jannon types were not used again until they appeared in a specimen book issued by the office in 1845 in which they were called *Caractères de l'Université,* and ascribed to Claude Garamond. When these types were revived in 1900 they became the model for many of the present-day types which bear the name Garamond.

September 6

George Clymer, teacher, carpenter, cabinet-maker, and indefatigable inventor, received on September 6, 1827 a patent for a platen press capable of printing, as the specification read in part, "two forms of double royal paper at one time, being a surface of four feet six inches by three feet three inches, which is twice the size of the largest newspaper at present printed."

This monster probably was never actually built. Its inventor's reputation remains secure for the development of another press, called the Columbian, which was a distinctive contribution to the history of the hand press. Clymer, who at the age of sixteen had invented a new type of plow for use on his father's Bucks County, Pennsylvania farm, had begun to experiment with printing presses as early as 1800. The first Columbian press was built in 1813 and by April of the following year its manufacturer was ready to make deliveries. The Philadelphia *Aurora,* in its issue of April 26, 1814, printed a panagyric to Clymer, describing two of his presses and their purchase:

"Mr. George Clymer, of this city, with a spirit of persevering industry seldom combined with genius, has directed his attention principally for the last twelve or thirteen years, to the improvement of the *printing press.* Every scheme that appeared at all likely to answer the desired end, has been successively tried by him. . . . The defects of the common press are so numerous, that it is impossible to provide a remedy for every evil. Perhaps there never was a machine invented to effect any purpose that leaves so much to depend on the skill and attention of the workman. To construct a press possessing none of these evils, required the exertions of an ingenious mind cooperating with a mechanical hand. Mr. Clymer has united in himself, those advantages to an eminent degree, and has applied them with a perseverance that deserved and attained success. He has completed, of the most durable metals two presses and through [sic] these are constructed on distinct or different plans, they approach as near perfection as it appears possible. All the defects of the old press are conquered in these. They are planned and perfected on true mechanical principles; not subject to alter or get out of order: there can neither be *adjusting, regulating, levelling, mackling, slurring,* nor *doubling:* they possess so much power that no exertion of strength is required of the workman on the heaviest form. The impression is given at once, by what is termed a double platen, and is equable, clear, and perfect. . . ."

The Columbians were two iron presses, of intricate manufacture, and were considerably more expensive than the then popular Ramage press. As a result, American printers were slow to take advantage of their superiority. Clymer therefore journeyed to England where iron presses were already being produced, and arranged for the manufacture of his press. The Columbian was a resounding success with English printers, in spite of the American eagle which was mounted as a counterweight along with the rattlesnake looped around the nameplate— and of course the name of the press itself. Until the Albion press was introduced, it outsold all of its competitors.

September 7

"September the seventh, 1480, thirteenth indiction. The most honorable tradesman, Nicolas Jenson, alien and printer of books, dwelling at Venice in the Parish of Saint Cancianus, being, by the grace of God, sound in mind and understanding though infirm of body, did send for me, Hieronymo Bonycardi, Public Notary under imperial license, and did seek of me this, his last Will and Testament, the which I have drafted conformably to the law-customs of the Empire, at the desire, consent, and express command of the said testator, in this form, to wit . . . ."

Thus began the will of the French craftsman, Nicolas Jenson, who rose to be master of the mint at Tours and was sent by Charles VII to Mainz to learn the new art of printing. However, along with numerous early practitioners of this craft, he chose instead to journey to Italy rather than to return home. In 1470 Jenson set up a press in Venice, receiving a privilege to print in that city when the monopoly of John of Speier was cancelled.

His first book, the *Epistolae ad Atticum* of Cicero, was composed in a roman font, based upon the humanist manuscripts so much admired in Italy. This letter, cut in a size of about 16-point, was used for scores of books which issued from the press prior to Jenson's death in 1480.

The Jenson type has become justly famous as the first purely roman letter to be cast in metal. It is not known that it was cut by Jenson himself or at his command, but the letter itself has been model for countless recuttings.

The typographic historian Stanley Morison quotes with some approval the encomium of an associate of Jenson concerning the type: ". . . the quality and value of his types is another marvel to relate. . . . the characters are so methodically and carefully finished by that famous man that the letters are not smaller or larger or thicker than reason demands or than may afford pleasure."

Probably the most famous of all the Jenson books was the *De evangelica praeparatione,* written by the 4th century theologian Eusebius, which issued from the press in its first year. William Morris first revived the type used in this volume in the form of his Golden type in the last decade of the 19th century, and it was also the model for the famous Doves Press type of Cobden-Sanderson.

The best of all the modern copies is Centaur, designed by Bruce Rogers, the first use of which—aside from a few private press books— was in the monumental two-volume folio bible which Rogers designed for Oxford University Press. No doubt echoing the praise of many typographers, Centaur is presently being advertised for sale in fonts as "the noblest roman of them all!"

September 8

"The British compositor is wedded to a very unhealthy practice," stated a memorandum of the British Master Printers' Federation, dated this day in 1907, "and with few exceptions, in nearly every office, one of the boxes in the upper case is filled with snuff from which frequent pinches are taken. Lately a feeling has arisen against this practice, and the Master Printers' Federation has issued a notice forbidding snuffing and chewing tobacco as habits conducive to lead poisoning, an industrial disease that renders the employees liable under the new Compensation Act if the worker is laid up through it."

Here was a new twist, aside from the unique use of one of the boxes in the upper case not generally described in the printing manuals. During the long history of poor working conditions in the printing offices of both Europe and the United States, the workers became addicted to snuff, tobacco, and of course alcohol, in order to seek refuge *from* such disorders as lead poisoning and tuberculosis and other respiratory diseases.

As late as 1865 the London compositors were requesting that the length of the work week be limited to fifty-eight hours, and that overtime be additionally compensated. At that time it was not unusual for a printer to be called upon to work for sixteen straight hours with not the slightest additional pay. When requesting the reduction of hours, the compositors cited the statistical information that, according to the report of a Royal Commission, "the death rate of printers is 47 percent higher than that of the whole community, and that 70 percent of the deaths occurring are ascribable to some form of chest disease."

Refuge in tobacco or alcohol was a simple route to escape the despair of working conditions during much of the 19th century. Charles M. Smith wrote of the mid-century printing offices and found it necessary to publish his remarks anonymously:

"The house in which I found myself located bore the stamp of antiquity and dirt, both to a degree perhaps unrivalled in London. . . . Everything like comfort, order, economy, and even decent workmanship, was sacrificed to the paramount object of dispatch—the turning out of the greatest possible quantity of work in the shortest time. . . ."

Describing the scene after he had worked all night long all of the previous day, Smith wrote:

"Morning, dank, misty and foggy, looks in upon the hot, smoky and reeking den. By this time, the atmosphere of the series of black caverns in which business is carried on is becoming disgustingly nauseous, as well as stiflingly hot. Notwithstanding the cold and raw weather without, the perspiration streams from every face within. The entire building is one huge vapour-bath of dismal stenches, from the rank steam of which the soot-black walls and ceilings glisten with moisture. The most severe and inveterate catarrh is sweated out of the system, to be renewed with increasing intensity, at the first contact with the outdoor air. As the dull, wintry light steals on by slow degrees, the candles one by one disappear, and now a few hands who, from feeble health or advanced age, have been allowed to escape the nightwork, reoccupy their frames. Coming in from the fresh air, they are struck aghast with the horrible odour which prevails, and make some attempts at ventilation, which, being clamourously resisted by the majority, they are compelled to relinquish. . . . . By eleven o'clock comes the Ganymade again, with his bunches of clean pots, but the same unwashed face as yesterday. 'Beer' gentlemen!—gentlemen, beer!' meets the same ready response as usual."

September 9

William Bulmer, English printer, died upon this day in 1830 in his seventy-fourth year. His name would appear prominently upon any list compiled of the great English printers of all periods, and he fully deserves this recognition. After serving a Newcastle apprenticeship, Bulmer journeyed to London, where he was employed by John Bell, one of the more careful printers of the period. His career really began, however, with a chance introduction to the King's bookseller, George Nicol, who was at that time in the midst of plans to publish a monumental edition of the works of William Shakespeare.

Another important factor in Bulmer's eventual fame in the annals of English printing was Nicol's selection—prior to meeting Bulmer— of the Birmingham punchcutter, William Martin, to produce the type for this venture. It is the use of this type (which incidentally, in its modern re-cutting, bears the name of Bulmer), that helped to bring to Bulmer the admiration of typographic critics ever since. Martin, a brother of Robert Martin, who was Baskerville's apprentice, produced a letter which while bearing a resemblance to the type of Baskerville, also favors the designs of Giambattista Bodoni, which were at that time greatly admired. The result is a type which, in the words of one writer, "is unquestionably one of the very best ever evolved, both for intrinsic beauty and for its unequalled combination of marked individuality with general applicability."

With Nicol's help, Bulmer set up the Shakspeare Press. In 1794 he completed the first volume of Shakespeare, immediately establishing his reputation as a fine printer. In 1795 he printed the *Poems of Goldsmith and Parnell,* using Martin's types and the wood engravings of his boyhood friend, Thomas Bewick. This volume is considered to be one of the finest productions of the Shakspeare Press and represents possibly the finest printing of the Bewick engravings. In its introductory pages the book carries a notice from its printer indicating his desire to produce first-rate printing:

"To raise the Art of Printing in this country from the neglected state in which it had long been suffered to continue, and to remove the opprobrium which had but too justly been attached to the late productions of the English press, much has been done within the last few years; and the warm emulation which has discovered itself amongst the Printers of the present day, as well in the remote parts of the Kingdom as in the metropolis, has been rightly patronized by the public in general. The present volume, in addition to the SHAKSPEARE, the MILTON, and many other valuable works of elegance, which already have been given to the world, through the medium of the Shakspeare Press, are particularly meant to combine the

various beauties of PRINTING, TYPE-FOUND-
ING, ENGRAVING, and PAPER-MAKING; as
well with a view to ascertain the near approach to perfection which those arts have
attained in this country, as to invite a fair
competition with the best Typographical
Productions of other nations."

September 10

The life of a proofreader in France was made
more carefree this day in 1572 when a royal
edict was published, saying, "The master
printers shall deliver to compositors only
copy which has been revised, edited, and put
in proper form, to the end that the labor of
typesetting shall not be slowed down by defective copy."

Some thirty years previously François I
had issued regulations for the control of
printing in Paris which had placed upon the
proofreaders the complete responsibility for
the production of correct texts. The controversial section of these regulations stated:
"If the master printers producing books in
Latin are not learned enough to correct the
books which they print, they are required
to employ capable correctors, under penalty
of arbitrary fine. These correctors must correct the books with care and diligence, making their revisions in accord with classic
standards, and in all respects do their duty.
Otherwise they will be held liable for dam-
ages incurred through errors for which they
are to blame."

The exactness of the texts of books being
printed in Paris during this period was a
matter of great controversy among the scholars at the University. Chartier, a professor
of medicine who was editing an edition of
Hippocrates in both Greek and Latin, was
unable in 1637 to obtain a corrector who had
sufficient competence for the task and found
it necessary to enlist the services of a learned
friend. In some dudgeon, the Professor suggested that regulations be set governing the
problem: "1. That all printed books in which
appeared a certain number of errors should
be suppressed. 2. That no master printer who
did not know Greek and Latin should engage in the trade. 3. That the salaries of
correctors should be generous and that only
the most capable should be employed. 4.
That there should always be three correctors

who should read each proof in succession."

It was observed that such proposed regulations were not practical as in themselves
they did not explain just how and where
such savants were to be obtained. Nevertheless the propositions were included in new
regulations, although they were not rigidly
enforced.

Finally in 1744 a Decree of Council provided that booksellers and printers who desired to act as correctors of their own editions could do just this, but that they would
be responsible for any errors, which had to
be corrected prior to the publication of the
book.

G. A. Crapelet, writing in Paris in 1831
about the responsibilities of the proofreader,
stated: "It is, in fact, impossible for a master printer, in addition to his general business
responsibilities, to read proofs with that
complete tranquility of spirit essential to this
type of work. Education, intelligence, good
memory, taste, patience, application, love of
the art, and especially the typographic eye
constitute the minimum qualifications required in the corrector to whom is entrusted
the proofreading of the office."

September 11

"To bring together the posies of other men
bound by a thread of one's own choosing is
the simple plan of the editor of the Bibelot.

"In this way those exotics of Literature
that might not immediately find a way to
wider reading, are here reprinted, and, so
to speak, resown in fields their authors never
knew. . . . Besides this, to more widely extend
the love of exquisite literary form, it must be
shown by example that choice typography
and inexpensiveness need not lie far apart."

Thus wrote Thomas Bird Mosher, of
Portland, Maine, who was born this day in
1852. The statement appeared in the first
number of a little periodical for book lovers
which was published monthly for twenty
years, between 1895 and 1915. Mosher, the
son of a State of Maine sea captain, himself
followed his father's calling for a five year
period, but finally decided upon a landsman's
career when he came of age. He went to
work as a clerk in a law-stationer's office
in Portland, but finding law books unsuited
to his tastes, he spent a year or two as a

clerk in a bookshop in St. Louis, Missouri.

Returning to Portland, he again became connected with law publishing, becoming a partner in the firm of Dresser and McLellan. A love of literature and fine books promoted his establishment of his own firm, the Mosher Press, in 1891. At 39 years of age he began a career and became, in the words of Norman Strouse, his only biographer to date, "One of the most remarkable printer-publishers in the private press movement on either side of the Atlantic."

In England, William Morris was ready to embark on his own effort to promote the printer's craft, although his route was not at all that of Mosher, whose desire was to make literature readily available in tasteful format at a low price, while Morris catered to the purse of the wealthy book collector.

The first of 332 titles which Mosher was to issue from his press prior to his death in 1923, was George Meredith's *Modern Love*. Its physical appearance was to set the pattern which makes the Mosher books easily recognizable, although each book received an individual treatment. Most of the books were issued in series, all small volumes.

With the publication of the Andrew Lang translation of *Aucassin and Nicolete* in 1895, Mosher was involved in charges of piracy, as Lang, in England, accused him of printing without permission. Mosher wrote a letter to the English book periodical *The Critic,* in which he said, in part, that he was opposed to "the fad with authors and their publishers to kowtow to the wealthier classes and at the same time play into the hands of the speculative bookseller." He also argued that the translation was not in copyright, and that the limited and high priced English edition did not receive the wide circulation it deserved. Later on Mosher met Lang in London, and after a discussion they parted friends.

Bruce Rogers, who always disliked the American propensity to match any individual with an historical figure, thought enough of Mosher to call him a "XIX Century Aldus," which was a fitting comparison indeed.

September 12

Born in Baltimore, Maryland on September 12, 1880 was Henry Louis Mencken, one of the great American men of letters of our time. No matter how fine a reputation Mencken enjoyed as a writer, critic, philologist, he was most content to consider himself a newspaperman. As such he always had an affinity for printers, particularly those he knew during the early years of his career, the first decade of the century. Toward the end of his life when he had been incapacitated by a stroke, he was asked his opinion of present-day printers. He stated that they were not the same breed he had earlier worked with, and remarked that he had recently heard that printers now played golf. "This is almost obscene," he remarked.

Of course whenever printers are discussed professionally, their capacity for alcohol becomes an item of the conversation. In the second volume of his autobiography, *Newspaper Days,* Mencken describes some of these attributes on the part of the printers and newspaper people of the day.

"Between 1899 and 1904 there was only one reporter south of the Mason & Dixon Line who did not drink at all, and he was considered insane. In New York, so far as I could make out, there was not even one. On my first Christmas Eve on the *Herald* but two sober persons were to be found in the office—one of them a Seventh Day Adventist office-boy in the editorial rooms, and the other a superannuated stereotyper who sold lunches to printers in the composing room. There was a printer on the payroll who was reputed to be a teetotaler—indeed his singularity gave him the nickname of the Moral Element—, but Christmas Eve happened to be his night off. All of the rest were full of what they called hand-set whiskey. This powerful drug was sold in a saloon next door to the *Herald* office, and was reputed to be made in the cellar by the proprietor in person—of wood alcohol, snuff, tabasco sauce, and coffin varnish. The printers liked it, and got down a great many shots of it. On the Christmas Eve I speak of its effects were such that more than half the linotype machines in the composing room broke down, and one of the apprentices ran his shirt-tail through the proof press. Down in the press room four or five pressmen got hurt, and the city edition was nearly an hour late."

*   *   *

"The hero of the *Herald* composing room in those days was a fat printer named Bill, who was reputed to be the champion beer drinker of the Western Hemisphere. Bill was a first-rate linotype operator, and never resorted to his avocation in working-hours, but the instant his time was up he would hustle on his coat and go to a beerhouse in the neighborhood, and there give what he called a setting. He made no charge for admission, but the spectators, of course, were supposed to pay for the beer. One night in 1902 I saw him get down thirty-two bottles in a row. Perhaps, in your wanderings, you have seen the same—but have you ever heard of a champion who could do it without once retiring from his place at the bar? Well, that is what Bill did, and on another occasion when I was not present, he reached forty. Physiologists tell me that these prodigies must have been optical delusions, for there is not room enough in the coils and recesses of a man for so much liquid, but I can only reply *Pfui* to that, for a record is a record. Bill avoided the door marked "Gents" as diligently as if he had been a debutante of the era, or the sign on it had been "For Ladies Only." He would have been humiliated beyond endurance if anyone had ever seen him slink through it."

September 13

On September 13, 1587 the Italian language was first printed in England, with the august permission of John Whitgift, Archbishop of Canterbury. The vehicle for this initial publication was, surprisingly, *The Decameron* of Giovanni Boccaccio. Whitgift certainly did not have the reputation of admiring light literature, but Timperley reports that permission was granted primarily because of the wide popularity of Italian in this era of English history.

Queen Elizabeth had elevated Whitgift to the see of Canterbury in 1583 so that he might exercise his gifts in suppressing the Puritan uprising. This he proceeded to do with some relish, tracking down a number of printers, who were convicted for publishing ideas heretical to both Crown and Church, and forthwith executed. He undoubtedly had some cause to be harsh in his method, as the printers moved about from place to place, defying authority while castigating the ecclesiastics at every opportunity. Eventually the controversy died down,

and Elizabeth's "little black husband," as she called the Archbishop, survived the harsh period and lived to pray at his Queen's deathbed in 1603.

Following the printing of the Boccaccio, the Bishop of London allowed to be printed another work by the same writer, entitled *Amourous Fiametta*. The titlepage of the latter work reads: "Wherein is sette down a catalogue of all and singular passions of love and jealousie, incident to an enamored young gentlewoman, with a noble caveat for all women to eschewe deceitful and wicked love, by an apparent example of a Neapolitan lady, her approved and long miseries, and with many sound dehortations from the same."

September 14

"The Typophiles of New York greet you, Sjoerd Hendrik de Roos, on this your seventieth birthday, & wish you a long continuance of health and years in which to minister to the arts of the book. May your dedicated craftsmanship in type design, in printing and in binding inspire in the rising generation of bookmakers a quickened sense of the worth and the dignity of the printed book. In token of our regard for yourself and for your versatile talents we sign this message collectively, and send you separately some recent Typophile publications, suitably inscribed. We wish to be considered your admiring friends, proud to belong (with you) among the world's kindred of booklovers. And since bookmakers (no less than their books) too have their fates, may the world's celebration of your 70th birthday teach all nations to unite in preserving civilization even as we now unite in honoring you. 1877-1947, The Typophiles De Roos Day, 14 September."

S. H. de Roos, typographer and type designer, shared with his countryman Jan van Krimpen, the honor of being the outstanding typographer of his time in Holland. As a boy he had studied art, with the result that, following evening courses at the Royal Academy of Fine Arts in Amsterdam, he acquired sufficient talents in lithography to accept commissions in that field. Simultaneously, through a developing interest in the art of the book, he bcame a bookbinder. Through his work with books he enlarged his viewpoint to include the typography of the book, studying in particular, the book design of England, Germany, and the United States.

In 1903 de Roos was given the opportunity to design the format of the Dutch edition of *Art and Society,* by William Morris. His admiration of Morris as an artist and as a printer inspired him to produce a book which was enthusiastically received and is now considered to be one of the important books in the history of Dutch typography. His growing reputation as a book designer prompted the Typefoundry Amsterdam to engage him as artistic advisor. This association was to last for a period of thirty-five years, and to result in a number of printing types for that foundry which have enhanced the reputation of Dutch typefounding.

The first type design was a Javanese letter, followed by one of his most successful types, Holland Medieval, a letter styled upon the types of the great 15th century Venetian typographer, Nicolas Jenson. Medieval has proved to be exceedingly popular, now being available in a series, accompanied by initials. The next types of de Roos were Erasmus, a somewhat lighter letter, and Meidoorn, which was inspired by the Subiaco type of Sweynheim and Pannartz. The type which made de Roos well-known in the United States was Egmont, cut in 1932.

Possibly the best known of all the de Roos types is the uncial letter, Libra, which was offered by the foundry in 1939.

De Roos died in 1962 at the age of 84, honored as a great typographer whose influence has extended far beyond the borders of his native land.

September 15

In the city of Paris on this day in 1712 was born into the family of the printer and typefounder Jean Claude Fournier, a son— Simon Pierre or as he is more commonly known, Pierre Simon. The younger Fournier made a unique contribution to typefounding, both in theory and practice, by inventing a system of type measurement and by writing a book on typefounding in which he outlined his methods. "The invention of these points is the first service which I rendered to printing, 1737. Obliged then to commence a long, painful, and laborious career by the graving of all the punches necessary to form the establishment of my foundery, I found no rule established which could guide me in fixing the body of the characters which I had to make, and I was thus under the necessity of forming them for myself."

Finding the lack of standards in the size of type most annoying, Fournier *le jeune* set to work to correct the situation by a method best described in his own words: "This then is what engaged me to disentangle this chaos, and to give these matters an order which they have never before had. I think I have the happiness to succeed in it, with an exactness and precision which leaves nothing to be desired, by the invention of *Typographical Points.* It is nothing more than the division of the bodies of characters by equal and determinate degrees, which I call *Points.* By this means, the degrees of distance and affinity of the bodies may be known exactly. They can be combined together in the same manner as numerical signs; and as two and two make four, add two, it will become Nonpareille, which is equal to six points, added to another Nonpareille will make together a Cicero, which has twelve points, add again a Nonpareille, you will have eighteen points, or a Grosromain . . . .

"In order to combine the bodies, it will be sufficient to know the number of *Typographical Points* of which they are composed. . . . For this purpose, I have fixed these points at the exact sizes they ought to have, in the scale which is at the head of the *Table of Proportions* . . . . The table exhibits at the top a fixed and definite scale, which I divide into two inches, the inches into twelve lines, and the line into six typographical points; the total is 144 points. The first small divisions are of two points, which is the exact distance which there is from a Petit-texte to a Petit-romain, or from that to a Cicero, &c."

While the point system today varies mathematically from that of Fournier, the terminology remains the same. The Anglo-American Point System, evolved in 1886, has as its basic unit a point of .01383″ while that of Fournier measured .0137″. Neither of these measurements, nor the present-day European system devised by Didot, adhere to the metric system and are of course inexact by modern mathematical standards.

But we must credit Fournier with the first overture towards precision procedures in the composing room.

September 16

With Thomas MacKellar in the chair, a meeting of the typefounders of the United States began on this day in 1886, in the Spencer House at Niagara Falls, New York. The press release stated: "The representatives of twenty of the largest and best foundries in the United States were present, and never was there a congregation of men more in earnest, and resolved to change the aspect of affairs. Typefounding is a grand art, and demands the exercise of the mental capacity in a very high degree."

Although the great thing that was accomplished at this convention was the adoption of a system of point sizes for American types, nobody seems to have told the printers. In a letter to *The Inland Printer* in October, 1886, an anonymous person named "Typo" wrote:

"The standard of Marder, Luse & Co., Chicago, and the new standards of the Central Type Foundry, St. Louis, and the Johnson Type Foundry [MacKellar, Smiths & Jordan], Philadelphia, are exactly the same, being .966″ to six picas, and the quads and spaces from either of these foundries work perfectly together. There is not the imperceptible difference that you allege, nor is there any difference, these foundries having all in fact adopted the same *interchangeable* standard of the Chicago Type Foundry."

The following month in the same periodical, "Typo" was answered by "Cerberus" in this manner:

"Your correspondent 'Typo' in the October number, undertakes to correct you on the subject of type bodies, but even *he* does not get at the 'bottom facts.' When he says, 'the new standards for the point system, adopted by the Johnson type foundry, Central type foundry, and Marder, Luse & Co., are based on the same standard pica' he says truly; but when he said, 'these foundries adopted the standard of the Chicago type foundry' he did *not* inform you from whence that foundry obtained it. Did it fall from the clouds? Certainly it was not a heavenly *body*. Else it had not chosen 'wicked Chica-go' for an abiding place. As is well known to many old printers in Chicago and the West, the Chicago type foundry was established as a branch of the old New York type foundry (now Farmer, Little & Co.) who made the first type cast in Chicago. The original pica standard has never been changed; and as a natural sequence, it follows that the standard now almost universally adopted by the founders of the United States is that of Farmer, Little & Co."

September 17

"This cannot be an easy life. We shall have a rugged time of it to keep our minds open and to keep them deep, to keep our sense of beauty and our ability to make it, and our occasional ability to see it, in places remote and strange and unfamiliar; . . ."

This quotation, from the pen of the physicist, Robert Oppenheimer, was read at the memorial service for a fine American printer on September 17, 1955. To Arthur W. Rushmore the words represented his own credo and he had them printed in the *Golden Hind Commonplace Book,* completed a short time prior to his death over the imprint of his private press. Rushmore had been introduced to the printing of books in 1904, when he went to work for the firm of Harper & Brothers. Here he remained until his retirement in 1950, at which time he was director of design and manufacture.

The Golden Hind Press began with a 14 x 17 hand press which had been discarded by the Harper cut room. To it was added somewhat later a 24 x 36 Washington hand press, which would enable Rushmore to print anything "we should ever be ambitious enough to try." The type collection of the new enterprise soon included some distinguished designs. From Fred Goudy's Village Letter Foundery come Goudy Text, Deepdene, Medieval, Truesdell, and Goudy Antique. To these were added ATF Bulmer and Garamond, along with that perennial private press favorite, Original Oldstyle Italic of the now defunct A. D. Farmer & Son foundry. The European foundries were represented with Lutetia from Enschedé in Holland, and Wallau, Weiss and Elizabeth from Germany. Few private presses in the land were so well endowed, but of course even fewer boasted a proprietor so professional.

In addition to an annual Christmas keepsake, the Golden Hind Press produced almost eighty limited edition books for the Harper imprint. The best known were the special editions of the poems of Edna St. Vincent Millay. By 1950 the output of the Press had reached a total of 180 books. As Rushmore then stated, "Type, galleys, and books creep like a rising tide through the house. But the compensations have been many: it has brought us the nicest possible friends; it has deepened our respect for fine work wherever we see it; and, the best of all, we have enjoyed that pleasure which only creative work seems to give. Who could ask for more?"

September 18

The art of printing came to Venice this day in 1469 upon the granting of a privilege to print to a Bavarian printer, Johannes da Spira, by the Senate of the city. The privilege gave Da Spira the exclusive right to print for a period of five years, a practice which became quite common in the Italian city states when printing was gaining a foothold. If a printer could exercise a monopoly, he was quite ready to establish himself in any locality which could offer it to him.

Da Spira brought with him his brother Wendelin, and the pair began at once to set up their printing office. Their selection of Venice was dictated by strictly commercial reasons. In fact the German traders in that city were instrumental in helping Johannes to secure the privilege. From its geographic location Venice was at the time the center of European trade, and it was natural that printing be a part of it. Latin was then the universal language of the scholar wherever he might be located. Thus the early Venetian printers were in an excellent position to print for the whole of Europe, utilizing the first class transportation routes maintained by the traders, which spread from Venice in every direction. Within a relatively short period there were over two hundred printers in Venice. According to E. P. Goldschmidt, "Barrels of books left Venice every day." He was of course referring to the method of printing then used in book production which was to print the books and ship them in sig-

natures. The bookseller or the private customer of the printer preferred to have his books bound in his own style, some of the wealthy purchasers maintaining binding establishments of considerable size.

The first book to be issued by Da Spira was a folio edition of Cicero's *Epistolae ad familiares*. The type for this volume is a roughly hewn roman letter in the style of the humanist scribes but with gothic characteristics. Stanley Morison, the great historian of typography, says of Da Spira's roman that "it is fine for its time, broad but spoiled by ill-proportioned capitals, too heavy for the lowercase and ungainly in cut."

The Cicero of Da Spira thus became the first book to be produced in what became the first great printing center, which according to Bernard saw the printing of over two million copies of books by 1500, a period of just thirty-one years.

September 19

The Council of Venice, on this day in 1492, appointed Giovanantonio Tagliente as writing-master in the Chancery of the Council. The appointment was over a year late, as Tagliente had addressed to the Council a Supplication for employment in May, 1491:

"Most Illustrious and Excellent Prince, pious and glorious council! Humbly and devotedly sheweth for his part your faithful servant and subject Giovanantonio Tagliente, citizen by birth. Whereas, persuaded by many virtuous gentlemen and citizens that he should settle again in this renowned city, in order to make known and teach the true art and mystery of writing every variety of letter that a man can write, as manifestly throughout all Italy and likewise in this dominion he hath by experience demonstrated [can be done] briefly and at little cost. And resolving to live and die in his native place, and under the shadow of your Sublimity, and to demonstrate such a secret to the servants and signatories of your Signory, and to every person who would delight in such a faculty or science. Reverently maketh supplication that it may please your illustrious Signory to provide him with some convenient stipend, so that by means of it the said (Giovanantonio Tagliente) may live with his family under the shadow of your Sublimity. Offering himself to teach and instruct chancery writing with its rules to all the young men dedicated to your Exellency's Chancery without other expense. Further, to any other person who would wish to learn to write, for two ducats only, for every sort of letter he would like, whether *antiqua, cancelleresca, mercadantesca, moderna* or *bastarda*. To your eminence and grace he humbly commendeth himself."

Tagliente's position as one of the triumvirate of great calligraphers of the early 16th century, which included Vicentino Arrighi and Giovanbattista Palatino, ranks him in third place. But as a noted teacher his influence was undoubtedly of greater importance within the ranks of calligraphers than that of his fellow writing-masters. It was in 1522 that Arrighi, who was employed in the Papal Chancery, published his book on writing, the *Operina*. No doubt Tagliente was spurred into action by the immediate popularity of the Arrighi work, as just two years later he produced his own writing manual, *Opera di G. A. Tagliente*. Unlike the *Operina*, which was directed toward a study of the chancery hand, Tagliente's book covered the variety of scripts used in legal and documentary work. Its success was immediate. During the 16th century it was reprinted at least thirty times under various titles.

The Italian writing-masters of that period called the cursive writing which they produced, *cancellaresca corsiva*, a term which, in the present-day revival of calligraphy is sometimes confusing. Actually a chancery was any office from which correspondence of various kinds was issued, and they were located all over Italy. The issuance of Arrighi's *Operina* has frequently misled a number of writers to refer to the Arrighi hand as the only example of what we call chancery writing. During our own period, most of the writing styles of the Renaissance are simply recorded under the rather general heading of calligraphy.

September 20

On this day in 1900 was born the charming lady who made her reputation as a man. Well! Who ever heard of a woman who knew anything about type? So it was quite natural that when Beatrice Warde completed her research which proved that Garamond type was not originally designed by Claude Garamond, she could not possibly publish the brilliant paper under her own name. Thus "Paul Beaujon" became its author, and when the English Monotype firm invited M. Beaujon to London to offer him a position, she showed up, overwhelmed the officers of the company, accepted the job, and is still there, fortunately having proved during the last forty years that a lady very definitely can be a most knowledgeable typographer.

When Mrs. Warde left Columbia University as a young librarian she was most fortunate in securing a post as assistant to Henry Lewis Bullen, librarian of the American Type Founders Library. The world's printers may also consider themselves fortunate that BW entered a typographic library for that first job, as her great enthusiasm for the production of the printed word has brought her international recognition as an outstanding authority of the printer's craft.

Mrs. Warde has made herself a spokesman for first-rate typography and has never lowered her standards. During visits to most of the English speaking countries, she has been primarily interested in talking to printing students, holding before them the finest examples of the typographer's art and demanding that they seek out the best. She has fearlessly faced modern art students and has told them how important it is to attempt to understand the viewpoint of the practical printer. Appearing before the annual meeting of the National Society for Art Education, BW said, in part, "Do not confuse him (the student) by the modern phrase 'closed trade': use the technical term our ancestors used and call composition an *Art and Mystery* (sometimes requiring arduous initiation): show him why it is the most responsible manual art known to civilization. . . . Use, exploit that pang of envy to build in him a profound respect for compositors, a habit of respect which will be invaluable to him when the time comes for *him* to command *their* respect as the coordinator of the whole job."

BW's inscription, "This Is a Printing Office," is unquestionably the most widely distributed tribute of its kind ever to be written. Along with several pieces and her many reasoned essays on typography, it has been the means of stimulating countless imaginations concerning the art of the printer. A tireless salewoman for what she believes, BW is no stranger to America, although she has lived in England since the Twenties. No matter how frequently she returns to these shores, she is sure to be feted by all the groups devoted to typography. She is just as sure to renew her personal testimonial to all that is the best in her field.

September 21

On the evening of September 21, 1899, Edward Johnston stood up and faced the seven students who represented his first class in writing and lettering at the Central School of Arts and Crafts in London. At that point Johnston placed himself among those who were solidly responsible for the revival of interest in fine printing in the early years of the 20th century.

A teacher's effectiveness can best be measured by the inspired direction he uses to motivate his students. In this respect Johnston was a resounding success. Eric Gill, Grailey Hewitt, Anna Simons, Percy Smith, and Harold Curwen were all to look back to Johnston's classes as the beginning of outstanding careers. Perhaps Gill paid his former instructor the most eloquent tribute when he wrote in his *Autobiography:*

"It was through Edward Johnston that I threw off the art nonsense of the Chichester art-school. . . . I won't say that I owe everything that I know about lettering to him . . . but I owe everything to the foundation which he laid. And his influence was much more than that of a teacher of lettering. He profoundly altered the whole course of my life and all my ways of thinking. And as a writer with the pen, a calligrapher—it will have to be sufficient if I say that the first time I saw him writing, and saw the writing that came as he wrote, I had that thrill and tremble of the heart which otherwise I can only remember having had . . . when I first heard the plain-chant of the Church (as they sang it at Louvain in the Abbey of Mont Cèsar) or when I first entered the church of San Clemente in Rome, or first saw the North Transept of Chartres from the little alley between the houses. . . . But these more sudden enlightenments are rare events, never forgotten, never overlaid. On that evening I was thus rapt."

From his lectures Johnston published in 1906 *Writing & Illuminating, & Lettering,* a text which had far-reaching influence in the study of letterforms and which has subsequently gone through many editions. During his career Johnston illuminated and drew initials for many of the great private presses, such as Doves, Ashendene, and Cranach. His most important public commission came in 1919 with the sans serif lettering for the London Underground. It was this style of letter which had a marked influence in the revival of sans serif types just a few years later in the program of the Bauhaus movement in Germany.

Johnston died at the age of 72 in 1944. Four years later there appeared the privately printed *Tributes to Edward Johnston* in which James Wardrop wrote: "Better than anyone else since the days of Charlemagne, he understood, and learned to manipulate that infinitely complex, but universal and elementary thing we call the alphabet."

September 22

The present writer has discovered, inserted in a copy of the famous specimen book issued by American Type Founders Company in 1892 (the first to include the offerings of the various foundries which had amalgamated in 1892), a printer's billhead for the sale of one thousand letterheads in two colors. The invoice was dated this day in 1884, but the most interesting thing about it was its design, representing as it did, the height of typographical fashion for its period. It was printed in four colors and contained, in addition to the name of the firm, two triangles of different size, a semi-circular scroll, and a dozen or so rules twisted into various shapes.

No doubt the compositor who designed this piece was immensely proud of his craftsmanship, since it was a splendid representative of the technique called rule-bending. During the 1870's and '80's, rule-bending reached the proportions of a craze, with each comp trying harder to outdo his brother typo in making up the most intricate and involved ornaments with brass rules. The practice represented for a time the *avante garde* typography of its period. But it was quickly accepted as a standard and was thus allowed the opportunity to flower and then to wither. While the practice lasted, however, the compositor who could twist rules with imagination was an important man in any commercial composing room.

To adequately handle this typographic contortion, the comp needed more equipment than the simple bodkin and tweezers. Alongside his frame, if he was an "artist," was a glue-pot and quite probably a supply of plaster of paris. Another item he required was something his present-day brother lacks, and that was time—time to plan a design and hours to contort both rules and type to his purpose. The equipment manufacturers came forward with a rule-bending apparatus, "which enables brass rule to be curved to various ornamental shapes with ease." The directions further stipulated that it was better, "when using metal rules, to hold them over a gas or spirit flame before bending."

Next in line to keep the craze rolling were the typefounders, anxious to supply the myriad range of sorts which were added to the rule-bending for more artistic effect. The firm of MacKellar, Smiths & Jordan stated that, "at no time since the invention of their art have printers been so fully supplied as at present with typographic implements for producing exact and beautiful work. . . . Among late novelties are several beautiful series of ingenious adjustable characters for the ornamentation of display lines, both straight and elliptical."

At about the time that even the most versatile comps could do no more than produce what everyone else was doing, the trend shifted—away from the curves and the bends to panels and angles. This practice became even more widespread than the bending, as, to be fully effective, the panels had to be intricately interwined with one another throughout the job being composed, were it a title page or a full-page advertisement.

September 23

Benjamin Franklin, in his role as entrepreneur, inserted in the columns of his newspaper, the *Pennsylvania Gazette,* on this day in 1742 an advertisement on behalf of his friend William Parks, the pioneer printer of Virginia: "An honest and diligent Person, that is capable of building a good Paper-mill, and another that understands the Making of Paper, are wanted to undertake and carry on that Business in a neighboring Colony. Any such Persons that want Employment, will meet with a Person who will give good Encouragement, if they apply to the Printer of this Paper on the 25th Instant."

A Pennsylvania papermaker, Johan Conrad Schütz, applied for the job. Later he went down to Williamsburg, where he constructed the first paper mill in the state of Virginia. He returned home early in 1744, presumably having taught the local people the craft. Having the mill, however, did not assure Parks of a continuous supply of paper to be used in his printing operations. The problem which plagued his mill was the lack of rags with which to make the paper. Franklin, of course, was ready to supply these, at the standard rate of exchange, which was 4*d* a pound for "Fine pick't rags," and 1½*d* for the ordinary variety. In a four-year period Franklin sold to Parks over eleven thousand pounds of rags at these prices, part of which was paid for by the production of the mill.

In an attempt to secure a local supply, Parks inserted the following *Ode* in his own newspaper, the *Virginia Gazette,* issue of July 26, 1744:

"Tho' sage Philosophers have said,
Of nothing, can nothing be made;
Yet much thy Mill, O Parks brings forth
From what we reckon nothing worth. . . .
(And long that gen'rous Patriot live
Who for soft Rags, hard Cash
will give!). . . .
Ye Fair, renown'd in Cupid's Field,
Who fain would tell what Hearts
you've killed;
Each Shift decay'd, lay by with care;
Or Apron rubb'd to bits at—Pray'r,
One Shift ten Sonnets may contain,
To gild your Charms, and make
you vain;
One Cap, a Billet-doux may shape,
As full of Whim, as when a Cap,
And modest 'Kerchiefs Sacred held
May sing the Breasts they once conceal'd."

Evidently this plea in verse did not have the results which Printer Parks expected. In this respect his position was no different from that of any of the other colonial papermakers, as the difficulty of securing rags was one of the hazards of the craft.

September 24

On this day in 1905 one L. E. Cassatt, foreman of the Idaho Springs *Gazette,* took pen in hand to inform the Queen City Printing Ink Company of Cincinnati about a job of printing he had produced using the firm's ink. "Dear Sirs," wrote Mr. Cassatt, a compositor and pressman of forty years' experience, "Today I take the liberty of sending you a prospectus printed with your 'H.D.' book ink. At first glance you will say that the presswork is not so extraordinary, but when you learn the conditions under which the work was done, you will agree with me that it is remarkable and would be impossible to accomplish with any other ink than the Queen City 'H.D.' book ink without serious offsetting.

"This work was done on an old two-roller Chicago Taylor press. This press was brought over the plains with an ox team before the advent of railroads. It was put in commission in Denver and run for a number of years. It was repaired and sent to Leadville, during the great mining excitement in that city, where it was operated for a long period. After it was supposed to have been worn out in Leadville, it was repaired again and shipped by jack (or burro) to Aspen. On its way from Leadville to Aspen, a peculiar accident happened. One of the side frames, being strapped on the backs of a couple of burros, the animals lost their equilibrium on a narrow mountain pass and side frame and animals went down the precipice almost perpendicular, some five or six hundred feet. The burros were killed outright and it is almost needless to say the frame was broken in a dozen places. After the press reached Aspen, the broken parts were riveted together and the old machine entered upon another long period of usefulness. After being worn out for the third time, and supposed to be beyond redemption, it was shipped back to Denver, where both ends of the cylinder shaft were spliced and the machine otherwise repaired. It was sold to the Idaho Springs (Colo.) *Gazette* some twelve or fifteen years ago where it has been in commission ever since. And this is the history of the old machine on which I recently printed the prospectus which I send you to-day. I claim there is no two-roller press in existence, and especially a country cylinder, that can print cuts such as are in this prospectus without the aid of the Queen City 'I.D.' book, which stands without a peer for fine cutwork."

September 25

"It is designed, that the Countrey shall be furnished once a moneth (or if any Glut of Occurrences happen, oftener,) with an Account of such considerable thaings as have arrived unto our Notice."

Thus, bravely, did Numb. 1 of *Publick Occurrences Both Foreign and Domestic,* appear on the streets of Boston on Thursday, September 25th in the year 1690. A four-page newspaper with a type page just 4-7/8 x 8-5/8 inches, *Publick Occurrences* can claim the distinction of being the first American newspaper. The sheet also may be listed as competing for the title of being the shortest-lived paper to appear on this continent. Unfortunately, its publisher, Benjamin Harris, had neglected to check out his operation with the local authorities.

On September 29 the Governor and Council of Massachusetts issued a statement to the effect that the newspaper had published "Without the least Privity or Countenance of Authority." They further expressed their "high Resentment and Disallowance of said Pamphlet," and forthwith ordered "that the same be Suppressed and called in; strictly forbidding any person or persons for the future to Set forth any thing in Print without License first obtained."

Quite possibly the authorities were not at all amused by the sprightly handling of the news by Editor Harris, as his sheet was better written than many of the officially accredited newspapers which began to appear about fifteen years later. In their suppression statement they had hinted "that therein is contained Reflections of a very high nature: As also sundry doubtful and uncertain Reports." Such a reflection was perhaps the gossip concerning the immoralities of the King of France, in addition to some irreligious remarks about the recently completed French and Indian War.

Ben Harris, the publisher of America's first newspaper, was an English bookseller who had come to Boston four years earlier after serving a prison sentence for his connection with the Popish Plot, a supposed conspiracy of English Catholics to burn London and kill off all the Protestants. A contemporary account says of Harris:

"He was a brisk asserter of English liberties, and once printed a book with that very title. He sold *A Protestant Petition,* in King Charles's reign, for which they fined him £500, and set him once in the pillory; but his wife, (like a kind rib,) stood by him to defend her husband against the mob. After this [having a deal of mercury in his natural temper,] he travelled to New England, where he followed bookselling, and then coffee selling, and then printing, but continued Ben Harris still; and is now both bookseller and printer, in Gracechurch-street, as we find by his *London Post;* so that his conversation is general, (but never impertinent,) and his wit pliable to all invention. But yet his vanity, (if he has any,) gives no allay to his wit, and is no more than might justly spring from conscious virtue; and I do him but justice in this part of his character, but in once travelling with him from Bury fair, I found him to be the most ingenuous and innocent companion that I had ever met with."

September 26

Writing on notepaper bearing the imprint, "at the Fleuron, 10 Adam Street, Adelphi, w. c." Holbrook Jackson addressed himself to Oliver Simon Esq., at the Curwen Press, on this date in 1922:

"Dear Simon, Thanks for yours of the 19th. I have spoken to Morison and he agrees with you and me that The Fleuron Society has petered out, and I think there is nothing more to be done than to admit this. There has been no expenditure save the printing of the paper on which this letter is typed and I have asked Morison to supply the amount due from each of us, which will be only a few shillings. The only subscriptions paid were Morison's and my own. The requests for subscriptions from other members did not develop into cheques. I am therefore returning Morison his cheque. Mr. Newdigate has never answered any of my letters

so I imagine he never considered himself a member."

Late in 1921, an informal group of men interested in promoting the cause of good printing had begun to meet to discuss the ways and means of such a venture. One of these individuals, Oliver Simon, made the suggestion that a society be formed which would undertake the production of one book a year. The purpose would be to prove that machine-set and machine-printed books could match the quality of the books which had been produced by the great private presses, whose influence was still very strong.

Several members of the original group evidenced interest in Simon's proposal and agreed to meet to plan such an undertaking. They were Francis Meynell, Stanley Morison, Holbrook Jackson, Bernard Newdigate, and Oliver Simon. It soon became evident that no real agreement could be reached on a publishing program, particularly since Newdigate was of the opinion that the practices of William Morris at the Kelmscott Press should serve as the model of the Fleuron publications. It was upon this rock that the Society foundered.

However, out of the discussions and exchange of ideas, there did emerge a most worthwhile venture. Simon and Morison decided to collaborate on the production of a periodical devoted to typography, to be called *The Fleuron.* With contributions from all the original members of the Fleuron Society, the first number—set in the new cutting of Garamond which Morison had suggested the Monotype firm produce—appeared in the Spring of 1923. The regular edition consisted of one thousand copies, with 120 copies of a *de luxe* edition being printed on hand-made paper. The price set for the ordinary edition was twenty-one shillings. The second number was limited to but 750 copies, with the same number of *de luxe* copies as in the first number. By the time the third number was ready, it was evident that *The Fleuron* was a success and the print order was returned to one thousand.

Seven numbers of the journal were printed. Unquestionably they represent the high point of typographical publishing in this century, each issue containing the most authoritative and scholarly writing of any periodical devoted to the art of printing. The first three numbers were edited by Simon, and the last four by Stanley Morison, helping to establish a reputation which has been virtually without parallel in the field of typographic history. Today almost no collector specializing in printing books considers his library complete without a set of *The Fleuron*. Of course the going prices reflect this distinction, a set costing up to $300.

September 27

"In the seventh year of Henry VIII. September the 27th (1509). The King gives to Richard Pynson Esquire, our Printer, Four Pounds annually, to be paid from the receipts of the Exchequer during life." Thus honored by royal decree, Richard Pynson, one of the great triumvirate of early English printers, which included William Caxton, and Wynkyn de Worde, and by all odds the best printer of the group, thereafter used the title of Esquire proudly. The colophon of an edition of *Statuta* read: "Richard Pynson Squyer and prenter vnto the kynges noble grace."

Pynson's early life is not well documented. He was a native of Normandy, probably learning the craft of printing in the city of Rouen. He began printing in England in 1491 or 1492. His first dated book, the *Doctrinale* of Gallus, was completed on November 13, 1492. However, he had produced a number of books, undated, prior to this time, one of which was a splendid folio edition of Chaucer's *Canterbury Tales*. Pynson was the first printer to use roman type in England.

As a printer noted for his fine editions, Pynson was frequently the victim of piracy. In 1525 a printer named Robert Redman "borrowed" the device of Pynson for the printing of a law text. When Pynson himself produced an edition, he hotly brought the matter before the public, much in the way of his Italian contemporary, Aldus, who was victimized in much the same manner. At the end of an edition of *Lyttleton's Tenures,* "moost truly correctyed and amended," Pynson wrote: "Richard Pynson, the Royal Printer, Salutation to the Reader. Behold I now give to thee, Candid Reader, A Lyttleton corrected, not deceitfully, of the errors which occurred in him; I have been careful that not my printing only should be amended, but also that with a more elegant type it

should go forth to the day: that which hath escaped from the hands of Robert Redman, but truly Rudeman, because he is the rudest out of a thousand men, is not easily understood. Truly I wonder now at last that he hath confessed it his own typography, unless it chanced, that even as the Devil made a Cobbler a Mariner, he made him a Printer. Formerly this Scoundrel did profess himself a Bookseller, as well skilled as if he had started forth from Utopia; he knows well that he is free who pretendeth to books, although it be nothing more; notwithstanding he is a Buffoon who hath dared to engage in it, his reverend care for the Laws of England should knowingly and truly have imprinted them all. Whether the words which I give be profitable, or whether they be faithful he can tell, and do thou in reading Lyttleton excuse his care and diligence in that place where thou dost see it. Farewell."

It was Pynson, as Royal Printer, who printed the famous attack on the principles of Martin Luther by Henry VIII, *Assertion of the Seven Sacraments against Martin Luther,* issued in 1521. "What serpent so venomous," wrote the King, "as he who calls the pope's authority tyrannous?" Luther replied with equal ardor, calling Henry a lubberly ass and a frantic madman. Although Henry later led England into the Reformation, he remained estranged from Luther and German Protestantism. The Pope, however, named the King *Fidei Defensor,* or Defender of the Faith.

September 28

On this day in 1651, it is recorded that William Pynchon deeded his property to his son John and made preparations to return to England. One of the original patentees of the Massachusetts Bay Colony, Pynchon was a wealthy Englishman who had arrived in the Colony in 1630. He had helped to found the town of Roxbury and had later traveled into the wilderness a hundred miles west of Boston. Here he established, on the Connecticut River, a trading post which later was named Springfield, after Pynchon's English home.

The town became an important outpost of the Colony, situated as it was at the head of navigation in the river, ideally located to receive the furs which were trapped to the north in the Hampshire Grants.

While amassing a large fortune from the fur trade, this Colonial functionary became disenchanted with the narrow limits set by the Governors of the Colony. He had published in London in 1650 a tract entitled, *The Meritorious Price of Our Redemption,* in which he vehemently disagreed with the then orthodox theological viewpoint relating to the atonement. While his criticisms were subsequently regarded as constructive by later generations of more liberal divines, they were not so accepted by the clergy in Massachusetts. In fact, the book was considered to be so offensive that Pynchon was brought before the General Court in October, 1650. Agreeing with the theologians that august body condemned Pynchon's treatise forthwith. In a self-righteous statement the court declared:

"The Courte, having had the sight of a booke lately printed under the name of William Pinchon in New England, Gent., doe judge meete, first, that a protest be drawn, fully and cleerly, to satisfy all men that this court is so farr from approving the same as they doe utterly dislike it and detest it as erronjous and daingerous; secondly, that it be sufficjently answered by one of the reverend elders; thirdly, that the sajd William Pinchon, gent., be summoned to appeare before the next Generall Courte to answer for the same; fowerthly, that the sajd booke now brought ober be burnt by the executioner, or such other as the magistrates shall appointe, (the party being willing to doe it,) in the markett place in Boston, on the morrow immedjately after the lecture."

The book was burned the following day, as directed, and is probably the first instance of bookburning in the land which became the United States of America. Ironically, Pynchon returned to England to attain the very freedom for which he originally left his home. Finding the atmosphere more congenial and liberal, he lived to write a number of other theological tracts prior to his death a decade later.

Fortunately, book burning is an activity which has never been popular in the United States, although it is threatened on frequent occasions by groups of even narrower viewpoint than the General Court of Massachusetts in 1650.

Typical of the doggerel written by printers who fancied themselves as poets, and commonly seen in trade periodicals and even in the public prints up to a few generations ago, is *The Merits of Printing, A Song* anonymously contributed to the New York *Public Advertiser* in its issue of September 29, 1808.

"When Learning and Science were both
      sunk in night,
And Genius and Freedom were banish'd
      outright.
The Invention of *Printing* soon bro't all
      to light,
    Then Carol the praises of Printing,
    And sing in that noble art's praise.

"Then all who profess this Heaven taught art,
And have Liberty, Virtue and Knowledge
      at heart,
Come join these verses, and now
      bear apart,
    Then Carol, etc.

"Though every Composer a galley must have,
Yet Judge not from that a Composer's
      a slave,
For printing hath often dug Tyranny's grave,
    Then Carol, etc.

"If *Correction* he needs, all mankind does
      the same;
When he *Quadrates* his matter, he is not
      to blame,
For to *Justification* he lays a strong claim,
    Then Carol, etc.

"Tho' he daily *Imposes* 'tis not to do wrong,
Like Nimrod he follows the *Chase*
      all day long,
And always to him a good *Slice*
      does belong,
    Then Carol, etc.

"Tho' friendly to peace, yet *French Cannon*
      he loves,
Expert in his *Great* and *Long Primer*
      he proves,
And with skill and address all his
      Furniture moves,
    Then Carol, etc.

"Tho' no Antiquarian, he deals much
in *Coins,*
And freedom with loyalty close combines,
And to aid the Republic of Letters
he joins.
Then Carol, etc.

"Extremes he avoids and a *Medium* invites,
Tho' no blockhead he often in
Fool's Cap delights
And handles his *Shooting stick* tho' he
ne'er fights.
Then Carol, etc.

"But the art to complete, the stout
pressmen must come,
And make use of their *Balls, Frisket*
and *Drum,*
And to strike the impression the *Platten*
pull home,
Then Carol, etc.

"But as the old proverb declares very clear,
We're farthest from God when the church
we are near,
So in all printing *Chapels* do Devils appear.
Then Carol, etc.

"On the press, *Truth, Religion,* and
Learning depend,
Whilst that remains free, Slav'ry ne'er
gains its end,
Then my *Bodkin* in him who is not
Printing's friend.
Then Carol the praises of printing
And sing in that noble art's praise."

September 30

The Rev. Charles Henry Olive Daniel, Provost of Worcester College, Oxford, was born on the last day of September in 1836. One of the beloved teachers of his period and a scholar of note, he yet was able to devote much of his leisure to the operation of a press which he had begun as early as his ninth year and which he continued until his election as Provost of the College in 1903.

In the annals of the private press movement the Daniel Press occupies a unique position, predating as it does the first full flowering which occurred at the close of the 19th century when such presses as Kelmscott, Doves, and Ashendene made their lasting contributions to the printing art. Daniel's first impression was made on a toy press, which was used for several years for the ephemeral production of the press, although a small Albion was obtained about 1850. A larger Albion was used from 1882.

In addition to exciting the interest of literary men in the format of the book, Daniel's great typographical accomplishment was the revival of the splendid old fonts which had been brought to Oxford in the 17th century by Bishop Fell, and which had been lying idle for a hundred and fifty years. An essay on Dr. Daniel appearing in Rothenstein's *Oxford Characters* stated: "His signature is the warrant to the lettered world of a fair impression of good literary work, worth printing, worth buying, worth reading, and worth keeping."

Falconer Madan, Bodley's librarian and biographer of Henry Daniel, attempts in his Memorial published in 1921 to place the Daniel Press properly in perspective with relation to other private presses. He lists six different groups in which private presses may be classified. First is secret propagandism—perhaps best expressed by the underground press of protest, religious or political. In the second group are those which exist for the personal pleasure of their owners, and in the third group are the presses which are used to preserve special literature, such as in the case of the writer who cannot find a publisher, a sort of amateur "vanity" press, although this more modern idea was then outside of Madan's experience. A fourth *raison d'etre* is to serve aesthetic or artistic purposes —in other words to improve the quality of the printer's art.

Into the fifth group are placed those operated for commercial profit, a worthy venture indeed, and one which escapes most of the private printers, who have the greatest difficulty in even coming close to meeting their cost of materials, not to mention long hours of labor. If a private press is an outstanding aesthetic success its output will of course be valuable, although as in the case of paintings, this may happen long after the operator has been removed from the scene.

Falconer believed that the motivation of the Rev. Daniel brought his press into a sixth category—that of giving pleasure to literary friends. Daniel never sought to be a great printer, but attempted to do the best work of which he was capable.

October

October 1

On this date in 1961, the late Rachel Hunt—one-time apprentice bookbinder to Cobden-Sanderson at the Doves Press and later patron to Porter Garnett at the Laboratory Press at Carnegie Institute of Technology—initialed and okayed a sheet of letters titled "Trial Letters for Hunt Roman." The letters were from the drawing board of the accomplished type designer, Hermann Zapf. With the approval of Mrs. Hunt, the production of the type began, to be completed in Frankfurt, Germany in the plant of the Stempel Typefoundry in 1962.

Hunt Roman is a type which can be placed in the category of private types, in the tradition of such designs as the Golden Type of William Morris, made for use at the Kelmscott Press, along with the Troy and Chaucer types. The Kelmscott Press types were the inspiration for a number of other designs of the same period, such as the Doves Press type, the Ashendene Press "Subiaco" type, and the font of the Vale Press.

While the idea behind the creation of a private type received its greatest impetus from the private press movement, there have been a number of types which have bridged the gap between such restrictive use and the commercial world of print. Such a letter is the ubiquitous Cheltenham, possibly the best-known American type ever produced. It was originally designed for the Cheltenham Press of New York City but was later released for commercial production, with resounding success. Most typographers would agree that the Centaur type of the late Bruce Rogers would qualify as the most distinguished example of a type designed for private use (by the Metropolitan Museum of Art), which became one of the highly regarded typefaces of our time when it was adapted for monotype composition in the splendid Oxford Lectern Bible of 1935. Centaur is now proudly used by all printers conscious of the qualities of a fine letter.

The prolific Frederic W. Goudy designed a number of types upon special commission. His first popular success in type designing was Kennerley, cut for the composition of *The Door in the Wall,* by H. G. Wells, and published by Mitchell Kennerley.

Several other Goudy private types have since been relegated to the hell-box, such as Nabisco, Saks Goudy, and Companion Old Style (for the *Woman's Home Companion*). Two others were more fortunate. The Aries font, re-designed for the famous Grabhorn Press under the name of Franciscan, has been used in several notable books from that press, including its monumental *Bibliography;* the University of California Oldstyle has been made available to all printers under the name of Californian, after the University agreed to release its exclusive right to the type.

October 2

By decree of the English Parliament, from this day in 1543, it was enacted that no person or persons "should take upon him, or them, to read, openly, to other, in any church, or open assembly, within any of the king's dominions, the Bible, or any part of Scripture, in *English*, unless he was so appointed thereto by the king, or by anie ardinarie." The law further stipulated that, "every *nobleman,* and *gentleman* being a householder, might read or cause to be read, by any of his familie servants in his *house, orchardes,* or *garden,* and to his *own familie,* any text of the Bible or New Testament; and also every *merchant-man,* being a householder; and any other persons other than women, prentices, &c. might read to themselves privately the Bible, &c. But *no women* except *noblewomen* and *gentlewomen,* who might read to themselves alone, and not to others, any texts of the Bible &c., nor *artificers, prentices, journeymen, servingmen* of the degrees of *yomen* or under, *husbandmen,* nor *labourers* were to read the Bible or New Testament in *English* to himself or to any other, privately or openly."

A hundred years following this decree, a printer named John Field, later to be Printer to Cambridge University, issued a bible set in Pearl (5-point) type. This bible, a 32mo, was notable for its errors, caused, no doubt, by its diminutive type. These *errata* were to cause the divines of the period a great deal of trouble. It was reported that when a reverend doctor of divinity sought to reprove some "libertines" for their licentious behavior, these worthies brought forth Field's 32mo as evidence that they were but following the scriptures.

For example, Roman vi. 13 read: Neither yield ye your members as instruments of righteousness unto sin. First Corinthians, vi. 9 stated: Know ye not that the unrighteous shall inherit the Kingdom of God?

Some of Field's errors might well have been intentional, as it is known that at one time he had accepted a bribe of some fifteen hundred pounds to corrupt a text which, in the sixth chapter of Acts, appeared to sanction the right of the people to appoint their own pastors. The Field bible contained upwards of six thousand errors, making it a worthy rival to the famous Vulgate of Pope Sixtus V. In his account of Printer Field, C. H. Timperley seemed to be as outraged at the size of the bible as at the number of errors which it contained, of which he said, "if one book can be made to contain near four thousand errors, little ingenuity was required to reach six thousand."

October 3

On the tombstone of one Adam Williamson, a pressman printer who died in Edinburgh, Scotland on this date in 1832, is inscribed:

All my stays are loosed;
my cap is thrown off; my head
is worn out
my box is broken;
my spindle and bar have lost
their power;
my till is laid aside;
both legs of my crane are turned
out of their path;
my winter hath no spring;
my rounce will neither roll out
nor in;
stone, coffin, and carriage have
all failed;
the hinges of my tympan, and frisket,
are immovable;
my long and short ribs are rusted;
my cheeks are much worm-eaten,
and mouldering away;
my press is totally down!

The volume of my life is finished!
not without many errors:
most of them have arisen from bad
composition and are
to be attributed more to the case
than to the press;
there are also a great number of
my own;
misses, scuffs, blotches, blurs, and
bad register:
but the true and faithful Superintendent
has undertaken
to correct the whole.
When the machine is again set up,
(incapable of decay),
a new and perfect edition of my life
will appear,
elegantly bound for duration, and
every way fitted for
the grand library of the Great Author.

And so many a printer went to his rest eternal, comforted no doubt by the knowledge that such remarks on his craft would appear on his headstone. The last half of the epitaph of Pressman Williamson bears some resemblance to that written—but never used—by Benjamin Franklin during his fanciful youth. In the years of his age and wisdom

Franklin directed that a simple marker should read "Benjamin and Deborah Franklin," along with a date.

Printers, being on the whole a literate group of men, frequently wrote stylish epitaphs utilizing their craft terminology, seeking no doubt to immortalize their simple workaday lives. It is amusing to note that in the Edinburgh epitaph Pressman Williamson continued to his grave the classic rivalry between compositor and pressman which has existed throughout the long history of the art of printing.

October 4

On or about this day in 1796, William Henry Ireland published in London *An Authentic Account of the Shakspeare Manuscripts,* in which he confessed the sensational forgery of several Shakespeare manuscripts. Ireland wrote:

"I solemnly declare first, that my father was perfectly unacquainted with the whole affair, believing the papers most firmly the productions of Shakspeare. Secondly, that I am myself both the author and writer, and had no aid from any soul living, and that I should never have gone so far, but the world praised the papers so much and therefore flattered my vanity."

Ireland, the son of a rare book dealer with a special interest in Shakespeare, had accompanied his father on a trip to Stratford-on-Avon in 1794, where he met John Jordan, who had admitted forging the last will of Shakespeare's father. The young man, just seventeen years of age, became curious about Jordan's methods. This forgery so excited his interest that he proceeded, primarily to please his father, to "discover" a number of lost Shakespeare documents, in the form of the actor's contracts, letters, and notes. His imitation of Shakespeare's calligraphy was close enough that the foremost bibliophiles and scholars in London accepted them as true copies.

Ireland was so delighted with the results of his forgeries that he even wrote a complete play, entitled *Vortigern and Rowena,* which was actually performed in the Drury Lane Theatre on April 2, 1796. The London drama critics were considerably more astute than the bibliophiles, with the result that the

pseudo-Shakespeare was quickly uncovered. In 1805, Ireland wrote his *Confessions,* in which he related his methods in duping the experts.

"It became necessary," he wrote, "that I should possess a sufficient quantity of old paper to enable me to proceed; in consequence of which I applied to a bookseller named Verey, in Great May's buildings, St. Martin's Lane, who, for the sum of five shillings, suffered me to take from all the folio and quarto volumes in his shop the fly-leaves which they contained. . . . As I was fully aware, from the variety of watermarks which are in existence at the present day, that they must have constantly been altered since the period of Elizabeth, and being for some time wholly unacquainted with the watermarks of that age, I very carefully produced my first specimens of the writing on such sheets of old paper as had no watermark whatever. Having heard it frequently stated that such marks on paper would have greatly tended to establish their validity, I listened attentively to every remark which was made upon the subject, and from thence I at length gleaned the intelligence that a *jug* was the prevalent watermark of the reign of Elizabeth: in consequence of which I inspected all the sheets of old paper then in my possession; and having selected such as had the jug upon them, I produced the succeeding manuscripts upon these; being careful, however, to mingle with them a certain number of blank leaves, that the production on a sudden of so many watermarks might excite suspicion in the breasts of those persons who were most conversant with the manuscripts."

October 5

Of the making of alphabetic sentences there is no end, but it must be admitted that it all started with printers. No doubt the first printer's devil hit upon the scheme in order to learn better the unique arrangement of the earliest type case. The practice was continued with the development of the keyboard operated devices from Dr. Church's machine to Mergenthaler's. The writer is reminded of such sentences by running across a little book of them completed on this day in 1950 by two students in the composing room of the School of Printing at the Rochester Institute of Technology.

In this volume, titled *The Twenty-six Letters,* the sentences are illustrated in several colors by intricate arrangement of ornaments, rules, and assorted dingbats. Naturally enough, the first entry is the most frequently encountered sentence of all, "The quick brown fox jumps over the lazy dog." Thirty-five letters!

Countless disciples of the Art & Mystery have attempted down the years to accomplish the inclusion of the twenty-six characters of the roman alphabet into a sentence that is both economic and literate—no simple task, if we examine the efforts of some of the most distinguished and gifted practitioners of the craft. The incomparable Bruce Rogers endeavored to reduce the brown fox quip to thirty letters in the beautiful specimen sheet which he designed for Fred Goudy's Italian Old Style type, in 1923. BR appended the original with "& (doesn't count) xvj brawny gods flock up to quiz them." It may be noted that the crafty typographer, just because he was working with Renaissance material, pulled a fast one with that "xvj," although he *said* that the quote was from "some lost mythology." BR also entered the lists in the same text with "Foxy judges track val'ble peach wine," but it is evident that the muse had left him. While he managed a certain frugality of numbers, he did so at the expense of leaving out two letters, and of course he weaseled with the apostrophe.

A really noble attempt to achieve par by one Edmund Thompson, resulted in "Quick zephyrs blow vexing daft Jim," a 29-letter gem which would annoy only a parsing seventh grade English teacher. A printer named Hank Bates reached the zenith in 1941 with, "Frowzy things plumb vex'd Jack Q." Again the refuge in the apostrophe, and a slight falling from grace with the initial, but admirable prudence in word selection.

Some of the more literate typos have scorned to limit their scope to twenty-six letters, preferring to amuse, if not inform, with their alphabetical prose style. George Trenholm, the genial Boston designer, set a high standard with "Exquisite farm wench gives body jolt to prize stinker," and "The exodus of jazzy pigeons craved by squeamish walkers." Trenholm proved his virtuosity

with, "Jail zesty vixen who grabbed pay from quack," a top-drawer performance besides such jaded efforts as, "J. Q. Plow might vex Z. D. Burk's fancy," by the believe-it-or-notter Ripley, who only proved that he was not a real printer, but merely a reporter turned cartoonist. But the returns are not all in—we haven't heard from the computers!

October 6

Under this date in 1868 *The Printer's Register,* a British periodical, published the following note:

"A Buffalo American Exchange says:—There is no type-foundry in the world superior—either in beauty or durability of its wares—to the famous Johnson Foundry of Philadelphia, now worthily carried on by Messrs. MacKellar, Smiths & Jordan, the successors of the lamented L. Johnson. The old Bruce foundry in New York and the White foundry in the same city (the latter now carried on by Messrs. Farmer, Little & Co.), although not up to the Philadelphia concern in variety of styles, are equal to any in the world in point of excellence in the cut, finish, and durability of their types. The Buffalo type-foundry, also, although not so extensive as either of these we have named ahead of it, makes a variety of types quite sufficient for the use of any newspaper, and of a quality inferior to none in all essential points. We can speak of the durability of its manufactures from long experience. As to their beauty and variety, for the purpose named, we may appeal to the appearance of the *Commercial Advertiser* and the *Courier,* of Buffalo, both of which concerns always buy their newspaper type of friend Lyman. Long experience with type of French, English, Scotch, and American manufacture, warrants us in denying the inferiority of the home article."

To which, in some high dudgeon, *The Printer's Register* added its own editorial comment:

"We insert the above in order to make the following statement. The founts of type used in printing the *Manchester Guardian,* the Leading Provincial Daily Journal in England, have been in daily use since January 1st, 1867, and have yielded twenty-five millions of impressions worked wholly from the type, whilst the condition of the founts at the present time are such, they will not require to be renewed for at least another twelve-month. We challenge any of our American friends to a similar test of durability, and shall be glad to elicit from them the largest number of impressions American hard metal type is capable of giving. The *Manchester Guardian* founts were cast in the Patent Hard Metal of the Type Founding Company, whose foundry is at 31, Red Lion-square, and both European and American printers are invited to inspect their manufacture."

One hundred years later, the controversy is still not resolved. The durability of type is the total of a number of variables, not the least of which is the comparative skill of the pressman who prints the type. Modern foundry type is composed of certain percentages of lead, tin, antimony, and copper, the exact mixture of which is in the category of a trade secret. In the 1860's the mixture was not very different, although iron and steel were sometimes used. Ringwalt lists the formula for a 17th century English alloy: twenty-five pounds of lead mixed with three pounds of iron stub-nails and antimony produced twenty-eight pounds of type metal.

October 7

Daniel Fowle, a printer from Boston, printed the *New Hampshire Gazette* at Portsmouth on this day in 1756—the first newspaper to appear in that state. Just two years previously Printer Fowle had been jailed by the Commonwealth of Massachusetts in an early case of freedom of the press. From his Anne Street shop in Boston he printed pamphlets which he himself sold. One of these, *The Monster of Monsters,* by Tom Thumb, Esq., so irked the legislature that a warrant was sworn for his arrest.

Brought before the House of Representatives, Printer Fowle was asked:

"Do you know anything of the printing of this book?"

After examining the pamphlet the printer told the House that it was not his work as he didn't have such types. When he was asked if he knew anything relating to its printing he said that he had purchased a few copies for sale in his shop.

Question. [by the speaker] Who did you buy them off?

Answer. They were I believe, sent by a young man, but I cannot tell his name.

Q. Who did he live with?

A. The young man, I believe, lives with Royall Tyler.

Q. Did you have any conversation with him [Tyler] about them?

A. I believe I might, in the same manner I had with many others; not that I thought him the author. It was never offered me to print.

One of the members then said to Fowle, "You do not know when you lie!"

Fowle replied, "Begging your pardon, sir, I know when I lie, and what a lie is as well as yourself."

Fowle was then confined for several hours in the lobby. At ten o'clock at night he was ordered to the common gaol, and "confined among thieves and murderers. His wife was not allowed to see him, and he was not permitted writing materials."

Royall Tyler, Esq. was next arrested and "carried before the house." When interrogated, he became probably the first printer in the land to "claim the Fifth," saying, simply, *"Nemo tenetur seipsum accusare."* It would be interesting to see the effect of such a statement upon contemporary Congressional hearings. Tyler was committed for contempt but released.

After five days in prison Fowle was released and there the prosecution ended. He made several attempts to obtain satisfaction for his "deprivation of liberty" with no success. Much put out with the government of Massachusetts, he removed himself to New Hampshire "at the request of several respectable gentlemen there" and thus became that state's first printer.

October 8

At about nine o'clock in the evening of this day in 1871 a fire began which engulfed three and a half miles of the city of Chicago and destroyed 17,000 buildings.

Legend has it that printers in the United States owe to this disaster their present method of type measurement, the American Point System. The actual facts seem to prove that there was no relationship between the two events. Among the industrial concerns which were destroyed on October 8 was the typefoundry of Marder, Luse & Co., best known of all American foundries serving printers in the Mid-West and West.

Some accounts of the early maneuvering of founders prior to the establishment of a point system state that when Marder, Luse & Co. rebuilt their foundry following the fire, they standardized, but there exists documentary evidence to the contrary. Upon receiving a delegation of printers asking that the Chicago Type Foundry instigate a standardized procedure, the firm stated in January, 1872:

"After the wholesale destruction entailed by the Great Fire we would have gladly conformed to a new and absolutely correct standard, but it was not reasonable to expect that we could suspend our business for two or three years, or until that standard could be definitely agreed upon. We can assure our friends that unless they are willing to pay a large advance upon the cost of type for some years, in order to make up for the loss sustained in making necessary changes, it is not likely that the change will ever be made. The loss would amount in the aggregate (to the entire typefounding industry) to several millions of dollars and we doubt if there are many printers who would be willing to bear their proportion of it."

Two years later Nelson Hawks, a former Milwaukee printer who had spent years attempting to interest founders in the change-over, became associated with Marder in the operation of a branch of the foundry in San Francisco. He took advantage of a visit John Marder made to him to sell him the idea. Apparently Hawks discussed the matter so eloquently that Marder was won over. In 1879 his firm formally announced that they were casting types to The American System of Interchangeable Type Bodies.

Following Hawks' advice, the Chicago firm took as a standard the pica em as produced by the Philadelphia foundry, MacKellar, Smiths & Jordan. This foundry was selected as its types were the most generally used by the American printers. The MacKellar pica em measured .166040" which was divided in 12 parts, to be called points (here following the ideas of the French typefounder Pierre Fournier who had introduced a system in 1737).

It needed only the agreement of all the typefounders to formalize this great step, accomplished in a meeting in 1886. In 1898 the British typefounders also standardized, using the American system.

October 9

At one of the sessions of the third annual meeting of the United Typothetae of America, on October 9, 1889, Andrew McNally, the president of the employers' association, harangued his audience with an account of the problems facing the members of the group. The probability of national acceptance of the eight-hour day was an important factor in the minds of employing printers, who were seeking means by which production could be maintained with shortened working hours. McNally asked that a national system of apprenticeship be formulated, which he hoped would guarantee a stable work force.

"The increasing inability of master printers to obtain a sufficient number of competent workmen," he stated, "notwithstanding the high rate of wages, forces upon our attention the urgent need of an apprentice system. I consider it of sufficient importance to be made a subject of national legislation.

"The compulsory education of children finds almost universal support, but it may fairly be questioned whether the compulsory education of boys in useful trades would not contribute in a greater degree to the happiness and prosperity of our country. We supply the American youth free facilities to cultivate the brain, the more keenly to feel, in manhood, the curse of his unskilled hands. The short-sighted policy of trades unions, in limiting the number of apprentices, and the fact that, in the absence of any system of apprenticeship, American boys are too generally 'Jacks of all trades and masters of none,' have kept the supply of proficient workmen far below the demand occasioned by the increased volume of business. We are, therefore, compelled to look to immigration for our supply of skilled labor.

"I appreciate the difficulties of inaugurating an apprenticeship system. The American workman is generally opposed to it, and the American public looks upon it as a species of slavery. Why, I cannot conceive. It should be the duty of the workman to have his boy trained as a skilled mechanic, else he is liable to become a day laborer, a pauper or a hoodlum. Franklin says: 'He that hath a trade, hath an estate, and he that hath a calling, hath an office of profit and honor.' "

It was not until the United Typothetae of America convention of 1914 that concrete proposals were made for the training of apprentices. At that time a permanent committee was set up and a Director of Apprentices appointed in the person of Dr. F. W. Hamilton, a well-known educator and former president of Tufts College. The movement to strengthen the education of printers continued when the UTA established a Department of Education, and cooperated in the forming of the School of Printing at Carnegie Institute of Technology. Printing education was thus raised to the college level and eventually bachelor of science degrees in printing were granted.

October 10

In a letter written from the Massachusetts Bay Colony at Salem to a friend in Bermuda on October 10, 1638, the Rev. Hugh Peter said: "Wee have a printery here and think to goe to worke with some special things, and if you have anything you may send it safely by these [Captain of the vessel delivering the message]."

The printery to which he referred was that established by a dissenting minister, Jose Glover, who had brought with him from England a press, types, and paper, and of course a printer, one Stephen Day from Cambridge. With Day were three manservants, his wife, two sons, and a stepson. Day had bonded himself and his men "to labor and worke with and for the said Josse Glover and his assignes in the trade which the said Stephen now useth in New England. . . ."

This bond described Day as a locksmith, and nothing was said about starting a press in the Colony. No doubt this was a subterfuge adopted to avoid problems with the government concerning the establishment of a press in America by the Puritans. The first printer of the English colonies may indeed have been a locksmith, as Day took up that trade when he retired from the printing office in 1647.

The first piece of printing to issue from the shop was a broadside, *The Freeman's Oath*, of which no copy is known to exist. This was followed by an eight-page almanac, which also has not survived. Then began the lengthy task of producing a book of psalms. The type used is a small-bodied "English" which is similar to the present-day size of 14-point. Larger types were used for display, along with Greek and Hebrew characters, and an assortment of ornaments which were set into the title page. As an example of the printer's art the little book of 294 unnumbered pages approximately 4½ x 7 inches in size, would receive little enough attention. The typesetting is extremely careless, abounding with errors of punctuation and word-breaking. But this first American book was not at all untypical of provincial printing in the England of the same period.

The press used by Day is purported to be in the museum maintained by the Vermont Historical Society at Montpelier, but as the Bay Colony printing office eventually used three different presses, there is some doubt that the Montpelier press is the one used to print the *Bay Psalm Book*.

Of the 1700 copies printed there are now but eleven known copies of the *Bay Psalm Book*, the most desirable American book in existence for collectors. Three of them are considered to be perfect, although even these are slightly marred. The only copy outside of the United States is in the Bodleian Library of Oxford University. The Van Sinderin copy in Brooklyn, New York is the only one still in private hands. The last copy to appear at auction was the one acquired by Yale University in 1948 for the sum of $151,000.

October 11

The journal kept by Benjamin Franklin Bache records for this day in 1784: "Began to cast a fount of St. Augustine." The senior Benjamin Franklin had brought his two grandsons, Temple and Benjamin, to Europe when he was appointed Ambassador to France. Towards the end of his stay there, he was determined to teach Benjamin the trade of printing, since he had without much success attempted to train Temple for public office. Young Bache, then fourteen years old, seemed an apt pupil, so his grandfather brought in a master typefounder to the private press he maintained at Passy to teach the boy typecasting.

The following year France's finest printer, François Didot, took Benjamin as an apprentice. This event was duly recorded in the journal:

"April 5. Went to Mons. Didot to learn punchcutting. To board in his house, but sleep elsewhere. Didot includes in his house engraving, the forge, the foundry, and printing.

"April 7. Engrave first punch, an O.

"April 8. Today an E.

"May 6. I have taken my grandpapa's press to pieces."

The training ended abruptly however when on May 2 Franklin was notified by Congress to return to the United States. The printer-statesman brought home with him, however, typefounding equipment from Pierre Simon Fournier, with which he set up his grandson in Philadelphia. That Franklin was aware of the need for the establishment of a typefoundry in the United States is apparent from a letter which he wrote from France in 1779: "I thank you for the Boston newspapers, tho' I see nothing so clearly in them as that your Printers do indeed want new Letters. They perfectly blind me in endeavoring to read them. If you should ever have any Secrets that you wish to be well kept, get them printed in those Papers. You enquire, if Printers Types may be had here? Of all sorts, very good, cheaper than in England, and of harder Metal. I will see any Orders executed in that way that any of your Friends may think fit to send. Very good Printing Ink is likewise to be had here . . . ."

In 1785 Bache established the foundry, but then left to continue his schooling, while his grandfather apparently kept the business until the young man should be ready. However, Bache decided in 1787 to go it on his own, and began his career as both a printer and a typefounder, issuing a specimen sheet showing types of French origin and also English Caslon. The young man soon became more interested in the printing side of his business.

In 1789 Bache was Franklin's secretary. He was present when the great old man died in his eighty-fourth year on April 17, 1790. Later that year Bache started a newspaper, the *General Advertiser,* which became known later as the *Aurora.* He died in 1798, just twenty-nine years old. His widow later married William Duane, who in 1806 sold Bache's typefounding equipment to Binny & Ronaldson, the Philadelphia typefounders.

October 12

In the city of Chicago the American Newspaper Publishers Association conducted on this day in 1891 a test to determine whether or not typesetting by machine was really efficient and practicable and to find which of the machines then under development was the best for newspaper purposes. The machines pitted against one another in this match were the linotype, the Rogers Typograph, and the McMillan.

In the report issued to its members the following January, ANPA reported that the McMillan machine produced the most type, 4,040 ems per hour, but that, "while exhibiting the highest typographical excellence in its composition, because justified by hand, nevertheless by reason of the fact that it requires three skilled workmen to produce its results, it is not to be preferred on the score of economy for use in newspaper offices under ordinary working conditions."

The next speediest was the linotype which turned out 3,082 ems, but the committee was not impressed. "That, so far as revealed by this test," the report read, "the linotype machine, while showing bursts of speed exceeding the capacity of its competitors, yet owing to the recklessness of the operator, the absence of any superintendent, and possibly to the too delicate and complicated mechanism, fell far short in the general result of accomplishing what had been claimed for its owners and others."

Although the slowest of the machines being tested (2,684 ems per hour) the Rogers Typograph was the most highly praised. "That so far as revealed by this test, the Rogers Typograph produced the best and most economical results. Its simplicity of construction was so great that it was set up ready for running in ninety minutes. For five consecutive working days no machinist or other party than the operator had anything to do with the machine, and it ran smoothly with scarcely a moment's interruption for the entire period of the test."

After four hundred and fifty years of typesetting by hand, by the closing decade of the 19th century it was evident that machine composition was getting ready to take over. Perhaps the substance of the opinions of comps about the upcoming automation is contained in a paragraph appearing in the trade press a year or so before the Chicago test: "Typesetting machines are getting more numerous, but printers do not seem to be greatly alarmed as no machine has yet been devised that can think."

As every issue of the trade periodical contained doggerel written by printers, it was natural that the typesetting machine would be the subject matter of some of the amateur rhymers. One laureate sang:

Ye printers, dear, what's this I hear,
    the news that's going round?
A great machine, to take your place,
    has surely now been found;
It'll set the type quite neatly, at a
    most tremendous speed,
And the clever printer man, they say,
    we shall no longer need."

October 13

Bibliophiles, and particularly collectors of Poe, undoubtedly noted with chagrin the letter written upon this date in 1893 by Francis A. Teall, a retired proofreader of Bloomfield, New Jersey.

"Being on a visit to my son, F. Horace Teall, I came across a paragraph in your September number containing a statement that calls for explanation, to wit: 'The proofreading department [of the new Standard English Dictionary] is in charge of the veteran proofreader F. Horace Teall, who says he remembers the proof of Poe's *Raven* and throwing the manuscript in the wastebasket.' Now, I suppose my son may fairly be called a veteran proofreader, his first experience in that line dating back some twenty years; but the 'veteran proofreader who says he remembers' etc., is myself, and the incident referred to occurred years before my son was born.

"The article containing the statement appears to have been going the rounds, for I saw it in the Philadelphia *Press,* while you quote from another paper. There I do not think it worth while to notice it; but among printers I would like to have the mistake rectified, for I take pleasure in the fact that I am a humble member of the craft, and have filled about every post in it—roller-boy, compositor, hand-pressman, proofreader, foreman, newspaper editor and publisher, and proprietor of a book office.

"It must have come about in this way. Many years ago I happened to mention the Poe incident to a friend (and never, I think, to anybody else, at least out of my own family); and having later in life done some things thought to make a biographical notice desirable, the gentleman wrote it, and inserted this anecdote from his memory. The reporter must have got it either from that notice or from the gentleman himself (circumstances rather favor the latter supposition), and mixed the junior and senior up. As to the anecdote itself, every experienced proofreader will know that it has no particular significance, for Poe was not then the famous man he afterward became, largely through this very poem, and proofreaders don't bother themselves with saving bits of magazine copy on the chance of future celebrity.

" Begging your pardon for troubling you with so purely personal a matter, I remain, very respectfully yours, Francis A. Teall."

October 14

Just three years prior to his death, Benjamin Franklin took the trouble to write to Signor Giambattista Bodoni of Parma, Italy. Under the date, October 14, 1787, Franklin wrote:

"I have had the very great pleasure of receiving and perusing your excellent *Essai des Caractères de l'Imprimerie.* It is one of the most beautiful that Art has hitherto produc'd. I should be glad to see a specimen of your other Founts besides this italic & Roman of the Letter to the Marq' de Cubières; and to be inform'd of the price of each kind. I do not presume to criticize your Italic Capitals; they are generally perfect: I would only beg leave to say, that to me the form of the *T* in the word *LETTRE* of the Title Page seems preferable to that of the *T* in the word *Typographie* in the next Page, as the downward stroke of *T, P, R, F, B, D, H, K, L, I,* and some others, which in writing we begin at the top, naturally swells as the pen descends; and it is only in the *A* and the *M* and *N* that these strokes are fine, because the pen begins them at the bottom."

Far from being offended by criticism from the infant nation across the Atlantic, it is recorded that Bodoni was so delighted that he confused Franklin's status. Updike says that "Bodoni was overcome with joy to have from the President of the United States this flattering letter, which he considered a title to glory and preserved with religious care."

The Duke of Parma, Bodoni's patron, was even more pleased than Bodoni, deeming the letter a tribute, no doubt, to his own acumen in selecting Bodoni as his printer. The Duke had it translated into Spanish to be sent to King Carlos III, the reigning monarch who was also a patron of Bodoni.

No matter how enthusiastic Benjamin Franklin was about Bodoni's types, Daniel B. Updike, another printing craftsman with roots in the city of Boston, considered them to be publicity types and disdained their use for the printing of books. Of course he was discussing the 20th century re-cutting of Bodoni, rather than the original. Updike believed Bodoni type to be "somewhat foreign" and suggested that it could be "utilized for short addresses, circulars, and advertising, with great success—as in the charming use of it by Mr. T. M. Cleland. To printer-designers as skillful as Cleland it may be recommended."

In spite of this criticism Bodoni ranks today as one of the universal types, popular for book and commercial printing.

October 15

In a report read before the full Faculty of the University of Paris, on October 15, 1532, the censors discussed the bible printed by Robert Estienne in "round character," i.e. roman type, and stated that they "did not observe that anything had been altered in the text used by the Church." Estienne was therefore allowed to proceed with the sale of his great Latin Vulgate Bible. This was the first instance on record of a series of annoyances to Estienne, all of which questioned his religious faith in the publication of theological works. The printer could very well have resorted to the printing

of simple texts or other secular works, but in the tradition of great scholar printers, he chose to produce instead editions of the New Testament in Greek, a Latin lexicon, and works in Hebrew

All of this activity brought him to the attention of the censors of the University, prompted by an assiduous approach to the Papal Bull *Exsurge Domine* of June 15, 1520, which forbade the faithful to read, print, or sell books containing the Lutheran errors therein condemned. For twenty-five years Estienne was so persecuted by the Paris theologians that he finally removed himself and his printing office to Geneva, saying, "If I must print nothing but under the censure of the Sorbonne, I must have abandoned letters and confined myself to the *Summa* of Mandreston, the *Logic* of Enzinas, the *Morals* of Angest, the *Physics* of Major."

However, such was the magnificence of his editions both as examples of the printer's art and of scholarly achievement, that he was appointed *Typographus Regius,* or Printer to the King, by Francis I in 1539. In his appointment the King did not consult the clergy at the University, and therefore, for the first time in the case of a King's Printer, Estienne did not occupy a chair at that institute of learning, nor was he ever invited to do so. Apparently Estienne was not concerned by this restriction, as he believed that the professors, the King's Library, and learned printing were all complementary to each other. He wrote of this in 1542 in praising the King's interest in learning:

"In the first place, offering rich renumeration, he has appointed as Masters of the best arts and studies in this University (the greatest in the world, to which all resort for study from every part) great scholars. . . . Then he has at great cost furnished and is daily furnishing a noble library of every kind of book, Hebrew, Greek and Latin, so that therein he has surpassed the efforts of the Kings Ptolemy and Eumenis; for . . . far from grudging to anyone the records of ancient writers which he at great and truly royal cost has procured from Italy and Greece, he intends to put them at the disposal and service of all men. With this in mind he has ordered that new and accurately copied forms of letters should be cut by distinguished craftsmen, in all the languages above-mentioned so that, by this method of writing, born and invented within the last hundred years, every excellent book—multiplied in any number of copies—might come into all men's hands."

October 16

John Luther Ringwalt was born in Lancaster, Pennsylvania on this day in 1828. He became a printer's apprentice in West Chester, Pennsylvania and at the age of seventeen was appointed the editor of the *Monroe Democrat* in Stroudsburg. For the next twenty-five years he worked in the Philadelphia area, performing editorial tasks and becoming a partner in a job printing firm. His great contribution to the history of American printing came in 1871, when he published the *American Encyclopaedia of Printing*. It is probably the most valuable source of information concerning the technology of printing in the United States during the 19th century up until the date of its publication.

In his Preface, Ringwalt set out immediately to demonstrate that his compendium was all-inclusive: "In the title of this work," he writes, "the term printing is used in its oldest and widest sense, so as to include not only all the established methods of multiplying fac-similes, but also the auxiliary processes essential to the production of a folded newspaper or a bound book. As an Encyclopaedia, it aims to traverse the circle of the art to which it relates, and therefore to describe its history, as well as its implements, its processes, and its products. . . ."

Actually, a great many of the 1,700 articles in Ringwalt's work had originally appeared in an English book by John Southward, *Dictionary of Typography*. This book was also published in 1871. The American copyright was owned by R. Menamin, who was Ringwalt's partner in the publishing of the *Encyclopaedia*. While the author does not acknowledge his debt to Southward, he does mention a number of his American collaborators. His wife Jessie, who had a great deal of experience as an editorial writer, was responsible for many of the biographical articles on American printers which were included in the book and which constitute such a valuable source of reference today.

The *Encyclopaedia* relies, as did so many other 19th century technical books in both England and the United States, on the earlier manuals, all the way back to the 17th century of Moxon. It remains, however, a fascinating source of exhaustive information. As a practical printer, Ringwalt's approach to his subject constituted a labor of love. He wrote: "The stereotyped phrase that printing is the art preservative of all arts, conveys a totally inadequate idea of its present position and utility, for it now not only preserves a record of all arts, but also converts them into useful auxiliaries, in the performance of its grand duties as the most beneficial, useful, and indispensable agent employed in human affairs; . . ."

October 17

"I have struck off 250 copies of the hymn beginning 'Behold the Saviour of Mankind,' with a chorus for occasional use. My press is very rude, but I am anticipating better days."

Thus reads the Journal kept by the Reverend James Evans, for this day in 1840. Many years later, the naturalist and author, Ernest Thompson Seton, wrote of Evans: "Take a map of North America and mark off the vast area bounded by the Saskatchewan, the Rockies, Hudson Bay and the Arctic Circle, and realize that in this region, as large as Continental Europe outside of Russia and Spain, one simple, earnest man, inspired by love of Him who alone is perfect love, invented and popularized a mode of writing that in a few years—in less than a generation, indeed—has turned the whole native population from ignorant illiterates to a people who are proud to read and write their own language."

The Rev. Evans had journeyed to Canada in 1823, as a missionary preacher, and working among the Ojibway tribe he had developed a written language which would enable the Indians to understand more readily the Christian message, in addition to preparing them to meet the responsibilities of the encroaching civilization of the white man. Evans evolved a system of syllabics in which the Ojibway tongue could be written with nine signs. Eight of these represented consonants, while the ninth, with four variations, stood for the vowel sounds. Before he managed to secure financial assistance to develop this method further, he was sent into the wilderness territory of the Hudson's Bay Company.

It was here that he encountered the Cree language, the standard tongue of the Northwest Indians. He soon found that the orthography he had developed for the Ojibways could readily be adapted for the Crees. He was, however, a thousand miles from the nearest railroad and completely without the means to accomplish readily the task of setting up a press in order to project his ideas. Evans stripped some lead from the Hudson Bay Company's tea chests, and "cut types in lead of two characters, and took molds in clay, chalk, putty, and other fruitless experiments." He next attempted to manufacture a sort of stereotype plate. He finally hit upon a solution, which he described in his journal: "I have got excellent letters considering the country and the materials and at last they make a tolerably good impression. The letters or characters I cut in finely polished oak. I filed out one side of an inch square bar of iron the square of the body of type, and after placing the bar with the notch over the letter I applied another polished bar to the face of the mold and poured in the lead after that had been separately melted to harden it. These require a little dressing on the face and filing to a uniform square and length, and answer well."

Evans next adapted a jack press, built to squeeze furs for shipment, and formulated ink from sturgeon oil mixed with chimney soot. For paper this indomitable man used birch bark, thus completing the entire printing process.

October 18

Alexander Wilson, who combined the craft of typefounding with the discipline of astronomy—a unique admixture of talents—died upon this day in 1786. Prior to the establishment of Wilson's foundry, there had been no typefounding in Scotland. Through his efforts the craft attained notable success in supplying types for both Scottish and English printers and also for many printing offices in the American colonies.

Alexander Wilson was born in St. Andrews in 1714. As a young man he went to London to learn the medical profession, becoming assistant to a surgeon. At this period he became excited about science, with emphasis upon astronomy. He spent a great deal of his time with other scientific amateurs, among whom was Lord Isla, who —attracted by Wilson's zeal in scientific matters—offered to sponsor his career.

However, an accidental encounter with the typefounding business occurred just about this time when Wilson visited a foundry with a friend who wished to purchase some type. Thomas Curson Hansard, writing in his manual, *Typographia,* published in 1825, discusses this incident, using as a source information he received from the Wilson family:

"While he was thus passing his time in a manner which he considered comfortable for one at his first entrance upon the world, a circumstance accidentally occurred which gave a new direction to his genius, and which in the end led to an entire change of his profession. This was a chance visit made one day to a letter-foundry with a friend, who wanted to purchase some printing types. Having seen the implements and common operations of the workmen usually shown to strangers, he was much captivated by the curious contrivances made use of in prosecuting that art."

Wilson sought the approval of Lord Isla, and upon receiving an enthusiastic response, he enlisted the aid of another young Scotsman, John Baine. Returning to St. Andrews, the two men opened the first typefoundry in Scotland. It was an immediate success, since the Scottish printers had been completely dependent upon the London founders.

In 1749 the partners agreed to go their respective ways, with Wilson becoming the sole proprietor of the foundry. He had become friendly with many of the distinguished faculty members of the University of Glasgow, particularly the printers to the University, Robert and Andrew Foulis. Wilson collaborated with the Press of the University in the production of Greek types for a series of classic texts being produced. These are now considered to be the finest monuments of Greek typography to be printed in Great Britain.

In 1760 Wilson was appointed to the Practical Astronomy Professorship at Glasgow University. A year or so later the foundry was brought into the environs of the University and managed by his two sons, who added still further to its reputation. During Wilson's entire tenure as head of the foundry, not a single type specimen is known to have been issued. As this covered a period of some thirty years duration, it represents a conspicuous lack from a typefoundry of such repute.

October 19

The New York printer, Hugh Gaine, advertised in the pages of *The New York Mercury*, dated this day in 1772: "Wanted an Apprentice to the Printing Business, and a Journey Man Printer, that is a good Press Man, at which Branch he will only be employed. Such a Person will meet with employ for a considerable Time by applying to the Printer hereof."

Printer Gaine's various advertisements constitute a record of the problems of the employing printer during the 18th century and indirectly of the problems of the employees. In 1762 he inserted the following notice in his newspaper columns: "Run-away from the Subscriber about 12 o'clock Yesterday, an Apprentice Lad, named Daniel Narraway: He is about 5 feet 6 Inches high, well made, pretty much pitted with the Small-Pox, wears his own Hair and is very much bloated by Drinking, to which he is most uncommonly addicted: Had on when he went away, a brown Coat, Jacket and Breeches, Shoes and Stockings, but no Buckles in his shoes, having lately sold them, and spent the Money: He is supposed to be lying drunk in some petty Tavern in the Out Ward of the City, or gone up to New-England. Whoever takes up the said lad, so that he may be lodged in the Work-House, shall receive a Reward of Five Dollars, paid by H. Gaine. N. B. All Masters of Vessels are forbid to carry him off at their Peril; and whoever harbours him after the Date of this Advertisement, shall be prosecuted as the Law directs in such Cases. This is the second time he has run away in a month."

Twenty years later, Gaine was still having problems in keeping his apprentices from roving. In 1783 he was complaining once more, in an advertisement in *Rivington's Royal Gazette:* "Absented himself from the Subscriber last Sunday, the 5th instant, An Apprentice Boy, named John Nullaan, Between 19 and 20 year old; about 5 feet 9 inches high; a well looking lad, with black hair: Had on when he went away, a dark colored coat, and it is supposed is gone on board a privateer, or merchant ship, as he is very fond of a seafaring life; therefore, all Masters of vessels and others, are forbid to carry him off, or entertain him on any account, as they will answer the same at their peril."

Contending with runaway apprentices was one of the common problems of the colonial printer, brought about by the terms of indenture, which sometimes bound a lad for ten years of arduous labor under conditions which not infrequently were scarcely less burdensome than actual serfdom. Throughout the period there existed a labor shortage, which printers attempted to alleviate with the hiring of apprentices, only to find themselves over-staffed during the seasonal lulls in the trade. And of course, printers were always well-endowed with an itching foot which kept urging them to seek out mysteries beyond the horizon.

October 20

Although the great Italian printer, Giambattista Bodoni, died in 1813, his native city of Suluzzo waited fifty-nine years before honoring him with a statue, unveiled upon this day in 1872. The inscription upon this statue, unfortunately, was most carefully composed in old style letters!

To a craftsman of the stature of Bodoni this was indeed a most unkind cut, since he was lionized during his lifetime for his sharply contrasted types which today form the basis for the "modern" classification of types. His reputation as the great printer of his era was well-earned, even if his status was immeasurably aided by a subsidy from the Duke of Parma, allowing him great freedom to print without any concern for the more commercial aspects of running a printing office—presumably a problem with many of his competitors.

As a typographer Bodoni was supreme. Everything which he undertook was produced with meticulous care. He was lavish with the use of white space in a period when most books appeared to be overcrowded with type, ornament, and illustration. His use of capital letters in title pages can not be faulted for optical spacing and careful selection of sizes and grouping of elements.

A visit to Parma to see Bodoni was considered to be a part of the Grand Tour of the continent indulged in by wealthy men and their families, along with notables of the literary and artistic world. The novelist Stendahl described his visit to Parma in an anecdote which is indicative of the attitude of the great printer to his work:

"To do my duty as a traveler I presented myself to Monsieur Bodoni, the celebrated printer. I was greatly surprised. This Piedmontais is not at all ostentatious but in love with his art. After having shown me all his French authors he demanded of me which I preferred, the *Telemaque* of Fenelon, the Racine, or the Boileau. I vowed they all seemed equally beautiful. 'Ah Monsieur,' cried Bodoni, 'you don't see the title of the Boileau?' I looked at it for a long time and was forced to admit that I could not see anything more perfect in that title. 'Ah Monsieur,' cried Bodoni again, *'Boileau Desproux* in one single line of capitals. I spent six months before I could decide upon exactly that type!' "

October 21

On this day in 1948 Alfred A. Knopf, the publisher, addressed the members of the Grolier Club in a little talk which he titled "Random Recollections." It can be said of Knopf that he has more than any other American publisher consistently applied the highest manufacturing standards. The list for which he has been responsible represents trade bookmaking at its best. At a time when the standardization of format is becoming a normal procedure in the trade, Knopf must receive the highest credit for his forthright position.

Discussing his relationships with designers, Knopf said:

"Contact between most type designers— there are very few exceptions—and a trade publisher would usually result in anything but friendship. A trade publisher must appear to a type designer, or to a fine typographer, either as a man who doesn't know a thing about the latter's art or as a good

enough chap but so restricted by costs, book-trade prejudices, and the like as to be all but helpless! . . .

"I've come little in contact with type designers as such. Bill Dwiggins I've known and loved and admired for a long time, but Bill never leaves Hingham and I'm lucky if I get to see him there for an hour or two once a year. And, anyway, I don't *know* him really—at any rate not chiefly as a type designer. Warren Chappell lives in New York and we do see a good deal of each other. Bruce Rogers, Goudy, Rudolph Ruzicka, Tom Cleland, I know, but I couldn't fill out a quarter hour with stories by or about *them;* while for me to talk about their work would be an impertinence.

"I have always tried to support a good designer against a recalcitrant author, and usually it works. It works because the author usually likes what a good designer does for him, but sometimes we have to stand up for the designer and explain to the author that we could no more expect the author to interfere with the designer than we would expect the designer to interfere with the author. . . .

"In 1923 we were laying plans with Mencken and Nathan for *The American Mercury* and it was only natural to turn over the complete design of the magazine to Elmer [Adler], who also did the initial prospectus and much other printed matter that we got out in connection with it. . . .

"I have lately run across a letter from Mencken, dating back to those days, which reads in part as follows: 'I have the Adler models for the new department. They look somewhat whorish, but so did *Americana* when he first showed it to us. I shall follow them.' . . .

"As for ourselves, the job we've done, as I see it, has been to sell reasonably well books by authors some of whom we honestly believe to be among the great ones of our times; to make those books as good-looking as possible; and to prove the fallacy of the remark I heard so often as a young man that so-and-so's book was too good to sell. Usually it wasn't quite good enough."

October 22

"You owe nothing to books; but books will give you, in the future, a lasting glory." So wrote Erasmus of Rotterdam to Jean Grolier, Knight, Lord Viscount of Aguisy, who died this day in 1565. The truth of the statement by the great humanist has been borne out in the four hundred years since Grolier's death, during which time the Knight has been honored as one of the most eminent of bibliophiles and his high standards have inspired countless admirers of books. Even more important, his motto, *Io Grolierii et amicorum* has been an example to not only collect books but to share them with friends.

Born to a wealthy family of Lyons in 1479, Grolier had both the interest and the funds to become a serious collector. Through his books he immersed himself in the literary society of his period. While serving as French ambassador in Italy from 1510 to 1535 he became friendly with many of the Italian printers, notably Aldus Manutius at Venice, continuing the relationship at the Casa Aldo with Francesco and Federico d'Asola, who were responsible for the establishment following the death of Aldus in 1515.

A letter written by Grolier to Francesco d'Asola, accompanying a book which he wished to have set in the Aldine types, expresses both the absorption of the bibliophile with the technical details of bookmaking and his intimate knowledge of them.

"You will care with all diligence, O most beloved Francesco," he wrote, "that this work, when it leaves your printing-shop to pass into the hands of learned men, may be as correct as it is possible to render it. I heartily beg and beseech this of you. The book, too, should be decent and elegant; and to this will contribute the choice of the paper, the excellence of the type—which should have been but little used—and the widths of the margins. To speak more exactly, I should wish it were set up with the same type with which you printed your *Poliziano*. And if this decency and elegance shall increase your expenses, I will refund you entirely. Lastly, I should wish that nothing be added to the original or taken from it."

When Grolier died, his library of 3,000 volumes remained with his family until 1675 and was then dispersed. These books, distinguished above all for their magnificent bindings, are now in many of the great libraries of the world, including that of the Grolier Club in New York. The warm relationship of Jean Grolier with the Aldine printers has been memorialized in the fine painting commissioned from the French artist François Flameng in 1889, titled "Grolier in the House of Aldus." It now hangs in the foyer of the Club, which with its splendid collection of books relating to the printer's art, fully exemplifies Grolier's motto, "and friends."

October 23

If ever an opportunity was missed to engage in a bit of promotion, the fact has gone unrecorded in the long career of Duff Green, a Kentucky politician who parlayed a chance meeting on an Ohio River keelboat with Andrew Jackson into a long series of spectacular schemes from most of which he emerged successful. One of these, however, resulting from his activities as Printer to the Congress, achieved only notoriety, but in no whit dimmed Green's appetite for enterprise. He announced, in a prospectus dated in 1834, the founding of the first school for printers, to be called the Washington Institute.

Green proposed to educate up to two hundred boys, aged eleven to sixteen, and furthermore to both feed and clothe them, in return for teaching them the printer's craft. The "schoolroom" for this undertaking just happened to be the printing plant owned by Green. In it he published a daily newspaper, *The United States Telegraph*, in addition to a monthly magazine. And of course there was also the printing for Congress, for which he held the contract.

Each lad who entered Green's Institute would be expected to devote eight hours to laboring for Green in addition to five hours of study in the languages and the arts. Presumably the balance of the day was his own, but he was allowed the opportunity to earn "additional" money (he was not to be paid for the eight hour stint) by working overtime. The boy was expected to wait until coming of age to receive this extra pay, but the prospectus assured him that, if he entered the school in his eleventh year, there would be awaiting his matriculation the opulent sum of seven hundred and twenty-eight dollars, "A sum sufficient to set him up in business as an editor, a lawyer, a physician, or if he prefers to plant himself as an independent freeman, to purchase and stock a farm in the rich lands of the West."

Green asked two of the subscribers to his publications to advance the capital to set up the school and to construct a building in which to house the students. The contribution requested was $150, for which Green would supply "in perpetuity" the publications produced by his plant, the normal subscription price of which was about $30 a year. The promoter mentioned that this "dividend" represented twenty percent on the investment.

The astonishing fact about this project was that it received the approval of a number of employing printers as a most desirable method of training printers. But the journeymen printers opposed the scheme with hoots and hollers, and under the leadership of the Columbia Typographical Society, they combined with members of Congress politically opposed to Green to block it.

October 24

Writing from his home in New Fairfield, Connecticut on October 24, 1931, Bruce Rogers explained his attitude upon judging exhibitions to Thomas Wood Stevens:

"Regarding your very complimentary offer, of the principal jurorship for the Fifty Book Show:—I am sorry to disappoint you, or to seem indifferent to your kindness in thinking of me in connection with it; but my one and only experience in serving on a jury for a printing show, was so unfortunate and unpleasant (owing to there having been some of my own unexpectedly entered) that I then and there resolved never to attempt to serve in a like category, under any consideration—a resolve that I have faithfully kept.

"Aside from this personal prejudice, I am not sure that I am in favor of the jury system—in printing or in general shows. I realize that something of the kind is practically necessary—but the grounds for judging bookmaking are so many and varied that I don't believe *anyone* should be empowered to say—by implication, at least—'This is good; that is bad' (which is what the selective system amounts to) unless at the same time they are able to give detailed grounds to the public for their acceptance of

one and rejection of the other—a thing manifestly impossible, unless theses were written about each book under consideration.

"I don't know what the new basis of selection is, that they chose last week; but the latest News-Letter contained enough to prove that there was need of one—whether it will result in a better and fairer choice of books remains to be proved. In fact the whole question of whether 'fine printing' as such, has any real justification, is still (to my mind) an open one:—but as it would perhaps seem like burning the scaffolding on which my own work has been erected, I am not going to argue it. Time alone will sift out the real from the pretentious—I mean, amongst my own books as well as others. I have made many merely pretentious ones.

"So, my dear Mr. Stevens, I hope you will excuse me with a good grace; and let me remain outside the controversies and criticisms that are bound to arise; whatever the method, and whoever the jurors are. It is doubtless a selfish instinct, but I fear I value my own quietude of mind, as a workman, above any educative influence I might conceivably exert in serving on a jury. What mental energy I possess is, to my thinking, much more profitably employed in countering the many difficulties and perplexities inherent in the actual production of books. Their after-fate is on the knees of the gods—one of whom I have no aspirations or inspiration to be—even temporarily."

October 25

"To the Editor of the *Providence Gazette, and Country Journal*. Sir, I am one of your Country Subscribers, and although I have no Learning myself, more than what I obtained by my own Industry, without Instruction, I value it in others." So began a letter, addressed this day in 1762 by a newspaper subscriber who signed himself simply, "Your Well-Wisher, A Countryman."

The letter continued: "There is generally too much Reflection cast on Country People for being illiterate and awkward; but if the Authors of such Reflections had any Candour, they would make all proper Allowances for narrow Circumstances, the constant Attendance which we and our Children are obliged to give in the Execution of our laborious Callings, the dispersed Manner of our Living, and the Want of Schools. Printing is the greatest Means of promoting Learning that was ever invented; and I hope that the setting up of that Business near us, may contribute to our Instruction, and be one Means of improving the rising Generation, and of wiping away the Odium cast on us, of being ignorant, rude, and unpolished."

As this letter appeared in just the second issue of the *Gazette,* it was undoubtedly written by its young and ambitious editor, William Goddard, who had begun—just one year out of his apprenticeship, served with William Parker in New Haven and New York—the publication of the first newspaper in Providence. Subscriptions for the early newspaper were seldom obtained in sufficient quantity to assure financial success. Goddard therefore sought to build his list beyond the limits of the town of Providence, which at that time had a population of about 4,000 inhabitants.

The publication of a newspaper was just one part of the operation of a colonial printing office. In the first issue of the *Gazette,* Goddard inserted an advertisement as a colophon: "Providence in New England: Printed by William Goddard, opposite the Court-House; by whom Advertisements are taken in, and all Manner of Printing Work performed with Care and Expedition."

In a later issue there was offered for sale at the printing office "A variety of Books and Stationery, to be sold cheap by the Printer hereof,—With all sorts of Blanks used in this Colony, neatly printed,—Also New York almanacks, for the Year 1763."

Thus the Colonial newspaper office was a print shop and a book store. As such it attracted the attention of the best informed residents of the community, the printer becoming, if not affluent, at least an important citizen. It is this factor which still attracts men of individuality to set up as newspaper publishers in villages and country towns, even with the competition of electronic communications.

October 26

In a letter addressed to Robert Frost on this day in 1912, Mrs. M. L. Nutt, an English publisher, wrote: "I have looked through your MS and I am personally interested in the treatment of your theme. I am therefore disposing to bring out your poems if the proposal I can put before you and which would be on the principle of a royalty payment will suit you. I cannot put a dry and cut proposal before you as yet, as I want to think a little about the most suitable form to give the book but I hope to be in position to do so very soon."

The "form" in which Frost's first book, *A Boy's Will,* finally appeared was scarcely in a class, typographically, with many of his later publications. The poet was most fortunate in his printers, becoming—as Paul A. Bennett has written— the "best-printed" American author. As early as 1912, when he was living in England and his initial effort had not been published, he was in correspondence with that distinguished entrepreneur of the limited edition, Thomas B. Mosher of Portland, Maine. Mosher was all for pirating some of the poems which were collected in *A Boy's Will.* Frost, extremely anxious to achieve circulation in the United States, was not particularly unhappy to have him do so, although he wrote of his publisher, Mrs. Nutt, that she would not look kindly on such a venture.

At about the same time, Frost wrote to Mosher telling him that he was thinking of offering some of his poems to the New York publisher, Mitchell Kennerley, in which case Frederic Goudy, then printing for Kennerley, might have become a Frost printer. Actually, the poet had to wait until 1928 to see his work issued from the press of one of the great printers, when the limited edition of *West Running Brook* was produced by Daniel Berkeley Updike at the Merrymount Press. The following year an early Frost play, *A Way Out,* was printed by John Fass at the Harbor Press. This edition, in Caslon type, received the accolade of selection for the Fifty Books of the Year.

In 1930 Frost's *Collected Poems* were produced for Random House by the printing craftsman who has since been most identified as *the* Frost printer, Joseph Blumenthal of the Spiral Press. This splendid book, handset in Lutetia type, was also a Fifty Book selection. In 1933 William A. Dwiggins had the opportunity to do a Frost poem, *The Lone Striker,* for the Alfred A. Knopf Borzoi Chap Book series.

In 1950 the Limited Editions Club issued a two-volume edition of Frost's poems, entrusting the typographic treatment to the hands of Bruce Rogers and the illustrations to the wood engraver, Thomas W. Nason. Two limited editions designed by Joseph Blumenthal, *A Witness Tree* and *A Masque of Reason,* were fine enough for inclusion in the Fifty Books, as were the Modern Library edition of the poems produced in 1946 and the trade edition of Frost's last book, *In the Clearing,* published in 1962.

October 27

Those printers who are interested in the equipment of a printing office in the American colonies during the 18th century are indebted to Benjamin Franklin for a concise list of materials which he helped to secure for the establishment of such an office. In a letter posted from Philadelphia on this date in 1753, Franklin wrote to William Strahan:

"I am now about to establish a small Printing Office in favour of another Nephew, at Newhaven in the Colony of Connecticut in New England; a considerable Town in which there is an University, and a Prospect that a Bookseller's Shop with a Printing House may do pretty well. I would therefore request you to bespeak for me of Mr. Caslon, vis

300 lb Longprimer, with Figures
    and signs sufficient
    for an Almanack
300 lb Pica
100 lb English
100 lb Great Primer
60 lb Double Pica
50 lb Two line English
40 lb Two line Great
    Primer
30 lb Two line Capitals, & Flowers
    of different Founts
20 lb Quotations

"As Mr. Caslon has different Long-primers, Picas, &c. I beg the Favr. of your Judgment to chuse & order the best.
  To which add,
  A compleat good new Press
  2 pair Blankets
  2 pair Ballstocks
  Some Riglets, Gutter Sticks, Side Sticks,
    Quoins, &c.

3 pair Chases of different Sizes, the
  biggest Demi
2 folio Galleys with 4 Slices
2 Quarto Galleys
A few Facs, Head & Tail pieces, 3 or
  4 of each
2 Doz brass Rule
2 good Composing Sticks
2 Cags of Ink, one weak the other strong
"If you can persuade your Pressmaker to go out of his old Road a little, I would have the Ribs made not with the Face rounding outwards, as usual, but with a little hollow or rounding inwards from end to end: And the Cramps made of hard cast Brass, fix'd not across the Ribs, but longways so as to slide in the hollow Face of the Ribs. The Reason is, that Brass and Iron work better together than Iron & Iron; Such a Press never gravels; the hollow Face of the Ribs keeps the Oil better, and the Cramps bearing on a larger Surface do not wear as in the common Method. Of this I have had many Years experience."

October 28

One of the rarest of the imprints of Colonial America was produced on this day in the year 1778 in Boston Harbor. Entitled *Déclaration adressée, au nom du Roi, à tous les anciens François de l'Amérique Septentrionale,* it issued from the press carried on board *Languedoc,* ship of the line in the fleet of Vice Admiral N. le Compte d'Estaing. The ship had completed a transatlantic voyage to aid the struggling colonies in their fight for freedom. The *Déclaration* was printed "de l'Imprimerie de F. P. Demauge, Imprem-eur du Roi & de l'Escadre." The New York Public Library owns the only known copy.

Almost as rare is a piece of printing produced by the printing office of another French fleet which arrived off Newport, Rhode Island in 1780, carrying some 6,000 soldiers. This press, l'Imprimerie Royale de l'Escadre, was carried on board *Le Neptune.* From it was struck off, in 1781, the *Calen-drier Français, Pour l'Année Commune 1781,* of which but two copies are known to exist. For a short period after the French fleet had anchored at Newport, the press was transported to the town, thus becoming one of the early colonial presses.

The *Calendrier Français,* an almanac, is the first volume of its kind to be printed in the French language in continental United States. It also represents the first Roman Catholic almanac to be printed in Rhode Island and possibly in the United States.

There are but four known works printed by Imprimerie Royale de l'Escadre, the press of *Le Neptune.* The largest was the first edition of *Voyage de Newport à Philadelpie,* by Chastelloux. Although the work has frequently been reprinted there are but seven copies of the original known to bibliographers. While it was known that the press also printed a newspaper, *La Gazette Française de Newport,* no copy has yet been found.

Unfortunately there exists no description of the equipment used to print aboard the naval vessels of the late 18th century period. Unquestionably the amount of space devoted to such an enterprise must have been limited indeed. There was never sufficient room even for the crews, since warships frequently were over-complemented for their size in comparision to merchant vessels.

October 29

"What do we mean by 'printing'?" The question was asked by Bruce Rogers in a letter written this day in 1927 to the editor of *The Saturday Review of Literature.* Rogers was attempting to clarify what he believed to be obscure terminology in discussions concerning the craft of printing.

The distinguished typographer went on to say, in part, "The artist printer finds himself in the complex situation of the architect who must consider the accord between the suitability of his building and its actual external appearance, or of the poet who must combine what he says—the contents of his poem—with his verse forms. In all the arts—and that is *why* they are arts—there must be this adjustment to make a successful work. The final harmony of these independent properties is never obtained automatically or by rote, but by a miracle, or after vast effort—or rather by inspiration and effort combined.

"A perfect book is both easy to read and beautiful to look at. Pleasure in the reading matter itself is enhanced by pleasure in

its suitable frame. An excellent balance of black and white lessens the effort of reading and the eye unconsciously approves of both ensemble and details without being distracted by them. . . .

"Typographical work permits no improvisations. It is the ripe fruit of experiment—the result of an art which preserves only the successful trials and rejects the rough drafts and sketches.

"The press holds up a mirror to the author in which he may see himself clearly. If the paper, type, and composition are carefully chosen and harmonious, the author sees his work in a new guise. He may feel keen pride or shame. He hears a firmer, more detached voice than his own—an implacably just voice—articulating his words. Everything weak, arbitrary, or in bad taste that he has written is pointed up and comes out in clear relief. It is at once a lesson and a splendid thing to be beautifully printed. . . ."

October 30

On this day in 1804 a young printer named James D. Bemis purchased half ownership of the *Western Repository* in Canandaigua, New York, the pioneer newspaper of Western New York. Just twenty-one years of age at the time, Bemis had already demonstrated the necessary acumen to become a driving force in the western expansion of the young American republic.

Although Bemis had but two years of formal schooling in his life, he had gained the liberal education of most printers of his time. As a result, when he became a journeyman printer, his abilities were recognized by the Albany booksellers, Backus & Whiting, who offered him a partnership in a bookshop which they proposed to establish in York (Toronto), Canada. Putting together a stock of books appropriate for the frontier trade, Bemis set out for his destination late in 1803. He arrived in the western town of Canandaigua on January 14th and thereupon sat down and wrote a letter to his sister, describing the frontier travel of his period:

"After being detained in Utica, upward of seven weeks, my patience was so far exhausted, that I determined, notwithstanding the badness of the roads, to make one more attempt to gain the place of my destination; and accordingly hired two wagons to take me to Canandaigua. They had proceeded about fifty rods, when one of them got mired to the hub!—'Good start' you will say. Well! we got out in about an hour, and travelled *eight* miles the first day.

"Next morning, after taking a warm breakfast, I again 'weighed anchor,' and trudged in solitude along the muddy waste, (for it is indeed solitary to have no company but swearing teamsters) 'till we reached Oneida village, an Indian Settlement, where, about dark, both wagons got again mired to the hub! Zounds and alack!—what a pickle we were in! How did I invoke the aid of old Hercules to give one tug at the wheel! However, after lifting, grumbling, hollowing, and tugging three hours and a half, with the assistance of an Indian, we once more got on land. It was ten o'clock, and no tavern within our power to reach. Cold, fatigued, and hungry, we were glad to get under shelter, and accordingly stopped at the first Indian hut we found, where there was no bed, and no victuals except a slice of rusty pork. After a night spent in yawning, dozing and gaping, we again got underway, . . . and we went on to Onondaga, where we arrived about ten at night. Here the house was full; and I obtained the privilege of sleeping with two strangers, by paying for their lodgings, and giving them a glass of bitters—an odd bargain to be sure! At Onondaga, the waggoners got discouraged, and despaired of the practicability of travelling! They accordingly stored the goods, and made the best of their way home again. Here I was obliged to remain *two* weeks; when a fine snow was falling, I hired a man with a three-horse sleigh, to carry me to Canada, and arrived at this place on Saturday evening, the 14th of January, after a 'short and pleasant passage' of sixty-two days from Albany!"

October 31

"Cut up and salt away beef. Take proof of 1st form." Thus reads the entry for this date in 1835 in the journal of the Rev. Jotham Meeker, printer to the Baptist mission at Shawanoe in the Indian Territory, in what later became the state of Kansas.

Jotham Meeker was apprenticed to the trade in Cincinnati in the early 1820's.

Shortly after hearing an address in his local church by Robert Simerwell, a missionary to the Indians in the wilds of Michigan, the young printer received a call to missionary work and journeyed to Michigan in 1825 to work with the Potawatomies. Here he became interested in the Indian language, a study which was to continue all his life.

While in Michigan, Meeker was licensed to preach the gospel, but in 1831 he found it necessary to give up his missionary work to return to printing in order to support his wife and mother. The following year, however, he was again prevailed to resume his mission at Sault Ste. Marie, where he remained until ordered by the Baptist Board of Foreign Missions to proceed to the Indian Territory and to organize a press with which to print and distribute the literature needed to win the favor of the Indians.

Meeker purchased a used Seth Adams press in Cincinnati, along with all the necessary types and equipment for a printing office. These he ordered to be shipped to the Shawanoe mission station. There on March 8, 1834 he printed the Shawanoe Hymn, the first recorded printing in the Territory.

Throughout his career as a printer and missionary, Meeker was intensely interested in the establishment of an Indian orthography by which the native Americans could more quickly assimilate the language of the white man. Meeker's approach to this system was to devise written or printed characters to represent certain positions of the organs of speech. Every uncompounded sound which could be distinguished by the ear was indicated by a character. In the Indian languages most of these sounds were what would be considered vowel sounds. Since Meeker used ordinary English characters, special types did not have to be devised for the written language.

The hardships of conducting a pioneer printing office may be noted from Meeker's journal in which he faithfully recorded the events of his life. On January 18, 1841 he wrote that he had translated all day but that the ink was freezing, making writing difficult. On November 8 he wrote that he was 37 years of age that day, had completed the translation of Matthew's Gospel and had printed part of it. On the 9th he observed that he had received some manuscript sheets "almost destroyed by mice—must spend some days in writing them over."

212

November

The first entry in the account book of Messrs. Binny & Ronaldson, typefounders of Philadelphia, is dated November 1, 1796 and lists one "John Scull of Pittsburg—$9.00." And so began the first permanent and successful typefoundry in the United States.

Archibald Binny, printer, and James Ronaldson, baker, had come from Edinburgh, Scotland, had renewed an earlier acquaintance in Philadelphia, and had decided to become typefounders in a location and at a period when there was virtually no typefounding activity. The firm rented a frame house on Cedar Street for $17.33 per month. The two Scotsmen added to their original equipment by purchasing the typefounding equipment of Christopher Sower II and that of Adam Mappa of New York, establishing a virtual monopoly in the manufacture of printing types in America.

In 1809 the firm published the first typefounder's specimen book to be produced in the United States, *A Specimen of Metal Ornaments Cast at the Letter Foundery of Binny & Ronaldson*. This book contained no type lines, but showed metal cuts and reproductions of wood blocks. In 1812 the company issued a book which contained actual types, the first volume of its kind to be published in America.

The types shown were romans and italics, English blackletter, fraktur, Hebrew, and Greek, and a decorative letter, in addition to borders. The romans were typical of the period, being of modern construction. There was a French Canon, very similar to the cuttings of the Baskerville letter made by the Fry foundry in England.

The most interesting of all the types shown is the Pica Roman No. 1. This type, a transitional letter cut as far as is known by Binny himself, was in wide use during the first three decades of the 19th century. When the Binny & Ronaldson firm went through successive ownerships prior to being part of the amalgamation which became the American Type Founders Company in 1892, the matrices for Roman No. 1 were retained. Mr. Joseph W. Finney, vice president of the new firm, made trial casts of the type and issued specimen sheets, naming the face Oxford.

Daniel B. Updike, the distinguished proprietor of the Merrymount Press of Boston, acquired the Oxford type and thought so much of it that he used it for the setting of his great two-volume work, *Printing Types, Their History, Forms, and Use*. When Princeton University Press engaged in the production of the multi-volumed *Papers of Thomas Jefferson* in 1950, the Binny & Ronaldson Roman No. 1 was recut for the linotype machine, receiving the name of Monticello. Jefferson is said to have admired the original, hence its selection for this edition.

November 2

In a letter to Horace Walpole, M. P., addressed from Easy Hill, Birmingham on this day in 1762, John Baskerville wrote:

"As the Patron and Encourager of Arts, and particularly that of Printing, I have taken the liberty of sending you a Specimen of mine, begun ten years ago at the age of forty-seven, and prosecuted ever since with the utmost Care and Attention, on the strongest Presumption, that if I could fairly excel in this divine Art, it would make my Affairs easy or at least give me bread. But alas! in both I was mistaken. The Book-sellers do not chuse to encourage me, tho I have offered them as low terms as I could possibly live by; nor dare I attempt an old Copy, till a Lawsuit relating to that affair is determined. . . .

"I have sent a few Specimens (same as enclosed) to the Courts of Russia and Den-mark, and shall endeavor to do the same to most of the Courts of Europe; in hopes of finding some one of them a purchaser of the whole Scheme, on the Condition of my never attempting another Type. I was saying this to a particular Friend who reproached me with not giving my own Country the Pref-erence, as it would (he was pleased to say) be a national Reproach to lose it. I told him, nothing but the greatest Necessity would put me upon it; and even then I should resign it with the utmost Reluctance. He observed, the Parliament had given a handsome Pre-mium for a quack Medicine; & he doubted not, if my affair was properly brought be-fore the House of Commons, but some Re-gard would be paid to it; I replyed, I durst not presume to petition the House, unless en-couraged by some of the Members, who might do me the honor to promote it, of which I saw not the least hopes or Proba-bility.

"Thus, Sir I have taken the Liberty of laying before You my Affairs, without the least Aggravation; and humbly hope Your Patronage; To whom can I apply for pro-tection but the Great, who alone have it in their Power to serve me?

"I rely on your Candor as a Lover of the Arts; to excuse this Presumption in Your most obedient and most humble Servant."

Horace Walpole paid no apparent atten-tion to this letter from Baskerville, so the typefounder attempted to sell his punches and matrices to France, for the sum of £6,000, using Benjamin Franklin as his agent. The American told him that the French government was too poor to purchase the types, as they lacked even the money to keep the public buildings in repair. It was not until after Baskerville's death that his widow advertised in 1776 for sale at auction, "Four accurate improved Printing Presses; several large Founts of Type, different Sizes; with Cases, Frames, screwed Chases, and every other useful Apparatus in that Branch of Trade."

A suggestion by the bibliographer, Har-wood, that the British government purchase the types as a start upon a national typog-raphy was disregarded. After every effort to sell the type in England had been investi-gated, Mrs. Baskerville finally disposed of them to the French dramatist, Beaumarchais, who was then engaged upon a printing of the complete works of Voltaire. The punches and matrices remained in France until they were returned to England in 1953 as a gift of the French government to Cambridge University. Copies of the original design con-stitute one of the universal types.

November 3

The revenge of a reigning Queen of England, Elizabeth I, was requited this day in the year 1579 upon William Page, publisher, and John Stubbs. Their crime was to write and print what the good Queen considered to be traitorous propaganda. In August the pair had combined with Hugh Singleton, a print-er, in producing a tract, the title of which stated in part, *The Discovery of a Gapying Gulf whereunto England is like to be swal-lowed by another French marriage, if the Lord forbid not the banes, by letting her majestie see the sin & punishment there-of.* . . .

Since Elizabeth had no intention of marry-ing the duc d'Alençon and was merely going through the motions for reasons of state, she was outraged at Stubbs' attempt to rally public opinion against her. She insisted that the trio pay for their crime by suffering the loss of their right hands. It took some fast footwork on the part of her lawyers to justi-fy this punishment as coming under an old law against the authors and publishers of seditious writings. Of the honest lawyers who spoke out against Elizabeth's decision, one had to resign his position as a justice and one was sent to the Tower of London to meditate upon his disobedience.

During the trial the printer Singleton, a very poor craftsman, was acquitted and allowed to perpetrate his bad printing upon the kingdom for the remainder of his life. Stubbs and Page were sentenced as the Queen had directed. The spectacle took place at Westminster before a large but quiet and sullen crowd. The public hangman did the job with an ordinary butcher's cleaver, a beetle, and a red-hot iron. Page said, while his stump was cauterized, "I have left there a true Englishman's hand." Following the hangman's blow Stubbs took off his hat with his left hand. "God Save Queen Elizabeth!" he cried.

Even in an England whose people were accustomed to severe punishments—in an ordinary year it is reported that eight hundred persons were hanged for such crimes as cutting down trees and stealing more than a shilling—public opinion reacted against the barbarity of the sentence to Stubbs and Page. Lord Cecil later awarded Stubbs a government job, with pension, to assuage his own shame at the proceedings.

November 4

In a preface to a type specimen book dated this day at the French town of Sedan in the year 1621, a master printer named Jean Jannon wrote:

"So, seeing that for some time many persons have had to do with the art who have greatly lowered it (so far doth ignorance and the lack of skill corrupt the most beautiful things in time:) the desire came upon me to try if I might imitate, after some fashion, some one among those who honorably busied themselves with the art, whom I hear regretted every day: such as, among others, a Conrad at Rome, a Manuce at Venice, an Estienne at Paris . . . a Plantin at Antwerp, a Wechel at Francfort, and some others who were very celebrated in their time. And inasmuch as I could not accomplish this design for lack of types which I needed to this end: not even being able conveniently to draw upon the typefounder, some of whom would not, and others could not, furnish me with what I lacked: I resolved, about six years ago, to turn my hand in good earnest to the making of Punches, Matrices and Moulds for all sorts of charac-

ters, for the accommodation both of the public and of myself."

Since Jannon had already used types secured from the Frankfurt typefoundry of Egenolff-Luther, the punches for which had been obtained by that founder from the widow of Claude Garamond, the Sedan printer was familar with their general style. His own design naturally followed the pattern of the Garamond letter.

Jannon was printer to the Calvinist Academy at Sedan, and his types were made for the exclusive use of the Academy publications. In 1642, when the forces of Cardinal Richelieu captured Sedan, Jannon's typefounding equipment and types were sent to the newly formed Royal Printing Office, where they were put to use in the setting of Richelieu's memoirs. The types were then stored and forgotten, until they reappeared in a specimen book of the same establishment in 1845 under the heading of *Caractères de l'Université*. The fonts were then attributed to Garamond. In 1898 the printing office, then known as the *Imprimerie Nationale,* revived the types for the printing connected with the Paris Exposition of 1900. Their use for this purpose naturally enough brought the types to the attention of the world's printers at a period when there was a tremendous interest in historic typefaces, following the 15th century revivals sponsored by William Morris at the Kelmscott Press.

The French National Printing Office still retained the exclusive use of the Jannon fonts, which were not allowed to be copied by French typefounders. Outside of France, however, there were no restrictions.

In the United States, Morris Benton of the American Type Founders Company, with the assistance of Thomas M. Cleland, cut a type inspired by the Jannon letter and called it Garamond. The "Garamond" revival had now really begun. The Monotype Company commissioned Frederic W. Goudy to cut a copy which was issued in 1923 and named Garamont. The Lintoype Company then brought out a Garamond, patterned from the true Garamond designs as shown in the famous Egenolff-Berner specimen sheet issued in Frankfurt in 1592. However, the Jannon features so evident in the ATF copy, were admired so much that Linotype found it necessary to cut a second Garamond identical to it, named No. 3. There are now Garamond cuttings from all the typefoundries of the world, some taken from the true Garamonds and some from the Jannon fonts, but none carry the name of the persecuted punchcutter.

November 5

Upon this day in 1733 appeared the first number of *The New York Weekly Journal,* published by a printer of the town named John Peter Zenger, who had been petitioned by a group of citizens opposed to the policies of Colonel William Cosby, Governor of the Colony.

Zenger, a German immigrant, had been apprenticed to the printing trade in 1710 by William Bradford, the Colony's first printer. Completing the period of his indenture in 1720, he pursued his craft in Chestertown, Maryland where he became a naturalized citizen. Returning to New York two years later, he again worked for Bradford before going into business for himself about 1726.

Within a year the content of the newspaper so angered autocratic Governor Cosby that he asked the House of Representatives to arrest and imprison Zenger for perpetrating "seditious libels." When Cosby's request was refused, he ordered the mayor and the magistrates to seize and burn the libelous papers. Upon their repudiation of his demands, he ordered his sheriffs to do so. His order was immediately carried out.

Zenger was then imprisoned and Cosby insured a trial favorable to the Crown by removing a judge sympathetic to the prisoner. Zenger asked that he be released upon bail, but the magistrate set the bail too high and none of his friends and supporters came to his aid. He had not been completely deserted, however, as his family was provided for. The governor's opposition simply wanted to make a martyr of Zenger. In this they succeeded beyond question even if the printer did have to spend thirty-five weeks in gaol where he enjoyed only, as he later wrote, "the liberty of speaking through the hole in the door to my wife and servants."

The issue became one of the great cases in which freedom of speech was a factor. Zenger's trial has since become one of the most celebrated of its kind. Zenger of course was most fortunate to have at his side one of the greatest of colonial lawyers, Andrew Hamilton of Philadelphia, who based his argument on his proposition that the common law used to charge Zenger was based upon the tyranny of the Star Chamber and should therefore be renounced in the light of modern liberty.

In his final argument Hamilton addressed his remarks to the jury rather than to the judges. He was eloquent, emotional, and effective, saying in part: "The loss of liberty to a generous mind, is worse than death; and yet we know there have been those in all ages, who for the sake of preferment, or some imaginary honor, have freely lent a helping hand, to oppress, nay to destroy their country.... the question before the court and you gentlemen of the jury, is not of small nor private concern, it is not the cause of the poor printer, nor of New York alone, which you are now trying. No! It may in its consequences, affect every freeman that lives under a British government on the main of America. It is the best cause. It is the cause of Liberty; and I make no doubt but your upright conduct, this day, will not only entitle you to the love and esteem of your fellow citizens; but every man who prefers freedom to a life of slavery will bless and honor you, as men who have baffled the attempt at tyranny; and by an impartial and uncorrupt verdict, have laid a noble foundation for securing to ourselves, our posterity, and our neighbors, that, to which nature and the laws of our country have given us a right,—the liberty—both of exposing and opposing arbitrary power (in these parts of the world, at least) by speaking and writing truth."

November 6

"In God's name, amen. Be it known to all who see or hear read this public document that in the year counted after the birth of Christ our Lord, one thousand four hundred and fifty five, in the third indiction, on thursday which was the sixth day of the month called Latin *November,* in the first year of the reign of the most holy father in God and Lord, our Lord Calixtus, by divine providence the third pope, between the hours of eleven and twelve at mid-day, at Mainz in the large refectory of the [convent of the] barefooted monks, in the presence of myself, a public scribe, and of the witnesses hereinafter named, there has appeared in person the honorable Jacob Fust, burgher of Mainz, and he has presented, spoken and declared on behalf of his brother Johann Fust, also there present, how a final date had been set, decided and named for today at this hour in the convent hall there, between the aforenamed Johan Fust, his brother, party of the first part, and Johan Gutenberg, party of the second part, for the just named Johann Guttenberg to see and to hear such oath being taken by the said Johan Fust as imposed and enjoined upon the same Johann Fust by wording and content of the judgment passed between both parties."

Thus, in the legal jargon dear to lawyer's hearts for centuries, did a Mainz notary by the name of Ulricus Helmasperger, record—with delightful inexactness of names—a public hearing in which a banker named Fust called in an inventor named Gutenberg for lack of payment of a loan. This document is one of the important sources of information which historians of printing cite as definite proof that Johann Gutenberg actually was a resident of Mainz at the period and that he did have something to do with a method of impressing metal characters called types to produce what is now called printing.

Unfortunately, Gutenberg never dated any of his printing, nor did he mention himself in a colophon, so it is necessary to fall back upon documents of this nature to prove that he is the inventor of movable type. The inventor did not himself appear at this hearing but he did enter a statement to the effect that Fust had loaned him money but had expected no interest. The money had been advanced for "instruments or apparatus" which were pledged to the banker in return for his loan. Further money had been advanced to pay for supplies and for workmen's wages.

While the mass of evidence points to Gutenberg as the inventor of movable type, there has been controversy for centuries over his claim. There is certainly substantiation upon a number of points which can be fairly well documented that the credit is his.

It is probable that the first tentative steps took place about 1440. This is the date accepted by modern scholars. It resulted in the world wide celebration of the five hundredth anniversary of the invention of movable type in 1940.

Eric Gill, printer, type designer, engraver, and long-established critic of the machine in the affairs of mankind, wrote to *G.K's Weekly* on this date in 1925:

"Sir: With reference to the letter of M.W. S. Roe in your issue of October 17. The matter of machinery is one to which you will be giving your official attention before very long, and I do not wish to anticipate. There is one point, however, which might as well be stated without delay, for it is one which has been missed by all your correspondents hitherto.

"Mr. Roe says, 'Learn how to control machinery and we shall get a much better result from that we already have, etc. . . .' Now before we can say *How* to control anything we must decide *who* is to control it—this is the fundamental point. Imagine an unruly child. People ask themselves how to control it. Is it not obvious that the problem wears an entirely different aspect directly we put it to ourselves, as we should do in the *first* place, in terms of *who*. Thus, is the father to control, or the schoolmaster, or the superintendent of the reformatory? The mere mechanism of control is entirely different according as it proceeds from one or the other.

"I do not propose now to write at length upon the question as to *who* should control machinery. I merely wish to point out that this question is antecedent to the question of *how* we should control machinery, and I think it is obvious that when the question of who is decided, the question of how will be much less difficult.

"Mr. Roe's letter ends with the sentence: 'To persuade a man to use a spade when he can employ a plough—well, I think it is a hopeless job.' Mr. Roe implies that the cultivator he envisages is able to choose his tool. Before we can make an implication as delightfully simple as that, let us ask ourselves, for example, whether the linotype machines used in Fleet Street are chosen by the compositors, or whether it is not possible that those machines are chosen by persons whose trade is money-making rather than 'comping.'

"P. S.—Mr. Roe quotes Carlyle's saying that man is 'a tool-using animal.' It is at least doubtful whether Lord Beaverbrook can justly be said to use the linotype machines he controls."

Gill was concerned with the dehumanization which occurs when the machine becomes so self-regulating that the individual has no responsibility other than that of manipulation, the final product being so homogenized that it has no character. As long as men with Gill's outlook continue to make their protest against the loss of intellectual responsibility in an increasingly mechanistic society, we can expect that the day of complete subservience to the machine will be, at the very least, delayed.

November 8

"Born in Nurnberg on 8 November, 1918, I spent my childhood in that factory town. My parents lived in a small settlement in the city's southern section, and I roved the bordering woods with my schoolmates and was seldom to be found at home. I chased butterflies, caught salamanders and gathered flowers and stones."

So wrote Hermann Zapf in his charming and informative book *About Alphabets*. In the post-World War II era he has developed into one of the foremost designers of type. Yet, as a schoolboy, his writing was so wretched that he felt himself fortunate to receive a B in penmanship.

"My first systematic attempts at writing with the broad-edged pen," he writes, "began in 1935. . . . The fashioning of letters may to many seem a trifling activity, but whoever has occupied himself with it intensively will properly understand a guest-book entry of 1932 by Rudolf Koch: 'The making of letters in every form is for me the purest and the greatest pleasure, and at many stages of my life it was to me what a song is to the singer, a picture to the painter, a shout to the elated, or a sight to the oppressed—it was and is for me the most happy and perfect expression of my life.'

"With tireless zeal in my spare time," Zapf continues, "I wrote pages of letters that often left me unsatisfied because the models in the books looked so much better—until one day I discovered I had been holding my edged pen in a false position, whereupon things began to look up. But of course no one who is self-taught can be spared such

roundabout journeys. Evenings and weekends I sat at home writing and writing— or rather practising, for the waste-basket was always full of written pages. My parents considered me almost out of my senses, father being annoyed by the added cost of electric current occasioned by my work at night. My friends went out for dancing and amusement; I stayed at home and bravely drew letters."

Such diligence was productive, however, as by the time he was twenty Zapf was commissioned by the famous Stempel typefoundry to design a type, a fraktur, named Gilgengart, and his career was fully launched. Zapf's approach to the problems of type design is traditional and is somewhat akin to that of the American type designer, Frederic W. Goudy, whom Zapf greatly admires.

A single paragraph in *About Alphabets* comes close to summarizing Zapf's thinking about letterforms:

"A new printing type has a long, often thorny way to completion. Before a type has come far enough to please outsiders, it adds gray hairs to its co-producers. Important in the matter is the type's design; a long time is needed to perfect all its details. The imaginary notion of letters from A to Z does not itself suffice, and by the time these more or less vague proposals and fancies attain a definite form, all may look quite different on printed paper. A design needs just not any forms, but good forms that harmonize with the remaining shapes, all distinguishable as signs and of noble character."

November 9

On this day in 1964 is recorded the death of Thomas Maitland Cleland in his eighty-fourth year. One of the great graphic artists of our time, he was not at all widely known during the last twenty years of his life, at least to the younger group of typographers. His insistence upon fundamental training in design and his traditional outlook were never more in evidence than in his famous talk at the Fifty Books Show in New York in 1940, entitled "Harsh Words." Having survived that polemic, he journeyed to Chicago in 1948 and addressed the Society of Typographic Arts in a similar vein.

"We are told by many writers and some designers," he said, "that the world has changed. The making of books, it seems, is no longer an art, but a vast quantity production industry and there must be a new 'aesthetic of the machine' and clearer concepts of form and function to meet this unprecedented state of affairs. These are brave and windy words and I am swept along by the great gust of emotion they arouse and dazzled by the visions they present, and altogether too excited by them to ask exactly what they mean. Before I could understand them I would have to overlook the fact that the world has, for a considerable number of years, been undergoing a process of change, and that since the invention of printing, the making of books has always been an industry, and sometimes an art, and frequently both; and that the hand-press was also a machine. There must be some good reason which eludes my aging comprehension, why the great presses of today—infinitely more efficient machines than hand-presses—can only print carelessly designed books or operate at full capacity with ill-proportioned margins; or why their speed and quantity would be curtailed by a well-composed title-page. As to function, I had always supposed that the function of books was to be read, and would suppose now that if there was any change at all, it would be in the direction of making them more easily read and not less so. There does not seem to be any great change in *how* they are read—people still stand or sit or lie right side up—that is they do not stand on their heads to read though some of the things they are given to read might make them feel that way. Some of the margins I see suggest that the books are intended to be held upside down, and murder mysteries may now be read in one of these new chairs made of bent pipe with no hind legs in which a more or less conscious sense of physical insecurity will contribute to the 'spine chilling' effect of the story. But just how even these innovations can account for bad presswork is still a spine chilling mystery to me.

"Modern:—that curious word which devours its own meaning with every tick of the clock, served as an explanatory label for any miscarriage of drawing or painting, until some of its users began to suspect the inherent absurdity of the word and came up with 'Contemporary' in its place. Another word which is on everybody's tongue these days is 'creative,' and the interpretation now given

it is that it consists in doing anything that has not been done before."

November 10

The townsfolk of Haarlem, in Holland, celebrated with considerable pride on this date in 1923 the fifth centenary of the invention of printing by a native of the town, Laurens Janszoon Coster. Of all the claimants to the place of Johann Gutenberg of Mainz, Germany as the first printer, Coster has survived the longest. It is many years since typographic historians have found it necessary to debate the question, but the Coster vs. Gutenberg controversy was a real hot potato, particularly during the 19th century. But probably the most widely quoted of all the writers who urged recognition of Coster as the father of the art was the Dutch historian, Hadrianus Junius, in his book, *Batavia*, published in 1575. In this volume Junius writes:

"About 120 years ago, Laurence Zanssen Coster inhabited a decent and fashionable house in the city of Haarlem, situated on the market-place, opposite the royal palace. The name of Coster was assumed, and inherited from his ancestors, who had long enjoyed the honorable and lucrative office of Coster, or Sexton to the church. This man deserves to be restored to the honor of being the first inventor of printing, of which he has unjustly been deprived by others.

"As he was walking in the wood contiguous to the city, which was the general custom of the richer citizens and men of leisure, in the afternoon and on holydays, he began to pick out letters on the bark of the beech; with these letters he enstamped marks upon paper, in a contrary direction, in the manner of a seal; until at last he had formed a few lines for his own amusement and for the use of the children of his brother-in-law. This succeeding so well, he attempted greater things; and being a man of genius and reflection, he invented with the aid of his brother, or son-in-law, Thomas Pieterison, a thicker, and more adhesive ink, as the common ink was too thin and made blotted marks. With this ink he was able to print blocks and figures, to which he added letters. I have seen specimens of his printing in this manner: in the beginning he printed on one side only.

"He engaged workmen, which was the source of the mischief. Among these workmen was one Jan—whether his surname be that of Faust, or any other, is of no great importance to me; as I will not disturb the dead, whose consciences must have smote them sufficiently while living. This Jan, who assisted at the printing press under oath, after he had learned the art of casting the types, setting them, and other matter belonging to the art, and thought himself sufficiently instructed, having watched the opportunity, as he could not find a better, he packed up the types and other articles on Christmas eve, while the family was engaged in celebrating the festival, and stole away with them. He first fled to Amsterdam, thence to Cologne, until he could establish himself at Mentz, as a secure place where he might open shop, and reap the fruits of his knavery. . . ."

November 11

The dedication of the Public Library of Haverhill, Massachusetts on November 11, 1875 was the occasion for the writing of a poem by John Greenleaf Whittier in which the printer's craft was noted, making it one of the very few such references in the works of any ranking poet. Entitled *The Library,* the poem first praised books, and then in the three middle stanzas it relates:

Age after age, like waves, o'erran
The earth, uplifting brute and man;
And mind, at length, in symbols dark
Its meaning traced on stone and bark.

On leaf and palm, on sedge-wrought roll
On plastic clay and leathern scroll,
Man wrought his thoughts, the
    ages passed,
And lo! the Press was found at last!

Then dead souls woke; the thoughts
    of men
Whose bones were dust revived again,
The cloister's silence found a tongue,
Old prophets spake, old poets sung.

    *   *   *

It is surprising that so little attention has been paid to the craft which has been after all responsible for the dissemination of the poets' own endeavors. Perhaps the professionals were appalled by the amateur versifiers within the craft itself who filled the printing periodicals with their songs, and who were ever ready to put into rhyme the ordinary details of their lives as printers.

Even the great Walt Whitman, himself a journeyman compositor, waited until near the end of his life before he wrote into the thirty-fourth book of his *Leaves of Grass* a short poem which seemed out of place among those verses in which the poet seemed so preoccupied with death. Immediately preceding the poem which began, "as I sit writing here, sick and grown old," appeared *A Font of Type:*

This latent mine—these unlaunch'd voices—
    passionate powers,
Wrath, argument, or praise, or comic leer,
    or prayer devout,
    (Not nonpareil, brevier, bourgeois,
    long primer merely,)
These ocean waves arousable to fury
    and to death,
Or sooth'd to ease the sheeny sun and sleep,
Within the pallid slivers slumbering.

November 12

On or about this day in 1739 a distinguished English master printer in his fiftieth year named Samuel Richardson reached into a new medium and began to write a novel. It was completed the following year and was published under the title of *Pamela, or Virtue Rewarded*. It became an immediate and resounding success. Richardson had originally been asked, by two London booksellers, to write a series of letters which could become patterns for illiterate country writers. He concluded that this could best be accomplished by instructing "handsome girls who were obliged to go out to service," informing them how to best "avoid the snares that might be laid against their virtue." From this inspiration grew his account of the adventures of a pure girl who resisted the advances of her amourous master and eventually married him

Printer Richardson followed up the success of his first novel with an even more popularly acclaimed tale, *Clarissa, or the History of a Young Lady*. Clarissa, a much less virtuous lady than her predecessor, Pamela, nevertheless captured for her author a world-wide audience. That acute and acidulous critic, Samuel Johnson, remarked of Richardson's prose style: "If you were to read Richardson for the story, your impatience would be so much fretted that you would hang yourself. But you must read him for the sentiment."

Richardson's novels were written for a middle-class audience, which responded by making the author the best-selling novelist of his time. He dared to present the thoughts of individuals in a period when such an invasion of privacy was but to be hinted at. While Lord Chesterfield derided his writing, Diderot, the encyclopedist in France, classed Richardson with Moses, Homer, and Sophocles, among other classicists. Perhaps his secret was best described by Lady Mary Wortley Montague, who wrote to her daughter, discussing *Clarissa,* "I was such an old fool as to weep over Clarissa Harlowe, like any milkmaid of sixteen over the ballad of the Lady's Fall."

In spite of his success as one of the most popular novelists of the century, Richardson continued his career as a printer, considering his writing to be simply an avocation. In 1754 he was appointed Master of the Stationers' Company, and in 1760 he became Law-Printer to the King's Most Excellent Majesty. Throughout his career as a master printer, he was notable for the treatment of his apprentices, many of whom achieved distinction in their craft upon completing their indentures under Richardson. He wrote a book of instruction for apprentices which was later rewritten in briefer form for presentation to each apprentice by the Stationers' Company. Written in 1734, this letter is still given to English apprentices.

Richardson died on July 4, 1761, in his seventy-second year.

November 13

In a letter dated this day in 1946 and addressed to a firm of Edinburgh printers, George Bernard Shaw said, in part: "So the great firm of R. & R. Clark is 100 years old; and I am only 90! It seems to me to have been ordained by Providence to be ready for me when my time came. At all events ever since it printed my first plays, *Pleasant and Unpleasant,* in 1898, it has been as natural a part of my workshop as the pen in my hand. It has given me no trouble, nor complained when I have given it a good deal, holding up its type sometimes for years. I have not had to think about my printing: I have left it to do itself, which means that R. & R. Clark had to do it."

Apparently no account has been written into the record by the production man at Clark's concerning Shaw's individualistic approach to the typography of his books. GBS was in the habit of purchasing the typesetting, printing, and binding of all his books and in turn selling the entire package to the publishers. This unique arrangement, for a best-selling author, was carried out during most of his active literary career. His selection of the Edinburgh firm was based upon his desire to engage a printer with trade union employees and upon his belief that Clark had the ability to produce "the book beautiful."

Holbrook Jackson on two different occasions endulged in extensive hyphenation when describing the GBS taste in printer's types, saying at one point that he was a "Caslon-Old-Face-man-at-any-price," and again that "Bernard Shaw throws back to William Morris, to the pre-Kelmscott-Caslon-Old-Face-Morris." The playwright did have a distinct fondness for Caslon, and furthermore demanded that the fine old letter be set in 12-point without leading, creating a rather solid page, which in addition could not contain rules. His dislike of rules was without question a fetish. "The only thing," he stated, "that never looks right is a rule; there is not in existence a page with a rule on it that cannot be instantly and obviously improved by taking the rule out."

Along with the Morris-inspired typographers, Shaw believed in tight spacing, even going to the trouble of rewriting a line in proof if the word-spacing was too wide. A probably apocryphal story is told of his predilection for mechanically-equal spacing. His instructions were followed so precisely by the Scottish typesetters that the article "the" was broke "t-he," and "an" was divided "a-n." GBS commented, it is said, with the statement, "Excellent; but please do not go so far as to prove the author is really a damn fool."

Until the 1920's, the dramatist demanded hand-setting in all of his books. The printer whereupon set two pages, one by hand and the other by monotype, and showed them to Shaw without identifying either page. Shaw selected the machine-set page, after careful consideration, thus justifying the printer's efforts. That he was well aware of the bibliophile's interests is evident in his statement that, "Well printed books are just as scarce as well written ones; and every author should remember that most costly books derive their value from the craft of the printer and not from the author's genius."

November 14

The Senate of Venice upon this day in the year 1502 granted to the publisher, Aldus Manutius, the exclusive privilege of the use of a new type introduced in April of the previous year. This type was a letter which the Italians called Aldino, but which in France became known as Italic, a subterfuge based upon the name of Italy to disguise its copying by the French printers, particularly those of the important printing center of Lyons.

The books of the incunabula period were generally large volumes, competing as they were with the manuscript texts still being widely used. Aldus believed in stimulating the advancement in learning via the printed word. After receiving some criticism concerning the more than adequate margins of his books, he began to experiment with the small format book.

He finally used as the model for his new type the sloped handwriting of the poet Petrarch. It offered space-saving qualities and indeed made it possible to produce books at a considerable saving, thus making them more readily available to a new group of purchasers, a process not discernibly different from present-day book marketing procedures.

The new style of type became so popular that Aldus used it for almost his entire "list," and according to Theodore L. De Vinne italic became for a century the rival of roman letters for book composition. For a number of years the capitals used with the italic lowercase letters were roman, or upright characters, and considerably shorter in height than the accompanying ascending lowercase letters.

Such capitals are now used by printers under the general term of small caps. Aldus was thus responsible for creating the "family" principle in types, so commonly utilized by contemporary printers for changes in typographical style when variants must harmonize with the originals. It is, in fact, now quite unusual for a new roman type to be introduced without its accompanying italic. Since the introduction of the two-letter matrix for line-casting machines, the mating of the two styles, roman and italic, has supposedly been canonized. While Aldus might have readily agreed with the economies represented by such a combination, he would have been distressed with the fitting of the italic characters resulting from such a partnership, depending upon mechanics rather than aesthetics.

November 15

"Let's make a new fount of type." With that statement was born on November 15, 1888 that unique creation known as the Kelmscott Press. The speaker was William Morris, craftsman in design, poet, painter, essayist, who was walking home with his friend Emery Walker following the latter's address before the Arts and Crafts Exhibition Society.

Using as his models two types designed by the Venetian printers Nicolas Jenson and Jacob Rubeus in 1476, Morris by photographic enlargements worked out his ideas, resulting in a letter which he named the Golden type. This name was taken from the title of *The Golden Legend,* a book with which he intended to initiate his new font. The purchase of equipment and the hiring of printers followed, and on March 2, 1891, the first Kelmscott sheet was printed. Morris next designed a blackletter type patterned on the types of Schoeffer of Mainz, Zainer of Augsburg, and Koburger of Nuremberg. This medieval type was cut, as had been the Golden type, by Edward P. Prince, who was to cut the punches for many of the private presses which followed in the footsteps of the Kelmscott.

The third type used by Morris was designed for his edition of Chaucer and given that name. It is the same type as the Troy but of smaller size, being 12-point as against

18-point of the earlier font. A fourth type was discussed but it was never produced.

Fifty-three books and nine leaflets and announcements constitute the output of the Press, all printed on Albion hand presses upon hand-made paper or upon vellum. The work remains an enduring monument to a man who knew what he wanted to do and how to write about it. In *A Note by William Morris on His Aims in Founding the Kelmscott Press,* Morris said, "I began printing books with the hope of producing some which would have a definite claim to beauty, while at the same time they should be easy to read and should not dazzle the eye, or trouble the intellect of the reader by eccentricity of form in the letters."

Of course he did not succeed completely in this endeavor. To modern eyes, the types of the Kelmscott editions are too heavy for easy reading. But as examples of the pressman's skill his books are all magnificent, each letter being stamped solidly into the paper. Today they remain as black and crisp as though they had just been imprinted. The Kelmscott books must be seen in the original in order to appreciate them fully as examples of the printer's craft. They will be recognized as such for a long time to come, no matter how the factors of legibility and readability may change.

November 16

A printer from Princeton, Indiana, named Donald McDowell Keys, wrote in a letter under this date in 1891 saying in part:

"I am an ardent admirer of typographical beauty and excellence wherever seen, and especially so in newspaper work, because of its comparative variety in this line. There may be handsomer sheets than the great dailies of Chicago (but they don't come into the hands of the writer), but let us concede the *Herald* and the *Tribune* the handsomest papers in America, in point of general typographical excellence, in quality of paper used, clearness of impression, cleanly appearance, neatness of display in advertisements, and the systematic, always well-arranged 'makeup' of the reading and all the other matter. Why is there such a marked difference in the general appearance of these papers, which are a delight to the eye, and the muddy, murky, slurred and (in many cases) illy made-up, shovelled-together-appearing of the other great dailies, say of Cincinnati, St. Louis, Boston, Washington and New York? Is the excellence of the Chicago papers maintained through the employment of better skilled labor and machinery than other papers? Are they produced at a higher cost than other papers of proportionate size and circulation? Are they printed as rapidly as the average presses turn out the morning papers of the country? What are the material causes for their excellence in appearance as compared with others mentioned? The Chicago papers always have the same neat, clean looks, while, sometimes, the dailies of the other cities are neatly printed, when they get a new dress for instance, and then in a short time their plates do not have a clean face; but they never equal the productions of the City of Wind and altitudinous architecture."

Printer Keys aroused a considerable controversy among the printers who worked for newspapers. The compositors of the period spent a great deal of time being concerned with the appearance of newspapers and were possessed of great loyalty for their own sheets. Mr. Mergenthaler's machine had not yet come along to displace the thousands of compositors who daily set up and distributed every word printed in every paper across the land. Their extra-curricular outlets were not the golf, bowling, and TV watching of their modern counterparts, but found expression instead in speed-typesetting contests, beer-drinking bouts, and of course long arguments about typographical skill.

There were so many competing newspapers that the spirit of competition ran high from the publisher down through the ranks in every office. It is doubtful today whether a compositor on the *New York Times* would take the slightest umbrage should a make-up man from another sheet tell him that the *Times* was a typographical monstrosity put together by three-fingered comps who didn't know an em quad from a shooting stick. In fact, the *Times* man would probably consider the other comp to be a screwball.

November 17

In a paper read at the annual Henrietta Hertz Lecture on Aspects of Art before the

British Academy in London on November 17, 1937, the typographic historian, Stanley Morison, discoursed upon the art of printing, attempting to apply his logical reasoning to just why and under what conditions printing could aspire to be an art. Morison began with the familiar account taken from the memoirs of the Florentine bookseller, Vespasiano da Bisticci, written in 1490, in which the bookseller described the magnificent library of his patron, the Duke of Urbino, in which no volume was imperfect, all being written on vellum and all beautifully illuminated. "Had there been one printed book," wrote Vespasiano, "it would have been ashamed in such company."

"It would thus appear just," stated Morison, "to regard printing as a sort of poor relation to calligraphy. It looks like writing; it clearly is not writing; therefore it is imitation writing. No imitation, as such, can possess any sort of artistic value. Thus, the subject upon which I have been asked to lecture today is easily disposed of, and there remains little excuse for my further detaining this audience."

Since no one in the gathering, typical of any group listening to Mr. Morison, took advantage of the invitation to withdraw, the speaker himself remained to enlighten his listeners, tracing the development of typography from calligraphic and inscriptional forms, and the effect of technological factors upon the reproduction of the printed word.

Mr. Morison finally endeavored to supply his reasoned definition of printing as an art. "Whatever the formal basis of printing may be—" he said, "calligraphy, engraving, or photography—the correctness of the text, the arrangement of the letters and lines, and their spacing, will continue in the future, as in the past, to prove whether a printer has a thorough understanding of his function. The arrangement or the design of a piece of printing should exhibit the highest possible degree of consistency—first, with the intentions and objects of the author; and, secondly, with the nature of the process by which these are to be expressed. When the text is efficiently articulated, and the process effectively exploited in accordance with specific requirements of illustration and multiplication, the product may please the understanding eye.

"That is to say, the understanding eye is pleased to recognize, in a piece of printing, the exactness, consistency, and lucidity that a thing of that kind ought to possess—be it book or newspaper or timetable—when read or even merely viewed in the circumstances intended by its author and printer. If a piece of printing should possess these qualities in an eminent degree, it may have some claim to consideration from such collectors of works of art as concern themselves with servant or applied arts. The primary claim of printing is not to be an art, but to be the most responsible of our social, industrial, and intellectual mechanisms; it must, like a transport system, be most disciplined, most rational. Nevertheless, if it is allowable to define art, in this connection, as the application of knowledge, reason, and skill to the service of writers and readers, it may not be rash to hope that some of the past, present, and future productions of the printer will, as multiplied productions of reason and skill, be counted worthy of rank as an Aspect of Art."

November 18

Mr. William Bowyer, printer of London, died upon this day in 1777 in his 78th year. An extract from his will follows:

"And now I hope I may be allowed to leave somewhat for the benefit of printing. To this end I give to the master and keepers, or wardens and commonalty, of the mystery or art of a Stationer of the city of London, such a sum of money as will purchase Two Thousand Pounds, three per cent. Reduced Bank Annuities, upon trust, to pay the dividends and yearly produce Thereof, to be divided forever equally amongst three printers, compositors or pressmen, to be elected from time to time by the master, wardens, and assistants, of the said company, and who at the time of such election shall be sixty-three years old or upwards, for their respective lives, to be paid half yearly; hoping that such as shall be most deserving will be preferred. . . .

"It has long been to me a matter of concern that such numbers are put apprentices, as compositors, without any share of school-learning, who ought to have the greatest: in hopes of remedying this, I give and bequeath to the said Company of Stationers such a sum of money as will purchase One Thousand Pounds three per cent. Reduced Bank Annuities, for the use of one journeyman compositor, such as hereafter be described, with this special trust, that the master, wardens, and assistants, shall pay the dividends and produce thereof half-yearly to such compositor: the said master, wardens, and assistants, of the said company, shall nominate for this purpose a compositor who is a man of good life and conservation, who shall usually frequent some place of public worship every Sunday, unless prevented by sickness, and shall not have worked on a newspaper or magazine for four years at least before such nomination, nor shall ever afterwards while he holds this annuity, which may be for life if he continues a journeyman: he shall be able to read and construe Latin, and at least to read Greek fluently with accents; of which he shall bring a testimonial from the rector of St. Martin's, Ludgate, for the time being: I could wish that he shall have been brought up piously and virtuously, if it be possible, at Merchant Taylor's, or some other public school, from seven years of age until he is full seventeen, and then to serve seven years faithfully as a compositor, and work seven years more as a journeyman, as I would not have this annuity bestowed on any one under thirty-one years of age; if, after he is chosen, he should behave ill, let him be turned out, and another be chosen in his stead. . . ."

The records neglect to mention the finding of such a paragon of compositors who could successfully apply for Mr. Bowyer's annuity.

November 19

On this day in 1937 the New York Club of Printing House Craftsmen met and honored as its guest of the evening the type designer, Frederic W. Goudy. A veteran of the lecture platform after countless appearances all over the United States, the seventy-two year old Goudy was completely at his ease. As the unquestioned leader of his profession, he was inclined to be somewhat whimsical in his comments. Following his remarks, the chairman announced that the type designer would be rewarded with a framed certificate honoring his long service to the craft. This testimonial was forthwith produced and held aloft for all to admire. The artist who had

lettered and illuminated it was also introduced. When the panegyric had been read to the great man, he took it in his hands and, referring to the principal line of the document, lettered in a semi-circle across its face, announced, "A man who would letterspace blackletter would steal sheep!"

Goudy hugely enjoyed the roar of laughter which greeted his remark, even it it did cost him for a few minutes the admiration of the artist, whom he took aside at the close of the meeting to congratulate for a fine job of lettering in spite of "unkind comments from an old man."

Goudy was a great story teller, and he loved a joke—most of the time. Earl Emmons—Jester to the Court of Goudy in addition to being its Poet Laureate—once told of attending a Typophile luncheon with Fred and then walking to Bryant Park, next to the New York Public Library. Since it was a sunny May afternoon they sat down on a bench so that Fred could watch the girls go by. Whenever he could distract the designer from this pleasant occupation, Emmons attempted to find out what Goudy thought of his doing a serious and definitive biography. Emmons had aspirations of becoming Fred's Boswell. As he advanced each point of his argument, the designer would nod and chuckle, but it soon became obvious that he was more appreciative of the passing show than of Emmon's proposal. When it was finally time for Fred's departure to catch the train back to Newburgh, he turned to Emmons. "Okay, Earl," he said, "go ahead and do that book. But don't be too damned flippant with me. And you can leave out Maytime in Bryant Park!"

November 20

A Harvard man who for thirty years was notably connected with Yale University died upon this day in 1960 at the age of 80. Carl Purington Rollins, one of the very fine printers of our time, served as Printer to Yale from 1920 to his retirement in 1948, when he was named Printer Emeritus. A year later the University honored him with the honorary degree of Doctor of Humane Letters, a fitting acknowledgement of Rollins' lifelong love of letters, particularly those in the printer's typecase.

As a boy, living in Newburyport, Massachusetts, Carl Rollins became interested in printing. He acquired a Golding Press and at the age of fourteen produced a tiny periodical called *The Stamp Journal*. When he had completed his studies at Harvard, he followed up this early regard for the craft by serving an apprenticeship as a compositor with the famous Boston firm of Heintzemann. In 1903 Rollins established a small printing office in Montague, Massachusetts, five years later moving it into the lovely old Dyke Mill in the same town. The Montague Press was maintained until 1918, when Rollins joined Yale as a typographic designer. It was in the Dyke Mill that Rollins worked with Bruce Rogers in the production of Maurice Guerin's *The Centaur,* from which is derived the name of the fine roman type designed by Rogers.

At Yale Rollins taught typography for thirty years. It is said of him that he redesigned or designed "almost every publication and piece of paper used at the University." For the Printing-Office of Yale University he designed some two thousand books in the thirty year period, most of which were distinguished examples of American bookmaking, and many of which were selected by juries in the Fifty Books of the Year Exhibitions sponsored by the American Institute of Graphic Arts. In addition to the Yale books Rollins designed numerous volumes for other publishers, a number of which he hand-set himself.

Typographically, Rollins was a traditionalist, with a great respect for such types as Caslon and Baskerville. He had no interest at all in the American cuttings of Bodoni, although he did use them on occasion. Throughout his long career he argued against the dependence of modern printers on the machine. He was a long way from being the typical "hand press" printer, but he reasoned that the problems of maintaining full production for machines took valuable time away from the printer who could better have spent it in a continuous search for perfection in everything he produced.

Friend and confidant of all the great printing figures of his time, Rollins was raised to the same pedestal as such figures as Updike, Rogers, Goudy, and Cleland by being the recipient in 1941 of the renowned medal of the American Institute of Graphic Arts.

November 21

Under the enthusiastic direction of the Chicago members of the American Institute of Graphic Arts, the "Fifty Books of 1923" Exhibition opened on this date at the Newberry Library. Excitement was generated by the idea of selecting fifty books out of the thousands published, as being outstanding examples of the printer's craft. A receptive audience was attracted by the poster produced by the inimitable hand of Oz Cooper.

The Catalogue of the Exhibition appeared as a supplement to the *AIGA News-Letter* in August, 1923, for the original showing in New York. In it an attempt was made to explain the need for such an exhibition: "Exactly what progress is being made in the United States in the direction of better printing and better book-making? In view of the conflicting opinions of experts, varying all the way from scathing rebuke to enthusiastic flattery, how can the men who are doing the work be sure whether their progress is slow or fast—or even whether it is backward rather than forward?

"The American Institute of Graphic Arts has long desired to render some aid in securing an answer to the query. It believes that the nearest approach to a specific answer will come through the adoption of some definite measure or 'yardstick' which can be applied at regular, stated intervals and in the presence of those most concerned. This belief has taken concrete form in the present exhibition. . . . Neither this first exhibition nor its successors will make any pretension of showing the fifty 'best' examples. The effort, rather, will be to show fifty *representative* books, as widely representative as possible of the various problems of printing and book-making and of the excellent work being done in different sections of the United States in successfully meeting these problems."

Forty-four years and 2,200 books later this statement is still essentially correct in most of its details. During this period the "Fifty" has been loudly praised and just as loudly damned, depending upon the viewpoint of the critical observer. While many of the selections may thankfully be forgotten, the list is assuredly "representative" of the best in American bookmaking in our time.

It is interesting to observe the typography of the books which were selected by the first jury of the "Fifty" and to compare it with the more recent selections. In 1923 Messrs. David Silve, W. Arthur Cole, and Burton Emmett chose twenty-two hand-set books and twenty-eight machine-set books. A number of the types used are seen rarely today, such as French Oldstyle, Suburban French, Franklin, Inkunabula, Walpole Italic, etc. In fact, of all the types used, only Caslon, Bodoni, and Garamond are likely candidates for present-day inclusion in the exhibition. And of course hand-set books are now quite infrequent.

In one category, the 1923 group was unique, and that was in the choice of paper. Twenty books were printed upon hand-made paper, even more unusual today than the hand-setting of books, except in private press printing. Both of these now singular practices were considered to be quite common in good book-making a half century ago.

November 22

The tragic death of the young 35th President of the United States on this day in Dallas in 1963 reminded printers of the statement written by Mr. Kennedy in January of that year. In it he paid tribute to the printer's craft:

"Thomas Carlyle once said that the man who invented the art of printing 'was disbanding hired armies, and cashiering most Kings and Senates, and creating a whole new Democratic world.'

"As the inheritors and protectors of that democratic world, we can see today how right Carlyle was—how much the things we most value depend on the printed word. The capacity of people to choose, to guide and to censure their own government—the vitality of the democratic idea itself—has always rested on the broad dissemination of facts and ideas which printing has made possible. Perhaps no invention in history so well illustrates the power of creative technology to liberate man.

"Nor has the impact of the art of printing been limited to the national state or culture. For print is the true international currency of the modern world. The printer's art has built the vast array of secular and religious thought, of technical and scientific achievement, which knows no national frontiers and which forms the fabric of today's dangers and possibilities.

"In celebrating International Printing Week, you celebrate a human achievement which has demonstrated far greater power to shape the world than all the force of modern weaponry. And it is appropriate that you have chosen the birthday of Benjamin Franklin for this celebration. That great scientist, philosopher, statesman—and printer—embodied for all time the tremendous fact that to affect the thinking of man is to influence the course of history."

November 23

It's not often that a contemporary typographer has the opportunity to practice paleontology and to experience the excitement enjoyed by the first translators of the Rosetta Stone. It was therefore with a spirit of adventure that our compositor picked up a copy of a fifty-cent Penguin book on this day in 1962, having read that just two days before, *Androcles and the Lion* had been published, in accordance with the directions set forth in the will of the playwright, George Bernard Shaw. What was unique about this edition was that it was composed in the Shavian characters which had been selected as the winning design in a competition for the creation of a phonetic alphabet. Shaw had directed that a large part of the income from his estate should be set aside for the development of such an alphabet "to be written without indicating single sounds by groups of letters or by diacritical marks."

The iconoclastic playwright spent a good part of his extremely long life talking and writing about the inconsistencies of English grammar, pronunciation, and spelling. He desired reform, and to round out the whole thing, he also wanted to have an alphabet which would be more condensed. He wrote, "To get such common words as son and science phonetically defined was hopeless. In what is called the Oxford accent son and sun become san; sawed and sword are pronounced alike, and my native city becomes Dablin. In Dublin itself I have heard it called Dawblin. The Oxford pronunciation of science is sah-yence: the Irish pronunciation is su-yence. Shakespeare pronounced wind as wined; and as late as the end of the 18th century an attempt to correct an actor who pronounced it in this way provoked the retort. 'I cannot finned it in my minned to call it winned.' "

The alphabet selected by England's Public Trustee was designed by Kingsley Read. The forty-eight characters of Read's alphabet were cut into a type by the Monotype Corporation of London in a 13-point size. When composed into pages in *Androcles* they make up about two-thirds of the facing page set in the conventional characters of 12-point Imprint. The saving of space is therefore not as economical as might be desired, particularly when the reader is expected to make the effort to learn to read phonetic characters.

Concerning the eventual acceptance of a phonetic alphabet, Shaw was more or less resigned to the recognition of the difficulties to be encountered. "The only danger I can see," he wrote, ". . . is the danger of civil war. Our present spelling is incapable of indicating the sounds of our words and does not pretend to; but the new spelling would prescribe an official pronunciation. Nobody at present calls a lam a lamb or pronounces wawk and tawk as walk and talk. But when the pronunciation can be and is indicated, the disputable points will be strong enough for the stupidest person to understand and fight about. And the ferocity with which people fight about words is astonishing. . . . Still we must take that risk. If the introduction of an English alphabet for the English language costs a civil war, or even, as the introduction of summer time did, a world war, I shall not grudge it. The waste of war is negligible to the daily waste of trying to communicate with one another in English through an alphabet with sixteen letters missing. This must be remedied, come what may."

November 24

Published on this day in 1644, the tract entitled, *Areopagitica: A Speech of Mr. John Milton for the Liberty of Unlicensed Printing, to the Parliament of England,* is one of the noblest statements ever written concerning freedom of the press. This pamphlet, the finest prose work of one of the great poets of the language, was written in protest against an Act of Parliament requiring the licensing by an official censor of all books printed in England. Milton took the title from Areopagus, the hill of Ares, meeting place of the highest council. In reasonable tones, without cant or the slightest touch of hysterics—unique for a pamphleteering attack—Milton asked that Parliament reconsider its censorship ordinance. He quickly arrived at the splendid passage, which began:

"I deny not but that it is of greatest concernment in the Church and Commonwealth to have a vigilant eye how books demean themselves, as well as men; and thereafter to confine, imprison, and do sharpest justice on them as malefactors. For books are not absolutely dead things, but do contain a potency of life in them to be as active as that soul was whose progeny they are; nay, they do preserve as in a vial the purest efficacy and extraction of that living intellect that bred them. I know they are as lively, and as vigorously productive, as those fabulous dragon's teeth; and being sown up and down, may chance to spring up armed men. And yet, on the other hand, unless wariness be used, as good almost kill a man as kill a good book. Who kills a man kills a reasonable creature, God's image; but he who destroys a good book, kills reason itself, kills the image of God, as it were in the eye. Many a man lives a burden to the earth; but a good book is the precious life-blood of a master spirit, embalmed and treasured up on purpose to a life beyond life. 'Tis true, no age can restore a life, whereof perhaps there is no loss; and revolutions of ages do not oft recover the loss of a rejected truth, for the want of which whole nations fare the worse."

Milton closed with an appeal: "This I know, that errors in a good government and in a bad are equally almost incident; for what Magistrate may not be misinformed, and much the sooner, if liberty of printing be reduced into the power of a few; but to redress willingly and speedily what has been erred, and in highest authority to esteem a plain advertisement more than others have done a sumptuous bribe, is a virtue (honoured Lords and Commons) answerable to your highest actions, and whereof none can participate but greatest and wisest men."

November 25

The irrepressible inventive spirit of the American male during the 19th century is evident in the hundreds of patents filed in the Patent Office describing devices by which the laborious operation of setting type by hand might be automated, and as a by-product the pockets of the inventor might be suitably garnished. One such patent, granted to O. L. Brown of Boston on this day in 1862, stated:

"This invention consists in placing the type in a case formed of cells of such a width as to admit of a single row of type, and using in connection therewith a sliding stick, together with a mechanism arranged in such a manner that the stick may be shoved along below the case, and brought to a proper relative position with any of the rows of type in the case, the type to be discharged from the case and properly deposited in the stick."

In a similar vein was the invention of Henry Harger, of Delhi, Iowa, for which a patent was granted in 1860, which consisted "in the arrangement of machinery in connection with the type case by which the types are fed to the composing-stick, and of an arrangement of fingers and levers in connection with the composing-stick, by which the lines may be taken from the case and set in line."

An even more wonderful and complicated mechanism is portrayed by the patent secured by D. B. Ray, of Circleville, Ohio, for a machine in which "tubes are so constructed that the type, as they are being distributed into hoppers by hand, shall be made to arrange themselves in passing through the tubes with the notched edges all turned the same way. The arm is twisted for the purpose of reversing the position of the type as it passes down. Catches are placed at the bottom of each tube to prevent the type from sliding out, which tubes are operated, when necessary, by a key. The composing-stick is so constructed, with a spring and slide attached, as to bring the type into a perpendicular position at whatever angle they may be dropped into the stick."

William H. Mitchell, of New York City, received a patent in 1853 for a device which "consists of means for distributing types from the form, and setting them up in rows, within grooves, a given letter in each groove or row, with the faces of the types upwards, and in a line. From these grooves the types are removed, each row of a given letter at a time, and placed within slides or conductors which supply them to an apparatus connected with finger-keys. The striking of any given finger-key drops one of the types upon a series of belts, which are moved by pulleys; the belts conduct the type to a composing wheel or conductor, in the order in which the keys drop them."

The following year Mr. Mitchell patented an improvement in his machine which "applies to the parts for dropping the types from the conductors on to the belt which carries it to the composing apparatus, and also comprises the invention of the wheel for setting up or composing type in a line."

November 26

"Where Liberty dwells, there is my country." So read the motto, attributed to Benjamin Franklin, which appeared at the masthead of the first newspaper to be printed in the city of Chicago upon this date in 1833. Six columns of type spread over four fifteen-by-twenty inch pages formed the *Chicago Democrat,* printed upon one of Sam Rust's Washington hand presses, introduced just four years previously.

Actually the *Democrat* can not lay claim to being the first issue of the Chicago press, as John Calhoun, printer, editor, and publisher of the sheet had turned out two weeks earlier two dollars worth of business cards for the Traveller's Home.

Calhoun had learned the case at sixteen years of age in Watertown in upstate New York. When he reached his majority he worked in printing offices in Albany and Troy, also doing a short stint in the Albany typefoundry of Starr & Little. This activity was followed by the founding of an unsuccessful newspaper in Oswego, whereupon he returned to Watertown to establish the *Eagle,* another sheet which quickly failed due to lack of proper financing.

At this point Calhoun heard enthusiastic reports about the opportunities for printers in Chicago and decided to try his luck there. He remained undiscouraged after a trip through Lake Erie in which his steam-

229

boat was turned back twice by a Great Lakes hurricane, finally running aground on the Michigan shore at Black River harbor. Walking twenty miles to Huron, Printer Calhoun embarked in another steamer bound for Detroit. Next he continued his journey to Chicago by slow stage coach.

Three years later Calhoun—beset by financial problems—negotiated the sale of his newspaper for the sum of twenty-two hundred and seventy-seven dollars and ninety-two cents, which included his press, types, cases, etc., and his good will. After all debts were paid, Editor Calhoun emerged with less than eight hundred dollars cash for his three years of struggling to keep the Chicago citizenry informed. The *Chicago Democrat* was published by its new owner as a weekly until 1840 when it became a daily. In 1861 the paper was absorbed by the *Tribune,* and its Democratic leanings thereby completely submerged.

November 27

On this day in 1518 in the city of Venice, there issued from the press of Daniel Bomberg his first *Great Rabbinical Bible.* It established his reputation as a scholarly printer of Hebrew, possibly the most eminent of them all, even to the point of his being termed "the Hebrew Aldus." Bomberg, a native of Antwerp, was the son of a wealthy man. Early in his life he decided to settle in Venice, the great trading center of Italy and a magnet for thousands of northern craftsmen during the late 15th and early 16th centuries. About 1515 he was persuaded by an associate, Felice da Prato, to take up the career of printing.

Although a Christian, Bomberg had learned the Hebrew language, and had a consuming interest in Jewish traditions. He therefore began the publication of Hebrew texts, although he was risking the investigations of the Inquisition by doing so. Thus he was entering an area of scholarship which offered no promise of success. There existed at the time a great deal of controversy in the Church of Rome concerning the treatment of the Jews, particularly from the Dominicans, although many of the church scholars, including Pope Leo X, were sympathetic to Hebrew theology and literature.

Bomberg found it necessary to request of the Venetian authorities that his proofreaders be exempted from the decree that Jews wear an item of clothing to separate them from Christian citizens, in this instance a yellow cap, which subjected them to molestation upon the streets of the city while traveling to Bomberg's printing office. The bible, which was dedicated to Pope Leo X, contained massoretic notes compiled by Felice da Prato, the purpose of which was the collection of traditional information by which the text of the biblical books was fixed beyond the possibility of change.

Bomberg's next great work was a complete edition of the Talmud, for which he requested and received the support of Leo X. This splendid work, begun in 1519, was completed in 1522. For the rest of his life this Christian printer printed the great works of Hebrew literature, at one time having as many as one hundred Hebrew scholars in his establishment to guarantee the authenticity of his texts. Accounts differ about the cost of his publishing enterprises, but he gave to it his personal fortune. It is estimated that in the thirty-two year period following the printing of the *Rabbinical Bible,* Bomberg's printing cost him three million crowns—a vast sum when it is recalled that it cost but twelve hundred crowns per year to rent his entire printing office.

November 28

Rummaging through a shelf-full of books in an open air church sale in a small Vermont village, the writer came across a rather plain little red book bearing a pasted-on label with the unmistakable stamp of the Merrymount Press. Furthermore, its title, *A Plan of Printing Instruction for the Public Schools,* related it to the printer's craft, making it doubly desirable for a typographic library.

The flyleaf of the little book bore the inscription, "To a true teacher of the Art," and was dated this day in 1927 and signed by Henry H. Taylor, the author. The book was one of a series produced by the American Institute of Graphic Arts. Mr. Taylor, of the distinguished firm of San Francisco printers, was presenting within the compass of forty-eight carefully printed pages a proposal for the teaching of printing in the schools, as a preparation for a vocation.

"Printing," wrote Mr. Taylor, "a process of rapid and inexpensive multiplication of manuscript, is, broadly speaking, a branch of the art of design, commencing with the design of the adopted type-face itself and ending with the correct placing and printing of the type-mass; that is to say, both from the utilitarian and critical points of view, any completed piece of work must be judged in the last analysis as a piece of design, into the production of which there has entered a knowledge of the technique of typesetting, presswork, and other operations, and the ability to perform these in a workmanlike manner. Therefore, instruction in simple design, as applied to the composition of type-matter, and its correct placing and make-ready and printing on a sheet of paper appropriate for the purpose, must go hand in hand with the purely technical instruction."

Would that this paragraph could serve as the introduction to the courses of instruction in the teachers' colleges! Taylor continues in the same vein:

"The solution of these new problems as they arise calls for the exercise of taste and judgment, and the success or failure of any work taken in hand will be dependent on the ability of the printer in the exercise of these faculties. Of course, in carrying on his work the printer must have a certain mechanical equipment, or "tools," with which to work; but his "intellectual tools" are the ones which he more commonly lacks, or more correctly speaking, are the ones which he least understands how to apply, for the reason that the training he usually receives is too specialized to allow him the opportunity to acquire them. But every printer, consciously or unconsciously, is applying them all the time, some successfully, others not so successfully, still others badly or almost not at all."

Mr. Taylor rightly advocated, at the first level, hand-work in both the composing room and the pressroom. "Hand-work," he stated, "being slower than machine-work, concentrates the student's attention on the work itself, and thus makes for thoroughness. Machines, on the other hand, being fascinating things in themselves, command attention to themselves primarily; the tendency of the boy is to look at the working of the machine as being the work itself. . . ."

The *Weekly Register* of Baltimore, published on this day in 1817, the first account to receive national publicity of the operation of the premier American papermaking machine, at a paper mill situated on Brandywine Creek, about two miles north of Wilmington, Delaware:

"We have lately visited the paper mills of Thomas Gilpin & Co. on the Brandywine, and witnessed the performance of their new machine for manufacturing paper on an extensive scale, which promises to be an important addition to the arts and manufactures of our country. This process of making paper delivers a sheet of greater breadth than any made in America, and of *any length* —in one continued unbroken succession, of fine or coarse materials, regulated at pleasure to a greater or lesser thickness. The paper, when made, is collected from the machine on reels, in succession as they are filled; and these are removed to the further progress of the manufacture. The paper in its texture is perfectly smooth and even, and is not excelled by any made by hand, in the usual manner of workmanship—as it possesses all the beauty, regularity and strength of what is called well closed and well shut sheets.

"It is with much pleasure that we announce the success of this machine; and we hope it will tend to secure our country against the importations from abroad, which have so much interfered with our own domestic arrangements; and we are also much gratified in believing, that its establishment on our own stream in the neighborhood of this place, will aid its improvement, and add to the valuable manufactures on the Brandywine."

The Gilpin machine, of the cylinder type, was undoubtedly adapted from the English machine of John Dickinson, which had become operative in 1809. The Gilpin Mill, the first in the state of Delaware, had been established in 1787 by Joshua and Thomas Gilpin, sons of Thomas Gilpin, an associate of Benjamin Franklin and founder with him of the American Philosophical Society. At the time that they began to manufacture paper, Joshua was but twenty-two years of age, and Thomas just eleven. The efforts of the brothers met with success, however, as may be determined from the journal of the famous French traveler, Jacques Pierre Brissot de Warville, who visited the mill during its first year and described the paper as "equal to the finest made in France."

The paper manufactured on the Gilpin machine was first used in the printing of the *American Daily Advertiser,* published in Philadelphia. The first book to be published in the United States on native American machine-made paper produced by the Gilpin Mill was *A Complete Genealogical, Historical, Chronological, and Geographical Atlas* by N. Lavoisne. This volume was printed by M. Carey & Son of Philadelphia in 1820.

The late Dard Hunter, historian of paper manufacturing, has stated that the Gilpin cylinder machine produced a thirty inch sheet at the rate of sixty feet per minute. The paper was notable for its uniformity of texture and color. An examination of books printed on its surface indicates that the sheet still retains its firmness and tone.

November 30

On this day in 1874 was born a man who never became a printer but whose life was devoted to the maintenance of the freedom of the printed word. Indeed, Winston Spencer Churchill may be credited as being one of the men of our times most responsible for our continued enjoyment of that freedom. As a writer and historian he appreciated the typographic art more than most of the men who have been Prime Ministers of Great Britain. His publishers, however, frequently took a dim view of his habit of revising and rewriting his own books from the page proofs.

At one time in his long career, Sir Winston was the honored guest at the 1934 meeting of The Printer's Pension, Almshouse and Orphan Asylum Corporation, which had been chartered in 1828 to "encourage provident habits and to promote self-respect among a body of skilled artisans to whom mankind is largely indebted," and which during these years has been outstanding in the furthering of these aims. Rising to acknowledge the toast, to Literature and the Press, proposed by the Rt. Hon. David Lloyd George, Churchill said:

"I have been entrusted with the task of replying to the toast of Literature and the Press. I have to deal with Literature only. There was a time when the two toasts were often lumped together and I was charged with both. But now I find that the press, essentially most immediately concerned with advertisements, has been removed from my custody, no doubt out of the increasing dignity which my years give me. . . .

"The English language is the foundation of English literature, and it is not a bad tongue either. I have not any great familiarity with other tongues, so I am able to pronounce with a considerable measure of authority that a more flexible and comprehensive medium of human speech has rarely been found in any quarter of the globe. It is a good thing that language should not remain in a dead and frozen condition. It should be added to from time to time. I myself have contributed several words to the English tongue. I remember some years ago being confronted with a hideous word 'hydroaeroplane,' as ugly to pronounce as to look at, and I invented the word 'seaplane,' which I think has obtained a definite root in the civilization of our times.

"The English language and English literature is one of our greatest and perhaps on the whole our most effective treasure. It is the bond which, more indisputably than anything else, unites the English-speaking peoples—not only the great peoples of the British Empire but the English-speaking peoples all over the world. It is a wonderful thing, a community that speaks and reads one language, an educated community in size beyond all rivalry that ever existed on the globe. They are proud of their past, and it seems to me that we should take every care we can to cultivate and develop our own language. . . .

"The printer, the author, the journalist, should not be more concerned in any matter than having the largest public in any language. . . . Do not underrate the great crafts with which we are all in one way or another associated. They all turn round words. Many mock at words, but words are the only things that last forever. . . . For thousands of years they survive, not as mere antiques, mummies, relics from a vanished past, from which we are separated by a gulf, they survive with living force, and even with growing force, and leaping across the gulf of time, they light the world for us today."

December

December 1

From Boylston Street in Boston, Massachusetts there was published on this day in 1919 an outrageous pamphlet which purported to be "Extracts from an investigation into the physical properties of books as they are at present published, undertaken by the Society of Calligraphers." A note explained: "The accompanying extracts from the Transactions of the Society of Calligraphers are published with the approval of the Society. They form a part of the exhaustive and unbiased Report returned by the Committee in charge of the investigation, which Report will be presented in its entirety in the Annual Bulletin. The report is of so surprising a nature that it was deemed unwise to withhold all notice of the findings until the annual publication. The Society, therefore, has the honour to present certain portions of the Inquiry, together with an abstract of the Committee's recommendations. (signed) W. A. Dwiggins, Secretary."

Here was Will Dwiggins in the role credited to him by his friend Watson Gordon, "a sort of self-appointed inspector of sacred cows; an exposer of their glandular effects. If it seems advisable in the public interest to send them to the glue factory, he is willing to drive the wagon." In the publication of this report Dwiggins was aided and abetted by his cousin, Mr. Laurance B. Siegfried.

American book publishers were taken completely by surprise when the *Extracts* were circulated. They were also shocked.

The committee had purported to have examined all books published in the United States from 1910, and its conclusions were that "All Books of the present day are Badly Made." The report itself was in the form of a dialogue between the Committee and people who were responsible for the various aspects of production in the publishing industry.

In the very first paragraph the tone was set:

"Q. Mr. B——,will you please tell the committee why you printed this book on cardboard?

A. To make it the right thickness. It had to be one inch thick.

—Why that thick, particularly?

—Because otherwise it would not sell. If a book isn't one inch thick it won't sell.

—Do you mean to say that people who buy books select them with the help of a foot rule?

—They have to have some standard of selection.

—So that it is your practice to stretch out the text if it is too short by printing it on egg-box stock?

—Not my practice, particularly. All publishers do it. We are obliged to use this and other means to bring the book up to a proper thickness. You must remember that our prices are not based on the contents of the book but on its size."

In summarizing, the Committee stated its intention of "forcing upon public attention such knowledge of the more elementary points of good taste as shall make impossible the further prostitution of standards." American publishers were agreed upon one

233

thing— the immediate lynching of the Secretary of the Society of Calligraphers, an act of revenge which fortunately did not take place. Retribution of a different nature was visited upon Dwiggins. He became a book designer. For the rest of his life he was more or less responsible for demonstrating through his own works his summarizations as a critic.

December 2

Dedicated to His Britannic Majesty, George III, on this day in 1783 was a curious pamphlet written by John Walter, former coal merchant and bankrupt insurance underwriter, who requested the royal patronage for a revolutionary scheme of typesetting. The title page of this pamphlet read: "An Introduction to the Art of Logography, or the Art of Arranging and Composing for Printing with Words intire, their Radices, and Terminations, instead of Single Letters. By His Majesty's Royal Letters Patent. By Henry Johnson, London, Printed Logographically, and Sold by J. Walter, Bookseller, Charing Cross, and J. Sewell, Cornhill, MDCCLXXXIII."

Walter was apparently attempting to recoup the fortune which he had lost when a fleet of ships underwritten by his firm fell victim to American privateers in 1776. He sincerely believed that setting type with logotypes rather than with single letters would revolutionize the printing industry. Meeting a printer named Henry Johnson, who had devised a logographic procedure to facilitate the setting of the numbers in the printing of the National Lottery, Walter secured the help of Caslon III of the typefounding family, and a printer and a bookseller. None of these partners proved to be satisfactory to him. Johnson turned out to be a swindler and Caslon refused to cast his type, acting under pressure from printers and booksellers who were opposed to the method. Nevertheless, Walter was enthusiastic and proceeded on his own. In his pamphlet he described the process:

"When I first undertook the arduous task, of Improving the Art of Printing by the use of cemented syllables, the whole English language lay before me in its copious and multitudinous mass, consisting of Ninety Thousand words, which I reduced immediately to about Five Thousand by separating the particles and terminations, also removing the technical terms and obsolete expressions." Following months of labor Walter had reduced his alphabet so that it could be accommodated in four cases, each 4½ feet by 6½ feet.

In order to impress the King, Walter secured the help of a number of the important men of his time, whose letters of support he included in his request for royal patronage. Among these was Benjamin Franklin, then serving as American Ambassador to France. The selection of Franklin as a supporter was a major error, as King George was outspoken in his dislike for the American statesman. The result was that Walter did not receive the patronage he needed.

He nevertheless determined to continue independently. By so doing he made a notable contribution to the history of world journalism. On January 1, 1785 he published the first issue of a newspaper, *The Daily Universal Register,* printed from his logotypes in an effort to prove to the public that they were practicable and economical. Exactly three years later he changed the name of his journal to *The Times or Daily Universal Register,* Printed Logographically. On the following March 18th, the name was shortened to *The Times* and so it has appeared each day ever since. About 1789 the logograph process was abandoned, but to it we owe the existence of one of the world's great newspapers.

December 3

The December 3rd issue of *Publisher's Weekly* in 1881 recorded the fact that a new book, entitled *Uncle Remus, His Songs and His Sayings—The Folklore of the Old Plantation* was ready for publication. Written by a Georgia printer-journalist named Joel Chandler Harris, *Uncle Remus* struck such a responsive chord that it quickly became a best seller, establishing its author as one of the most successful interpreters of Southern Negro folklore.

Harris was born in Eatonton, Georgia in 1848 and received an early love of books from his mother. Since she had been abandoned by her husband prior to the birth of her son, she encountered considerable difficulty in supporting the child. It was necessary for Joel to seek his first employment in his fourteenth year.

He answered an advertisement for a boy to learn printing in the office of a newly established weekly newspaper edited by Joseph Addison Turner, a wealthy plantation owner who had yearnings for a literary and journalistic career. This paper, the *Countryman,* was produced on Turner's large estate.

Harris was most fortunate in having the run of the plantation, including its library, and even more important to his subsequent career, he had the opportunity to observe at first hand its living conditions, particularly of the Negro slaves. He began to learn their legends and the sounds of their speech, acquiring an ear for dialect that was later to make his stories most authentic. In November, 1864, however, this instruction ended when the life of the plantation was completely disrupted by Sherman's march to the sea, forcing Harris to search for employment elsewhere.

Harris next took a job as a compositor with the *Macon Telegraph* and at the same time commenced free-lance writing. On the strength of this activity he was offered a job as assistant editor of the *Crescent Monthly* in New Orleans. Here he remained but a short time, returning to Forsyth, Georgia to edit the *Monroe Advertiser.* This was an unhappy experience, of which he later wrote: "I set all the type, pulled the press, kept the books, swept the floor, and wrapped the papers for mailing; my mechanical, accounting and menial duties being concealed from the vulgar hilarity of the world outside of Forsyth by the honorable and impressive title of 'Editor.' "

In 1870 Harris finally left the back shop to become an editorial writer for the *Savannah Morning News.* A friend later described his entry as a formal journalist: "I shall never forget the first night Col. Estill brought Joe Harris up into the composing room and sanctum and introduced him to us all. We thought at the time that he was the greenest, gawkiest-looking specimen of humanity our eyes ever rested upon. He was small of stature, freckle-faced, and looked like a typical backwoods country youth."

Even though, as a best-selling writer he acquired an outward polish, Harris always remained the country boy, never at home among strangers. While he accepted an invitation to visit the White House as the guest of Theodore Roosevelt, he was always much more content with Brer Rabbit in his native Georgia, which he never left, except for short trips, during his lifetime. He died in 1908.

December 4

Timothy Alden, of the sixth generation in direct descent from John Alden of Plymouth Colony and *Courtship of Miles Standish* fame, died on this day in 1858 in his thirty-ninth year, worn out from his endeavors in the creation of a typesetting machine. Born in Yarmouth, Massachusetts, he was apprenticed at the age of sixteen in the printing office of the Barre (Massachusetts) *Gazette,* remaining as a compositor there for eleven years.

During this period he began to dream of inventing a machine which would relieve the tediousness of much of the compositor's work, and at the same time appreciably increase his production. Observing that a competent telegraph operator could press keys at the rate of fifteen thousand an hour, he estimated that a typesetting machine equipped with a keyboard similar to that of a piano, could turn out work equivalent to that of at least seven compositors. Starting with this precept, he began serious work about 1838, finally traveling to New York in 1846 to seek financial support to continue his research.

The typesetting machine invented in England by Young and Delcambre had received an American patent in 1840, but up to 1850 no American patent had been granted to a native of this country. William H. Mitchell of Brooklyn did receive a patent in 1853, but the machine was never used or developed any further. In 1856 Alden was granted his first patent, and with additional capital his "practical" typesetter and distributor was ready for use. It was still, however, an imperfect mechanism, and in his efforts to remove the complications Alden destroyed his health.

The backers of the Alden machine continued their attempts to recoup their financial loss. They finally tested the typesetter in various New York newspaper offices, including that of the *Tribune,* where it was proved that it could produce the work of five comps, but, unfortunately, at the same cost as the labor of those same five. The device contained some 14,626 separate parts, and it weighed 1,560 pounds. The report to the stockholders of the company formed to develop and market the Alden Typesetter is listed by Bigmore and Wyman's *Bibliography of Printing* as an exceedingly rare book. Actually it represents an exclusive item in the incunabula of automated typesetting.

Bigmore and Wyman list the volumes as follows: "Yeaton (Charles C.). Manual of the Alden Type-setting and Distributing Machine: an illustrated Exposition of the Weight of every Piece, including Estimates of Cost of Labour and Material; a Summary of the Amount of Type-setting annually executed; an Authentic Sketch of the History and Progress of the Invention, with a Proposed Plan of Future Operations for the Alden Type-setting and Distributing Machine Company. New York: 1865. Royal Folio. pp. 246. Profusely illustrated with mechanical engravings."

What the company did not tell its stockholders was the fact that the one hundred copies of this edition cost approximately $11,000 to set and print!

December 5

William Blades, printer, bibliographer, and typographic historian, was born this day in the year 1824, in the London suburb of Clapham. A leading master printer and author of a number of books about printing, Blades is best known for his lifetime efforts to promote interest in the life of William Caxton, the first English printer.

At the age of sixteen, Blades was apprenticed in the printing office of his father, a well known printer specializing in the production of checks and bank notes. The period of William's indenture was seven years, during which he worked in every department of the firm, establishing the professional competency which was to aid him later in his bibliographical studies. It was during this period that he became vitally interested in the history of the craft of printing. He also began to acquire the splendid collection of books which eventually was to become the nucleus of the Printing Library of the St. Bride Foundation in London—now called simply St. Bride's, and one of the finest libraries of printing technology in existence.

Blades became particularly interested in the career of Caxton, and not being content to rely on secondary sources as written by Dibdin, Ames, and Herbert, he located and secured access to over 450 books produced by the Caxton Press in dozens of public and private libraries. He then proceeded to document every book, making a tabulation of the type being used. He was thus able to record every one of Caxton's types and to trace their use until they had been worn out. For the first time, the dates of printing these volumes became fairly well established. Blades proved that a serious study of typefaces was of immeasurable value in obtaining correct bibliographic information which had hitherto remained unknown.

In 1861 Blades published the first volume of his study, *The Life and Typography of William Caxton.* The second volume appeared in 1863. The work, in addition to helping to establish new bibliographic standards, also created a revival of interest in Caxton and his period.

During his lifetime Blades became involved in two controversies which engaged the interest of English printers. He took the part of the English inventor William Nicholson who had claimed that he was the inventor of the steam press rather than the German engineer Frederick Koenig. He also supported the claim of the partisans of Coster as against those of Gutenberg as the inventor of movable type and printing as we know it. In his short history, *The Pentateuch of Printing,* edited by Talbot Baines Reed and published in 1891, the year following Blades' death, he presents his opinions upon both of these arguments.

December 6

William Shakespeare built his King Henry VI trilogy upon the life of that most unfortunate of English Kings, who was born upon this day in 1421. During Henry's lifetime, the art of printing was established, but he was murdered in the Tower of London before it was brought to English soil. Shakespeare, however, in the second part of the play, puts a speech into the mouth of one of his characters—a speech which unquestionably represented the opinions of the established authorities of the period, although it is historically inaccurate. The rebel, Jack Cade, when Lord Say is brought before him, says:

". . . Thou has most traitorously corrupted the youth of the realm in erecting a grammar school; and whereas, before, our forefathers had no other books but the score and the tally, thou hast caused printing to be us'd, and, contrary to the King, his crown, and dignity, thou hast built a paper-mill. It will be proved to thy face that thou hast men about thee that usually talk of a noun and a verb, and such abominable words as no Christian ear can endure to hear. . . ."

No sooner had the knowledge of printing spread from Mainz, than it was realized that the craft must be controlled or suppressed. Possibly one of the earliest statements on this matter came from Mainz itself in 1486, when Archbishop Berthold appointed a book-censor, issuing a Penal Mandate under which it was forbidden to translate Latin and Greek into the vulgar tongue:

"Although by a certain divine art of printing, abundant and easy access is obtained to books on every science necessary to the attainment of human learning; yet we have perceived that certain men, led by the desire of vain glory or money, do abuse this art; and that what was given for the instruction of human life, is perverted to the purposes of mischief and calumny. For to the dishonouring of religion, we have seen in the hands of the vulgar certain books of the divine offices and writings of our religion, translated from the Latin into the German tongue."

The first general Papal Bull to be issued about printing came from the pen of Pope Innocent VIII, in 1487, stating in part:

"With the misuse of the printing press for the distribution of pernicious writings, the regulations of the Church for the protection of the faithful enter of necessity into a new period. It is certainly the case that the evil influence of a badly conducted printing press constitutes today the greatest damage to society. . . ."

King James I in 1607 stated the case for royal authority, when he condemned a book to be burned: "From the very highest mysteries of the Godhead and the most inscrutable counsels in the Trinitie to the very lowest pit of Hell and the confused actions of the divells there, there is nothing now unserched into by the curiositie of men's brains, so that it is no wonder that they do not spare to wade in all the deepest mysteries that belong to the persons of the state of Kinges and Princes, that are gods upon earth."

December 7

The last letter personally written by Samuel Johnson was composed this day in 1784 and addressed to William Strahan, his friend and the printer of a number of his works, including the *Dictionary:*

"Sir, I was not sure that I read your figures right, and therefore must trouble You to set down in words how much of my pension I can call for now, and how much will be due to me at Christmas."

Christmas, 1784 never arrived for Dr. Johnson, as he was dead a week later, on December 13th. In the closing days of his life he was apparently concerned about his pension, a term which he used for the payments now called royalties. Indeed, on December 10 he dictated another letter to Strahan requesting "whatever portion of my pension you can spare me with prudence and propriety." This letter proved to be the last ever to come from the lexicographer.

In spite of Johnson's oft-quoted aversion to Scotland and its inhabitants, he enjoyed the friendship of several Scotsmen, including of course Boswell and the printer William Strahan. Strahan had been apprenticed to the craft in Edinburgh in 1729 when just fourteen years of age. Upon the completion of his indenture in 1736, he worked as a journeyman in Edinburgh for about a year and a half and then proceeded to London where he had established himself in business in 1739, the first date which appears in the splendid set of ledgers in which he recorded meticulously every receipt and expense. These account books, now in the possession of the British Museum, are a most valuable source of information concerning printing costs during the 18th century.

In addition to being the printer of the first edition of Johnson's *Dictionary,* Strahan produced the first printings of Adam Smith's

Wealth of Nations and Gibbon's *Decline and Fall of the Roman Empire*. He also printed such popular fare as *Roderick Random*, *Peregrine Pickle* and part of *Tristram Shandy*. As a good friend of David Hume, he printed a great many of the works of the Scottish philosopher and historian, beginning with the second volume of *The History of Great Britain.*

Dr. Johnson, while most friendly with Strahan, did not hesitate to belittle his Scots ancestry from time to time, and even utilized his caustic wit to comment about the printing craft. Boswell records a conversation of Johnson with a poor boy whom he had induced Strahan to employ as an apprentice: "Well, my boy, how do you go on?" The lad replied, "Pretty well, Sir. But they are afraid I an't strong enough for some parts of the work." Johnson replied to this statement with, "Why, I shall be sorry for it; for when you consider with how little mental power and corporeal labour a printer can get a guinea a week, it is a very desirable business for you."

December 8

A professor of English achieved on this day in 1920 a certain kind of immortality not usual to his profession. He read a paper before the Fortnightly Club of Rochester, New York, which bore the title, *Printing and the Renaissance.* John Rothwell Slater was of course not an ordinary English professor as the content of this paper readily attests. In addition to possessing a sympathetic understanding of printing history, he had acquired the friendship of an outstanding practitioner of the craft, a fellow Rochesterian named Elmer Adler, who in turn counted among his friends a typographer named Bruce Rogers.

The end result of this circle of circumstances was a limited edition of *Printing and the Renaissance,* designed by Rogers and printed by *his* friend, William Edwin Rudge. With five hundred copies printed from Caslon type on antique wove paper, plus one hundred on French hand-made paper, Professor Slater was destined to appear in all of the BR bibliographies and exhibitions. All of this added up to Slater's real contribution to typographic scholarship,

which might otherwise have been lost forever. George Bernard Shaw once remarked to a fellow scrivener that if an author was to be remembered it would no doubt be through the medium of his printer. Shaw trusted no typographer to provide this particular brand of immortality, so he designed all of his books himself.

Dr. John R. Slater, however, had no need of the assistance of a printer to be long remembered. A member of the faculty of the University of Rochester from 1905 to his retirement in 1942, he served the school as its most distinguished professor emeritus until his death at the age of ninety-three in 1965. During most of this period he was the most admired teacher at the university, respected for his breadth of learning in the world of books and for his ability to inspire his students. The doors of the Rush Rhees Library on the college campus bear an inscription written by John Slater: "Here is the history of human ignorance, error, superstition and folly, war and waste recorded by human intelligence for the admonition of wiser ages yet to come. Here also is the history of man's hunger for truth, goodness and beauty which leads him slowly upward through flesh to spirit, from bondage to freedom and from war to peace."

In his Fortnightly Club paper, Dr. Slater paid tribute to the Renaissance printers, saying in part:

"An age full of contradictions and strange delusions, but an age of great vitality, great eagerness, great industry, patience, foresight, imagination. And in such an age it was the good fortune of these wise craftsmen who handled so deftly their paper and type to be the instruments of more evangels than angels ever sang, more revolutions than gunpowder ever achieved, more victories than ever won the applause of men or the approval of heaven. In the beginning the creative word was *Fiat lux*—let there be light. In the new creation of the human mind it was *Imprimatur*—let it be printed."

December 9

Oz Cooper, the fine Chicago artist and type designer, wrote on December 9, 1927, to Richard N. McArthur, then advertising manager of the typefoundry, Barnhart Brothers

& Spindler: "Dwiggins should be seduced, and I was thinking that I might write him some day and try to get him interested. Not with any definite proposal, you know. Just to get a groundwork laid. Whatever you think. There will be no hurry."

Cooper had been in a class in lettering with Will Dwiggins at the Chicago School of Illustration at the turn of the century. The instructor was Frederic W. Goudy. McArthur called them the Great Three of American lettering. "In Chicago," he wrote, "the Cooper style loomed boldly above everything else; in Boston a most intriguing style, having the flavor of the Old French, of which Dwiggins was the father; in Rome, where, in 1932 we addressed to Cooper a post card: 'Surrounded by Goudy old styles!' "

Dwiggins finally did get around to designing a type in 1929, after Barnhart Brothers & Spindler had gone the way of all the other American typefoundries and had been acquired by American Type Founders Company. The explosion of interest in the Bauhaus-inspired sans serif types which was then taking place was instrumental in helping to bring about what was to be a long term relationship between himself and the Mergenthaler Linotype Company.

In his great book, *Layout in Advertising,* published in 1928, Dwiggins had written: "Gothic in its various manifestations has little to commend it except simplicity. It is not overly legible, it has no grace. Gothic capitals are indispensable, but there are no good Gothic capitals. The typefounders will do a service to advertising if they will provide a Gothic of good design."

Harry L. Gage, Linotype's assistant typographic director, picked up this statement and forthwith issued WAD a challenge which resulted in his first type—a sans serif called Metro, still widely used, particularly in newspaper offices. It is probably fitting that Dwiggins designed his first type for use on a typesetting machine as his particular skill in type design was in the production of book types, which require a sublimation of the artistic ego since they are primarily intended to insure rapid comprehension of the printed word by the reader.

Dwiggins' best known type is Caledonia, completed in 1939 and now considered to be one of the really fine types cut in the last fifty years. A contemporary approach to the popular old Scotch Roman, with touches of Bulmer and Bodoni, Caledonia's popularity continues to grow.

In addition to several other book types, Dwiggins produced a number of decorative units for slug composition, which represent the most interesting ornamental material ever produced for the typesetting machine and which serve to keep alive that whimsical Dwiggins' touch in typographical decoration.

December 10

Between this date in the year 112 A.D. and December 9, 113 A.D. was cut the inscription which appears at the base of the majestic column erected in Rome to perpetuate an account of the Dacian wars of 101-06. The shaft of the monument rises 97½ feet, and is surmounted by a statue of St. Peter. The column has a spiral band which in twenty-three turnings, from the bottom to the top, contains a sculptured frieze 3½ feet wide and 800 feet long, depicting the events of the war. The Emperor Trajan appears in this account some seventy times.

The inscription, cut into a marble slab over the door at the foot of the column, measures 10 feet by approximately 4½ feet and originally contained 172 letters, 28 punctuation marks, and 3 numerical signs. These letters represent the finest examples of the greatest period of Roman monumental lettering. As such they have been the subject of study for many centuries and have appeared in countless books devoted to letter-forms.

The most recent of these studies, and the most authoritative, was made by Rev. Edward M. Catich from 1935 to 1939. Father Catich made a series of rubbings from the inscription. He published them, along with a treatise on the letters themselves, in 1961. Prior to this most informative work, the principal source of information on the inscription has been the plaster cast in the Victoria and Albert Museum in London. Dependence upon this source has been necessary owing to the difficulties of working with the original, a scaffolding being required in order to make rubbings or even photographs. In terms of obtaining precise information on letter proportion, the Victoria and Albert Museum casting, which was in turn made, in 1864, from a French metal copy, suffers from the distortions and defects of multiple copying.

The letters of the cast have been painted to simulate the original practice of painting inscriptional lettering. This has also introduced errors, as in some instances the paint has extended beyond the edges of the letters and in others has been short of the outlines, thus exaggerating certain letter features. In addition, there is distortion in the photographs of this cast, a serious matter, as most of the modern studies of the Trajan inscription are based upon these photographs.

In many of the books which discuss the Trajan letters, the authors have pointed out that their reproductions are made "in the spirit" of the original and encompass their personal aesthetic preferences. This is of course permissible, but it was the opinion of Father Catich that what needed to be done was to produce same-size reproductions from rubbings and tracings. This he did, making available for the first time for everyone interested in beautiful roman letters, the most magnificent examples of their kind that are now known to exist.

For many years Father Catich refrained from publishing his redrawn Trajan alphabet, but he decided to proceed with their publication when William A. Dwiggins enthusiastically recommended that he make them available to students of lettering. "Father Catich's portfolio," said Dwiggins, "will be a good tool in art schools—and elsewhere—for renovating standards that have become a trifle frayed in these revolutionary years."

December 11

Writing in bed at No. 7 Hammersmith Terrace on Sunday, this day in 1898, Thomas James Cobden-Sanderson stated in his journal, "I must, before I die, create the type for to-day of 'the Book Beautiful,' and actualize it—paper, ink, writing, printing, ornament and binding. I will learn to write, to print and to decorate."

Thus, at fifty-eight years of age, this proud, introvertish lawyer and fine amateur book-binder, began to think of becoming a printer, under the direct influence of William Morris for whose Kelmscott Press

Cobden-Sanderson had produced some magnificent bindings. His dream came to full fruition in the establishment of the Doves Press in 1900. From it was to come during the next sixteen years a stream of books which can only be described as being inspired.

Cobden-Sanderson's thoughts on printing are probably best known through his essay, *The Ideal Book or Book Beautiful,* published by the Doves Press in 1901 in which he wrote:

"The Ideal Book or Book Beautiful is a composite thing made up of many parts and may be made beautiful by the beauty of each of its parts—its literary content, its material or materials, its writing or printing, its illumination or illustration, its binding and decoration—of each of its parts in subordination to the whole which collectively they constitute: or it may be made beautiful by the supreme beauty of one or more of its parts, all the other parts subordinating or even effacing themselves for the sake of this one or more, and each in turn being capable of playing this supreme part and each in its own peculiar and characteristic way."

As the books produced by the Doves Press were without illustration and were ornamented only with initials, they can truly be said to be almost purely typographic. Cobden-Sanderson's statement on typography is one of the great short paragraphs on the art and should be required reading wherever designers attempt to work within the restrictions of the typographic art.

"The whole duty of Typography, as of Calligraphy," he wrote, "is to communicate to the imagination, without loss by the way, the thought or image intended to be communicated by the Author. And the whole duty of beautiful typography is not to substitute for the beauty or interest of the thing thought and intended to be conveyed by the symbol, a beauty or interest of its own, but on the one hand, to win access for that communication by the clearness and beauty of the vehicle, and on the other hand, to take advantage of every pause or stage in that communication to interpose some characteristic and restful beauty in its own art."

The ideal represented by Cobden-Sanderson was honored in the Doves Press books, both in their typography and in meticulous printing, but in the words of Sir Francis Meynell, "was not, in fact, sufficiently adventurous." There is a placidness about all of them, a feeling of perfection of detail, that in the long run is somewhat cold. Cobden-Sanderson himself became aware of this and in 1909 he told Edward Johnston that he wished that he could put up a notice on his workshop door, saying, "For God's sake do something careless!" The Doves press continues, however, to represent the private press idea at its finest and must remain a model for everyone who aspires to produce beautiful printing.

December 12

In his eighty-sixth year, John Boydell—engraver, publisher, and former Lord Mayor of London—died on December 12, 1804, having spent a good deal of his life in the service of the arts and leaving as a lasting memorial a magnificent edition of the works of William Shakespeare.

As a youth Boydell had learned surveying, but when he was twenty he had by chance seen an engraving of a castle by W. H. Toms, which so excited him that he walked to London, looked up the engraver and apprenticed himself in that exacting craft at an age long past the usual age for beginning indentures. After six years he had become a finer engraver than his master. He thereupon purchased his freedom and went into business for himself, soon opening, in addition, a small print-dealing business. At this time there was no market for English engravings, although the sales of prints produced on the Continent were extremely successful. Boydell set himself the task of popularizing English artists. In this endeavor he was so successful that by 1786 the export of English engravings was valued at £200,000 per year, as against £100 for imports.

In 1786 Boydell allied himself with a group of artists and printers which proposed a national edition of the work of William Shakespeare, to be illustrated by British artists and to be printed in a manner fitting to the subject. At this period English printing was in a poor state, so the problem of finding a suitable printer was serious. George Nicol, the King's bookseller, was a member of the group. Since he was knowledgeable about printing, he was charged with securing the printer. In the meantime the commissioning of the painting went on apace, along with the selection of the engravers who were to reproduce them.

In the Advertisement of *A Catalogue of the Pictures,* published in 1790, Nicol wrote: "The Printing is at present under the direction of a Gentleman who had already contributed much to the improvement of his profession, and who will now have the opportunity of showing the World that we can print as well in England, it is hoped, as they do in Parma, Paris or Madrid."

The printer selected was William Bulmer from Newcastle-upon-Tyne, then just twenty-nine years old. Nicol established him in London as W. Bulmer & Co., the Shakspeare Printing Office. Allied with Bulmer to cut the type for the project was another young man, William Martin, whose brother had been employed by John Baskerville. Nicol set Martin to work cutting "sets of type after approved models in imitation of the sharp and fine letters used by the French and Italian printers." The Martin letters do resemble such originals but they also retain a softness not present in the types of Bodoni or Didot, being somewhat closer in spirit to the letters of Baskerville.

Boydell must receive the initial credit for making it possible for Bulmer and Martin to combine their talents in a printing office which stands as one of the finest in the long history of English printing. The first volume of Shakespeare came from the press in 1791, and the final part emerged in 1804, representing a magnificent contribution to the art of typography in England. The bibliophile Dibdin wrote of the presswork, "there is scarcely one perceptible shade of variation, from the first page to the last, in the colour of the ink, the hue of the paper, and the clearness and sharpness of the types."

December 13

Under the heading of "A Year's Work," the Troy, New York *Daily Press* published on December 13, 1873 the following item:

"Fred W. Schneider, a compositor employed on this paper, in the year ending today set and distributed, in 312 days, 10 hours per day, 3,234,203 ems, an average of

10,366 ems per day; highest day's work, 17,-485; in 38 consecutive days he set an average of 12,000 ems per day, and for five weeks he averaged 70,000 ems per week. He had no department, and his work was straight matter from the hook."

Such items were fairly common in the period, when newspapers tended to boast about the typesetting speeds of their compositors. While typo Schneider's year of fast type-sticking seems prodigious to present-day compositors, it was not uncommon a hundred years ago. During the latter half of the 19th century, notices of typesetting feats became so regular that a spirit of competition was engendered, resulting first in challenges between the fastest comps, then matches in which newspapers competed with one another, and finally in the middle Eighties in full-size tournaments with large cash prizes and national honors.

Three of the record-holders—William Barnes, Joseph McCann, and Alexander Duguid—published a book on fast typesetting in 1887 which was a compilation of the matches and tournaments and short biographies of the comps who engaged in them. In the introduction they wrote:

"It is a fact that the compositors of to-day work at a greater speed than did the printers of thirty years ago. It is also true that the surroundings of the compositor of to-day are entirely different from those which then environed printers. In using the words 'compositor of to-day and printer of thirty years ago,' we have a purpose. We do not mean to apologize for the printer of those days. He has no need of the services of an apologist. He was in every way superior as a workman to the compositor of to-day. He could set type, impose forms and do presswork. He was what his title implies— a printer.

"To-day, the demands of modern journalism demand a subdivision of the printers' trade, and the matter of speed in each department has become the requisite of prime importance. As a consequence, we have compositors, pressmen, make ups, and few of them printers. This will explain why the compositors of to-day can handle type more swiftly than the printers of the ante-bellum days. Forty years ago the printer who could set 1,200 ems per hour was deemed a fairly quick hand; at 1,400 he was fast; at 1,700, wonderful, and 2,000 ems per hour was considered among the physical impossibilities.

Yet within sixteen years at least seven compositors have in public contests succeeded in surpassing 2,000 ems per hour."

At the exact moment when the typesetting tournaments were most popular, the speed typo was being relegated to the museum. It was in July, 1886 that Mergenthaler's Linotype machine received its initial trial in the office of the New York *Tribune*. In the first week of May in 1889 thirty-one compositors set on linotype machines 2,777,000 ems, exactly double the production of the same number of comps in 1885, the last year of total handset composition on the *Tribune*.

December 14

It was upon this date in the year 1497 that Fra Luca de Pacioli, of the Seraphic Order of St. Francis, completed the text of the work by which he is best known to printers —*De Divina Proportione,* a treatise on the proportion of Roman letters. The original book was concerned purely with mathematical proportion and is considered by modern mathematicians to be more of a compilation of known theories than an original work. When it was finally printed in 1509 by Paganino de Paganini in Venice, the section dealing with the proportion of letters was added. Again, while this addition was not original, it is considered to be the first appearance in print of any work dealing with the mathematical formation of letters, and a forerunner of the later essays on the subject by Albrecht Dürer and Geofroy Tory, both of whom were undoubtedly inspired by the Franciscan Friar.

Luca de Pacioli was born in the town of Borgo San Sepolcro, where St. Francis had preached and lived for a period in the hermitage of Mont Casale, given to him by the people of the town. The religious order founded upon the memory of St. Francis was active in the town, and it was natural that when Luca and his two brothers decided upon theological careers that they join the brethren of the Franciscans. The order was noted for its scholars who enjoyed a wide reputation wherever learning was admired. Since Luca had intellectual aspirations, he found the brotherhood most congenial.

Prior to being ordained, Luca had been employed in a business house in Venice where he had learned accounting and had become intensely interested in mathematics, acquiring sufficient skill in that art to be able to tutor the sons of his employer. Shortly after becoming a Franciscan, he was appointed professor of mathematics at the University of Perugia, where he wrote a treatise on his subject. It remained unpublished, although the manuscript is still in existence in the Vatican Library. For the rest of his life he lectured in mathematics, becoming one of the noted authorities of his time, and enjoyed the patronage of a number of the important men of the period, including the Duke of Urbino. From time to time he returned to purely religious duties for his order.

In 1494 he published what is considered to be his masterpiece, *Summa de Arithmetica, Geometria Proportioni et Proportionalita*. This work is not considered to be important by modern mathematicians, except for those sections dealing with a system of double-entry bookkeeping, which are still being reprinted. While not the originator of the method, Fra Luca is considered to be the first person to teach it and write about it.

December 15

Alexander Duguid, who proved himself to be the fastest compositor in the United States, was born this day in 1856 in Aberdeenshire, Scotland. A little more than twenty-nine years later, in the second National Typesetting Tournament, staged in Philadelphia in 1886, Duguid matched himself against the great professional speed typesetters and beat them all, with an average of 2,277⅓ ems of 6-point per hour. Duguid was described in a short biographical note written a year after the famous contest:

"He is about five feet seven inches in height, and weighs 135 pounds. When he was three months old his parents left Scotland and settled on a farm in Waterloo County, Ontario, where they remained until 1868. In 1872 Alexander, tired of the hard work of the farm, entered the Toledo *Blade* job pressroom, in which he remained a year and then began to set type. In 1883 he went to Cincinnati, and is now employed on the *Enquirer*. In six days on the *Enquirer* he set off the hook 101,800 ems. Inheriting a good constitution, which was strengthened and developed by the exercise and pure air of the farm, and being a total abstainer of intoxicants, and not using tobacco in any form, Mr. Duguid has successfully resisted the debilitating influence of a printer's occupation, and to-day enjoys almost perfect health. He has made a study of the philosophy of setting type and put his theories into practice. He sets type with about the same speed the year round. He was engaged to enter the Chicago tournament, but withdrew when the management insisted upon Sunday work. The Philadelphia contest was his first and only match.

"His best private record previous to this time was 2,093 ems solid minion in an hour. His best score in the last trial of the Philadelphia contest, was 3,416 ems in 1 hour, 30 minutes, an average of 2,277-⅓ ems per hour. Total gross score for the last day's work (3 hours) 6,804 ems; 6,635¼ ems net [deductions were made for errors]. Total for 33 hours, 71,119 ems gross; 69,200¼ ems net. As Mr. Duguid will not set type on a wager, he will probably not engage in any more matches."

Duguid wrote for his contemporaries the procedures which enabled him to pick up three pieces of 6-point type each two seconds:

"There is no royal road to fast typesetting. All must climb alike by hard, persevering work. A man must have a quick eye, steady nerves, ready, retentive mind and good health and physical strength. Moderate speed can be acquired by a slow, steady motion; about the same with a quick, stumbling motion; but to reach 2,000 ems an hour a *quick, steady* motion is required.

"In holding the stick incline it so that the type in it is almost horizontal. Let the arms do the work, do not move the body, except from side to side of the case. Pick up the type by the head, using the thumb and first finger. Get a type every time, bring it directly to the stick, hold it steadily with the left thumb and go for another."

December 16

On this day in 1816 the third Earl Stanhope died. Friend of the younger William Pitt and outspoken critic of the war with the American colonies as a member of Parliament, Stanhope was also an indefatigable experimenter in the sciences, producing among other things a fire-proof stucco, a calculating machine, and optical lenses. His legacy to the printing craft was an improved method of stereotyping and an iron hand press.

Earl Stanhope's press utilized a cast iron frame and a multiplied lever for turning the screw which allowed considerably more pressure to be applied by the pressman without additional effort. The combination of these features made obsolescent the wooden presses which had been used by printers for three hundred and fifty years. When the press was developed in 1800, its inventor "presented" it to the industry, refusing to patent the machine. Immediately his ideas were taken up by other inventors, resulting in such improved presses as the Columbian, the Albion, the Washington, and other hand presses, which for the next fifty years were responsible for most of the printing being produced.

Johnson, writing in his manual, *Typographia,* published in 1824, provides an excellent account of the Stanhope Press, from which most of the later descriptions have been drawn:

"This press is the invention of the late patriotic nobleman whose name it bears; who after many expensive and laborious experiments, at length succeeded, with the assistance of an ingenious machinist (the late Mr. Walker) in bringing the press to a state of perfection. The first press was finished in the year 1800, and its powers were tried at the office of Mr. Bulmer, (the Shakspeare Press) in which house it at present remains. They have undergone several alterations since the first of them were made, particularly in the rounce, and the ribs; the handle of the former was attached to a rod which crossed the plattin, this rod was connected with the spit by means of machinery; the carriage, instead of running on cramps in the ribs as at present, was carried upon wheels on a straight edge, which made a very disagreeable noise; the gallows for the tympans is also removed, and the bearings are attached to the ends of them. . . .

"His Lordship, having objected to the taking out of a Patent for his invention, it was consequently thrown open, upon which several Engineers and Smiths began to man-ufacture presses on the same principle; it is true some of them made trifling alterations, but in truth they were scarce worthy of notice; therefore, in order to find a market for them they sold them somewhat cheaper; but we can assert, without fear of successful contradiction, that those from the original manufactury were infinitely superior to what were made in other quarters. . . ."

Johnson's panegyric to the Stanhope Press concluded with illustrations and descriptions of each working part, which he hoped "will enable every pressman not only to put them together, but also to take them to pieces."

December 17

"Messrs. L. Johnson & Company had some time previously started the *Typographic Advertiser,* and the idea suggested itself to us that Western printers also should have an organ or trade paper. Well do we remember the evening on which the idea assumed definite form and the bantling was named. It was in our counting room on Randolph Street, something more than sixteen years ago. . . . Much fun was elicited in selecting a name for the new sheet, many a laughable and absurd one rejected, and finally the old time-honored *Printer's Cabinet* settled on. The paper was soon issued, and under the deft hands of the boys was the handsomest sheet then published in the West. It was well received by the fraternity, and from that day to the present, we think, has been a welcome visitor to nearly all the 'sanctums' in the West, as, indeed, we hope it long continues to be."

The *Printer's Cabinet* lasted another sixteen years, as did its founder, Sterling P. Rounds, who died on this day in 1888. The sheet never did attain the importance of MacKellar's *Typographic Advertiser* as a source of 19th century typographic information, as it contained about eighty percent advertising and its founder lacked the editorial skills of Mr. MacKellar.

Sterling Rounds was a Vermont farm boy who was taken to Wisconsin by his parents when he was but twelve years of age. As a preparation for a career in the law he was sent to an academy run by Louis Harvey, who was later to become Governor of Wisconsin. When Harvey purchased the Southport *American,* young Rounds received an opportunity to see the inside of a printing office for the first time. He thereby lost interest in his law studies.

By his twenty-first birthday Rounds had become part owner of a literary and temperance sheet, *The Old Oaken Bucket,* which quickly became a most lucrative enterprise. In 1851 he went to Chicago and persuaded James Langdon, owner of the largest printing plant in Chicago, to take him on as a partner. After several successful years this shop was sold to the Chicago *Times,* and Rounds opened a printer's supply business which grew to be the premier enterprise of its kind west of New York City. The firm is said to have completely outfitted over four thousand newspaper offices throughout the West, in addition to hundreds of commercial shops.

Rounds' reputation in the industry grew until his name was a household word among the fraternity of printers in the land. President Garfield, in response to the urging of over a thousand newspaper owners, appointed Rounds to the position of Public Printer. During his tenure of office, which ended in 1886, after Cleveland became President, Rounds revitalized the GPO, instituting numerous reforms which had long been needed in that establishment. His devotion to the job, however, allowed him little time to attend his own interests, which he had left under the care of his sons in Chicago. The business failed in 1884.

December 18

On this day in 1858 two printer-newsmen, W. L. Jernegan and Alfred James, set up a printing press in the village of Genoa in the Utah Territory and produced the first issue of a sheet which they called the *Territorial Enterprise.* The town was but a freighter's way-station between California and Deseret. The paper managed to subsist, although it was moved, within its first year, to Carson City. When gold and silver were discovered at the Comstock Lode in 1859, making Virginia City the center of the wildest and most extravagant area in America, the *Enterprise* made its last move, under the guidance of a new editor, Jonathan Williams. By 1861 the paper had become a daily, with another change of ownership. Editors Good-

man and McCarthy were reputed to have hauled the daily receipts home in water buckets, their sheet having struck an even richer vein than the Comstock itself, which within twenty years had produced over a half billion dollars worth of silver and gold.

Of the prospectors who were arriving by the thousand, one was a journeyman printer named Sam Clemens, who, finding that he could do better with a pen than with a shovel, began to write for the *Enterprise.* Discussing this experience, many years later, Clemens stated, "At first I roamed about the country seeking silver, but at the end of '62 or the beginning of '63 when I came up from Aurora to begin a journalistic life on the Virginia City *Enterprise* I was presently sent down to Carson City to report the legislative session. I wrote a weekly letter to the paper; it appeared Sundays, and on Mondays the legislative proceedings were obstructed by the complaints of the members as a result. They rose to questions of privilege and answered the criticisms of the correspondent with bitterness, customarily describing him with elaborate and uncomplimentary phrases, for the lack of a briefer way. To save their time, I presently began to sign the letters, using the Mississippi leadsman's call, 'Mark Twain' (two fathoms—twelve feet) for this purpose."

Reporter Clemens distinguished himself in reverse during his tenure on the frontier sheet. "In those early days," he recounted, "dueling suddenly became a fashion in the new territory of Nevada and by 1864 everybody was anxious to have a chance in the new sport, mainly for the reason that he was not able to thoroughly respect himself so long as he had not killed or crippled somebody in a duel or been killed or crippled in one himself.

"At that time I had been serving as city editor on Mr. Joe Goodman's Virginia City *Enterprise* for a matter of two years. I was twenty-nine years old. I was ambitious in several ways but I had entirely escaped the seductions of that particular craze. I had no desire to fight a duel. I had no intention of provoking one. I did not feel respectable but I got a certain amount of satisfaction out of feeling safe. I was ashamed of myself, the rest of the staff were ashamed of me—but I got along well enough. I had always been accustomed to feeling ashamed of myself, for one thing or another, so there was no novelty for me in the situation. I bore it very well."

December 19

"I began to set type when I was twelve years old, and have 'stuck' type in nearly every state in the Union." So began a letter written on this date in 1885 by Amos J. Cummings to the *New York Journalist*.

Cummings, as remarkable a man as the industry has ever produced, is now completely forgotten. He died in 1902, "with the printer's rule of his youth and the union card of his early manhood in the pockets of the clothes he wore upon his deathbed." Born in 1842 in upstate New York he learned the trade in the shop of his father, a minister who edited religious publications. Running away from home at fifteen, he became a traveling typo until he joined up with the William Walker filibustering Expedition to Nicaragua in 1847 in which he was captured by a U. S. naval vessel and returned to Mobile.

Cummings then journeyed to New York where he became a compositor on the New York *Tribune*. He next volunteered for service during the Civil War, in which he received the Medal of Honor for gallantry at Fredericksburg. He became a reporter for the *Tribune* after the war, becoming city editor. In 1868 he joined the *Sun* then edited by Charles A. Dana. "I am leaving the *Tribune*," he told Dana, "because they say I swear too much." To this the great editor replied, "You're just the man for me!"

On the *Sun* he became managing editor, remaining until poor health necessitated his removal to Florida, where he continued to serve as a political writer for national publication. He returned to the *Sun* in 1877, serving as a special correspondent. In 1886 he was elected to the Fiftieth Congress as a Representative from New York, serving through the Fifty-seventh Congress. In addition to his congressional duties he founded the *Evening Sun* of which he was editor for a short period. He maintained his journalistic career along with his political duties, and during the last twenty-five years of the century he was considered to be one of the nation's finest newspapermen.

Cummings in later life was fond of telling stories of his early career. One of his favorite anecdotes concerned his activities as a youthful printer in the West. He read a notice in a newspaper which stated: "Wanted, an editor to do the fighting for this paper. Weapons and whiskey furnished free. Wounds dressed by the editor's doctor; no charge. Funeral expenses at the expense of the village."

Cummings volunteered for the job, and requested the following supplies: six Winchesters, six Colt six-shooters, four butcher-knives, and twelve gallons of good whiskey.

On his first night, there was a knock on the door and two men demanded to see the editor. "I am the fighting editor," said the printer, "and here is my defense. Which weapons do you choose?"

"We'll take the whiskey," said one of the men. Cummings opened the jug and handed out tin cups, so they all sat down and discussed how they would settle the problem. They soon agreed that the easiest method was to have another drink. After a while in high good humor the visitors apologized for calling upon the editor in such a rough manner and dictated a statement exonerating the editor for having libeled them.

December 20

Appearing far down in the obituary page of *The Boston Sunday Herald* for December 21, 1958 was a short notice stating that George Trenholm, type designer, had died the previous day in his home in Weston. An eight-line paragraph covered his career, which is probably just the way he would have wished it. One feature of the notice would no doubt have pleased him, also, and that was the heading, which was set in the Metro type designed by his very good friend, William A. Dwiggins of neighboring Hingham, who had died just two years earlier, less a week.

The obituary stated that Trenholm was a native of Cambridge and had lived at Weston for thirty-two years. "He was, for many years, consultant and type designer for the Intertype Corp., and was past president of the Society of Printers and a member of the Salamagundi Club and the Typophiles Club."

Thus easily disposed of was a graphic arts career which had begun in 1905 when Trenholm completed high school and followed a natural bent for drawing by going to work for a small art studio. He continued his education during evening hours by studying painting with Charles Heil and attending the graphic arts classes conducted by the well-informed Vojetch Preissig at the Wentworth Institute. In 1916 he established his own studio and quickly acquired the reputation of versatility which marked his career, working with advertising agencies, printing firms, and typefounders.

The famous *Catalog 25-A* of the Chicago typefoundry, Barnhart Brothers & Spindler, the last ever issued by that concern, showed Trenholm's first effort as a type designer, a series named Trenholm Oldstyle, with italic, shaded capitals, and a boldface. For the same foundry Trenholm also created a useful series of ornaments and piece borders.

In 1940 the Intertype firm named Trenholm its typographic consultant, and from this connection came a series of decorative initials to be used with the Egmont type, and an excellent book type named Cornell, this title no doubt being suggested by the Intertype president, who happened to be a trustee of Cornell University.

Trenholm's one paragraph obituary did not mention his warmth and friendliness as a person, his willingness to be of assistance to anyone who called upon him. Working quietly and with reserve, George Trenholm never reached for the glaring light of publicity enjoyed by men with similar artistic capabilities, but among the graphic artists of our time he was of the first rank. He will never be forgotten by those privileged to be his friends.

December 21

On this great day in American history a weary shipload of travelers thankfully disembarked upon these shores in the year 1620. Among them were two printers, William Brewster and Edward Winslow, both of whom were to become leaders of the Plymouth Colony and who are recorded as the first members of their craft to set foot upon continental United States.

William Brewster had been a man of some wealth in England, having been in the diplomatic service. When in 1607 a group of people out of sympathy with the religious authorities in England journeyed to Leyden in Holland and established the Pilgrim Church in that town, Brewster went with them. It was there he decided to be a printer.

William Bradford, in his account of the Plymouth Plantation, wrote of Brewster:

"After he came into Holland he suffered much hardships; after he had spent most of his means, having a great charge and many children; and, in regard of his former breeding and course of life, not so fit for the many imployments as others were; especially such as were toilsome and laborious. But yet he ever bore his condition with much cheerfulness and contentation. Towards the latter part of those twelve years spent in Holland his outward condition was mended, and he lived well and plentifully. For he fell into a way, by reason he had the Latin tongue, to teach many students who had the desire to learn the English language, to teach them English. . . . He also had means to set up printing, by the help of some friends, and so had employment enough, and by reason of many books which would not be allowed to be printed in England they might have had more than they could do."

A number of the books which Brewster printed in Holland were considered to be objectionable in England. King James I personally attempted to coerce Holland for allowing him freedom to print. In 1619 Brewster's types were seized and he found it necessary to become a fugitive to avoid imprisonment.

Brewster, receiving in the Colony the title of Elder, was assistant to the Pastor and became one of the leaders of the group. His library, which contained some 300 volumes at his death in 1644, was an important factor in the development of the Pilgrim settlement.

Of the other printer, Edward Winslow, very little is known of his activities in the craft. It is probable that he worked in the printing office of Brewster in Leyden. In any case, along with his fellow printer he did not concern himself with printing after reaching the New World. He had charge of all negotiations with the Indians and became the official correspondent of the Colony with the London backers of the group. He was the first of the Pilgrims to return to England, doing so to represent their interests in the homeland. Fifteen years after the landing while on a visit he was imprisoned by Archbishop Laud for baptizing infants in the Colony without being ordained. One of Brewster's sons became Governor of Plymouth Colony from 1673 to 1680. Another descendant was Admiral John Winslow, who commanded the Union vessel *Kearsarge* in its battle with the Confederate raider, *Alabama*.

Although there were two printers in the Bay Colony in 1620, the colonists had to wait until 1638 before a press was established by Stephen Day, setting back the first printing in the United States by nineteen years. But the leadership supplied by the printers was undoubtedly of even greater value to the survival of the Pilgrim party than the benefits of a press.

December 22

Edmund Fry, M. D., and typefounder, died on this day in 1835, honored as the most learned member of his craft. A son of another medical man, Joseph Fry, who had left his profession to establish the Fry and Pine foundry in Bristol in 1764, Edmund Fry had been educated in medicine, but his vast enthusiasm for the study of philology, coupled with a tendency towards deafness, directed him to typefounding.

Coming into his father's firm in 1782, Fry immediately took an active part in its affairs and was probably responsible for the purchase of many of the matrices and punches of learned faces when the James Foundry was put up for sale. Under his guidance his own foundry tended more and more to specialize in such types, although in the specimen book which was produced in 1785, the founder stated that he had copied Caslon's types.

In 1799 Dr. Fry published a book upon which he had been working for over sixteen years. Entitled *Pantographia*, it was a philological study which contained some 200 alphabets, including thirty-nine Greek and eighteen Chaldee. With the advice of many of the foremost scholars of his time, Dr. Fry himself cut many of the characters which appeared in this notable work.

The changing of the name of the foundry to the Polyglot Foundry in 1824 certainly signified the direction it was taking. It is therefore not surprising that Fry was not at all sympathetic with the fancy types which English printers were then demanding. In 1828, after having spent forty-six years as a typefounder, Dr. Fry placed his business up for sale. Commenting that his father had begun with improved imitations of Baskerville's types in 1764, and that at the recommendation of customers the firm had then offered types based on those of Caslon, Fry stated that, due to lack of demand, these fine letters were being "taken from the shelves, and carried to the melting-pot."

Discussing the introduction of the decorative types then in style, Dr. Fry stated, "At which period a rude, pernicious, and most unclassical innovating System was commenced, which in a short time was followed by the most injurious and desolating ravages on the property of every Letter Founder and Printer in the kingdom, by the introduction of fancy letters of various anomalous forms, with names as appropriate—disgraceful in a profession, once held so *Sacred*, as to have its operations confined to consecrated Buildings and those of the highest class."

December 23

The third book produced by The Typophiles, published on this day in 1936, represented a happy occasion for *all* typophiles, not just the capitalized variety which has contributed so much to the literature of typography in our time. In his introduction to *Diggings from Many Ampersandhogs,* Paul A. Bennett, guiding star of the organization, asked, "Why a book on ampersands?" and proceeded to answer his question forthwith. Discussing the paucity of information concerning the ampersand, he stated: "Most of the contributions which follow owe their existence in varying degrees to impatience and exasperation, because little was available in English on the subject. Plus anger; be it confessed, a genial determination to amend that unfortunate omission."

And amend it the contributors did, by writing essays both serious and whimsical, in many cases printing the signatures themselves. The book contains thirty-five signatures and makes up the most solid of the shelf-full of Typophile books, which at this date number forty-eight.

The contributors also represented in themselves a typographic Who's Who. Bruce Rogers sent his poem, which begins, "& now comes Ambling Ampers& as tailpiece gr&.," and printed it on wrapping paper enclosed in a sandpaper frame which he called ampersand paper.

Fred Goudy really took his assignment to heart by thoroughly researching the subject and going so far as to design sixty ampersands which his son engraved into matrices and cast into type. The 56-page signature was printed by his friend Howard Coggeshall of Utica, New York.

Another offering, that of Clarence Hornung, included a re-drawing of 130 historic ampersands representative of the various countries. Edna and Arthur Rushmore of the Golden Hind Press retrieved an ampersand poem from an 1869 issue of *Punch*, the first stanza of which reads: "Of all the types in a printer's hand / Commend me to the amperzand, / For he's the gentleman (seems to me) / Of the typographical companie. / O my nice little amperzand! / My graceful, swanlike amperzand! / Nothing that Cadmus ever planned / Equals my elegant amperzand!"

The scholarly Professor Lehman-Haupt of Columbia University chose to keep his tongue in his cheek when he described the origin of the ampersand: "The Ampersand has its name from the little river Amper, which joins the Rhine not far from Mainz, where Johann Gutenberg spent his childhood years. Of warm summer afternoons little Hans would take off his shoes and play in the clean white sand of the riverbed. It was here that the clearly-marked outline in the moist sand of his footprints first suggested to him the idea of the sand casting mould, which, as we all have learnt to know, is the true clue to the invention of printing. From the incident of its discovery and on through the early experimental years the entire process of type production was called 'Ampersanding.' "

Edward Alonzo Miller contributed a geographical essay on the Adirondack Mountains, which contain an Ampersand Mountain, Lake, and Stream, the location of a Philosopher's Camp attended in the past by such figures as Lowell, Emerson, and Agassiz.

Altogether, the Typophiles never put together a more enjoyable potpourri of typographical whimsy.

December 24

On this day in 1572 a printer named Jacques Sabon became the owner of a typefoundry in Frankfurt for the sum of 425 gulden. This business had originally been set up by Christian Egenolff in 1530. It had been operated successfully until his death in 1555, when it was continued by his widow under the name of Egenolff's Heirs. Christian Egenolff II, preferring religious orders to printing, was unable to help his mother, so she turned to Sabon, a printer from Lyons, for practical assistance. Several years later he left for a period, working in several locations including Antwerp, where it is known that he worked for Christopher Plantin, completing a set of punches which had been left unfinished by Claude Garamond.

Sabon returned to Frankfurt to contract a liaison with Judith Egenolff, grand-daughter of the founder of the firm. The lady had already survived two suits of breach of promise, but Sabon's action resulted in marriage, which made Sabon a partner in Egenolff's Heirs in 1572. It is from this point that the foundry grew until it became the principal German typefoundry during the 16th and 17th centuries. Following Sabon's death in 1580, Konrad Berner married Judith and secured full ownership.

In 1592 Berner issued the first type specimen sheet ever to be issued over the name of a typefounder, that of Egenolff-Berner. This sheet has since become the best known of all early type specimens. The only known copy was reproduced by collotype by Gustav Mori in 1926 and returned to the Haeberlin collection at the Stadt-und Universitats-Bibliothek, where it was unfortunately destroyed during World War II. The types shown in the specimen are from the hands of some of the best of the European punchcutters, including Claude Garamond and Robert Granjon, although it is not known exactly how the foundry acquired these types. Several of the contemporary cuttings of the Garamond fonts were modeled from the letters shown here.

The 8-line heading of the specimen is set in Roman capitals and reads: "A specimen of characters or most approved types, arranged not for continuous reading but so as to show the gradations of the types, in the way most useful and convenient to the printer and to the writer of books."

The colophon of the sheet follows the tradition of the early printers' colophons by praising both the printer and his types: "Specimen and print of the finest and most beautiful types ever yet seen, assembled with great trouble and cost at first by the late Christian Egenolff himself, the first printer in Frankfurt, and then by his widow; and thereafter by the successors of the same, namely Jacob Sabon and Conrad Berner, with the utmost zeal collected together and published for the benefit of all who use a pen, but principally for the particular advantage of authors of printers' copy, so that they may judge in what type their work may best be done. . . ."

December 25

On this day in 1828 was born the first of America's great scholar-printers, Theodore L. De Vinne, in Stamford, Connecticut. De Vinne's father, a Methodist minister, had six sons, four of whom became printers. The other two became bookbinders.

De Vinne first visited a printing office when he was seven years of age, the occasion being the start of the apprenticeship of his oldest brother, John, with the firm of Harper Brothers. One of the owners gave the child a book during his trip through the plant. This book remained in Theodore's library the rest of his life. At fourteen years of age in 1842, young De Vinne was apprenticed to the trade in the office of *The Gazette,* in the Hudson River valley town of Newburgh. Following his indenture, he worked in plants in New York City from 1848 to 1850 when he became a journeyman compositor in the office of Francis Hart, where he was destined to spend his entire career as a printer.

The Hart shop contained one 23 x 28 inch Hoe cylinder press operated by a hand wheel, three hand presses and a Gillman card press. Illumination was supplied by five camphene lamps and twenty candlesticks. In a very short time De Vinne was named foreman and in 1858 was made junior partner.

By 1877, the year of Francis Hart's death, De Vinne owned a one-third interest in the establishment. By the terms of his partner's will he became full owner upon the gradual payment to Hart's widow of the sum of $160,-000. The firm of Theodore L. De Vinne & Company was then formed, and within a short period it had gained the reputation of being one of the best printing plants in America. Its owner became known as America's finest printer.

As the printer of *The Century* magazine, De Vinne's production methods excited the admiration of printers everywhere. Working with press manufacturers, paper mills, and with engravers and electrotypers, he developed what today would be called quality control procedures. The end result of these techniques was the best printed periodical in existence. His reputation was so secure that his customers actually preferred being placed upon a waiting list in order to be sure of the De Vinne imprint.

From the time that De Vinne first secured employment in New York, he had been continuing his education. As a member of the New York Typographical Society he spent a great deal of time in its library, which then contained some five thousand volumes. At thirty-one years of age he was editing a small publication entitled *The Printers' Miscellany,* contributing articles on the history of the craft and descriptions of new equipment and procedures. He began to take voluminous notes on printing history. In order to read source material he studied French, Italian, and German. From 1859 until his death in 1914, he was a constant contributor to technical journals.

In 1876 he published his greatest work, *The Invention of Printing,* which has not yet been surpassed as a study of the origins of the craft. His most widely known work was the four volume *Practice of Typography,* which continued the great tradition of printer's manuals begun in 1683 with the publication of Joseph Moxon's *Mechanick Exercises.* He also wrote a number of other books on typography, establishing his reputation as the first important American writer on the subject.

All of this activity was accompanied by his interest in the printing trade itself. He was a founder and first president of the United Typothetae of America and was extremely active in the promotion of good employer-employee relationships in the industry.

December 26

Any former employees, who for nostalgic reasons entered the cavernous but empty premises of the Chicago firm of typefounders, Barnhart Brothers & Spindler, on this day in 1933, would have felt a touch of sadness. Gone were the rows of typecasting machines which had produced so many of the popular types of American printers over a sixty year period. All that remained of a once thriving business were casters for the manufacture of leads and slugs, and even these were about to be dismantled, as in just five days the building was to be padlocked, thus definitely bringing to an end an enterprise which had made a notable contribution to American typography.

In 1869 the four Barnhart Brothers—Alson, Arthur, George, and Warren—who had originally left New York state to farm in Michigan, purchased from the Toepfer family a majority interest in the Great Western Type Foundry in Chicago, which had been organized just a year earlier. In spite of extremely strong competition from Marder, Luse & Company, and from Sterling Rounds, the Chicago agent for the Philadelphia firm of MacKellar, Smiths & Jordan, the Barnharts managed to prosper, by virtue of combative and vigorous enterprise.

When most of the typefounders in the United States joined together in 1892 to form the combination called the American Type Founders Company, the Barnharts maintained their individuality by remaining an independent and flourishing enterprise until 1911. Then they finally sold out to ATF in an agreement by which the firm retained its identity under its original name.

Contemporary printers who are now well into middle age will no doubt recall some of the BB&S types which were widely used during their youth, such as Parsons, designed by Will Ransom—a design which featured alternate characters with extremely long ascenders and descenders. Even though Ransom did not authorize these letters and disliked them intensely, they helped the design reach best-sellerdom. Without doubt the best known type ever cut by the foundry was Cooper Black, from the drawing-board of Oz Cooper. First offered in 1921, it became an instantaneous hit. Cooper himself would have been vastly amused at the recent revival, during the early 1960's, of this display type. Another Barnhart type which is still used is the style originally named Fifteenth Century. Available for a number of years, it met with little response, but when the name was changed to Caslon Antique in 1925, it received a new lease on life, although it in no way resembles that dignified English letter.

With the end of Barnhart Brothers & Spindler, there remained but a single firm dealing in standard foundry type in the United States, the American Type Founders Company. This organization, even with what might be called a monopoly in foundry type manufacturing, is kept on its competitive toes by the European foundries which are increasingly active in this country.

December 27

On this day in the year 1900, the most respected printer in America, the scholarly Theodore Low De Vinne, wrote a letter to his employees, thanking them for the Testimonial Dinner which they had tendered Mrs. De Vinne and himself upon the occasion of their fiftieth wedding anniversary and his own seventy-second birthday, on December 25th:

"Dear friends and Comrades of the De Vinne Press: Your present of this magnificent Pilgrim Shield on my anniversary was a great surprise. I did not expect it, and it is all the more welcome. I thank you for it heartily. It is a great gratification to me, in the last years of a long life, to know that I still retain the good will and love of our employees.

"The man in business, like the Pilgrim of John Bunyan, has to fight continually. To try to give the best workmanship to buyers who want the best only at low rates—to give the best wages to men who are often deserving of more than they receive—to be just and exact to all—are requirements not easily met.

"A fair employer has to be active and earnest as well as fair to meet the competition of rivals in business. He has to crowd and jostle. He often has to be aggressive. He may trample and strike where he does not intend to hurt. What is worse, he often has to postpone the proper recognition of valued helpers.

"I dare not say that I have always lived up to my ideal of what an employer should be. I have made mistakes which I regret. Yet I do say that I have always tried to be just, and I accept this testimonial, to which men have contributed who have been in the employ of our house for periods ranging from ten to fifty years, as evidence of their belief that I have always meant to be fair to all. That appreciation is dear to me.

"I don't intend to make a long reply. You have been active and willing helpers in the building up of a great business, and I am thankful and grateful. Let me beg of you to continue the same regard you have shown to me to my successors in the management of the house, who I am sure will go on in the path we have successfully trod, and will maintain the reputation of the house for the benefit of all."

December 28

On this day in 1879 the eminent English printer and bibliophile William Blades received from a bookbinder of Northampton a "fat little worm" which had been discovered in his shop in the binding of a very old book. Blades wrote about the creature with the enthusiasm of an entomologist:

"He bore his journey extremely well, being very lively when turned out. I placed him in a box in warmth and quiet, with some small fragments of paper from a Boethius, printed Caxton, and a leaf of a seventeenth century book. He ate a small piece of the leaf, but either from too much fresh air, from unaccustomed liberty, or from change of food, he gradually weakened, and died in about three weeks. I was sorry to lose him, as I wished to verify his name in his perfect state. Mr. Waterhouse, of the Entomological Department of the British Museum, very kindly examined him before death, and was of the opinion he was *OEcophora pseudospretella*.

"In July, 1885, Dr. Garnett of the British Museum, gave me two worms which had been found in an old Hebrew Commentary just received from Athens. They had doubtless had a good shaking on the journey, and one was moribund when I took charge, and joined his defunct kindred in a few days. The other seemed hearty and lived with me for nearly eighteen months. I treated him as well as I knew how; placed him in a small box with the choice of three sorts of old paper to eat, and very seldom disturbed him. He evidently resented his confinement, ate very little, moved very little, and changed in appearance very little, even when dead. This Greek worm, filled with Hebrew lore, differed in many respects from any other I have seen. He was longer, thinner, and more delicate looking than any of his English congeners. He was transparent, like thin ivory, and had a dark line through his body, which I took to be the intestinal canal. He resigned his life with extreme procrastination, and died 'deeply lamented' by his keeper, who had long looked forward to his final development.

"The difficulty of breeding these worms is probably due to their formation. When in a state of nature they can by expansion and contraction of the body working upon the sides of their holes, push their horny jaws against the opposing mass of paper. But when freed from the restraint, which indeed to them is life, they *cannot* eat although surrounded with food, for they have no legs to keep them steady, and their natural leverage is wanting.

"I remember well my first visit to the Bodleian Library, in the year 1858, Dr. Bandinel being then the librarian. He was very kind, and afforded me every facility for examining the fine collection of 'Caxtons,' which was the object of my journey. In looking over a parcel of Black-letter fragments, which had been in a drawer a long time, I came across a small grub, which, without a thought, I threw on the floor and trod underfoot. Soon after I found another, a fat, glossy fellow, so long . . . . . . , which I carefully preserved in a little paper box, intending to observe his habits and development. Seeing Dr. Bandinel near, I asked him to look at my curiosity. Hardly, however, had I turned the wiggling little victim out upon the leather-covered table, when down came the doctor's great thumbnail upon him, and an inch-long smear proved the tomb of all my hopes, while the great bibliographer, wiping his thumb on his coat sleeve, passed on with the remark, 'Oh, yes!, they have black heads sometimes.' That was something to know— another fact for the entomologist; for my little gentleman had a hard, shiny, white head, and I never heard of a black-headed bookworm before or since. Perhaps the great abundance of black-letter books in the Bodleian may account for the variety. At any rate he was an *Anobium*."

December 29

"The death of Daniel Berkeley Updike removed the last and the most widely influential of the notable group of Victorian writers, learned in both the practice and the history of the printing and allied trades, who, together, contributed a body of archeological research and industrial application whose richness and quality must arouse the admiration of future generations."

So wrote the typographic historian, Stanley Morison, of the death of America's great scholar printer, who died on this day in 1941, just two months short of his eighty-second birthday and the fiftieth anniversary of the founding of the Merrymount Press.

Updike, whose reputation as a fine printer was international, was asked by Harvard University to give a course on the Technique of Printing in the Graduate School of Business Administration. He accepted the offer, and from 1911 to 1916 lectured at Harvard upon that subject, giving particular emphasis to typographic history. The immediate result of this course was the enlargement of his lectures into a two-volume work entitled *Printing Types, Their History, Forms, and Use, A Study in Survivals,* published by Harvard University in 1922.

This great work has since established itself as one of the principal sources of present-day knowledge of the typography of the book through its first four centuries. Its even greater impact has been in the inspiration given to later scholarship, which in the last forty years has helped to fill in the gaps of our knowledge of the historic types. Stanley Morison, whose own career was in its formative years when Updike's book was published, has written, "No more need be said here than that this publication was the most exciting event of a decade. Its value to a country that had been starved of typographical literature since 1911 can hardly be imagined by Americans. To us at that time the book had a messianic quality. Despite the immense amount of research that has been done since, and which Updike's work was designed to inspire, *Printing Types* remains absolutely essential to the understanding of the subject. . . ."

The book went through three printings up to 1927. Ten years later it was revised, with some attempt being made to include the findings of the later scholars, particularly when important new facts had been brought to light. A third edition was published in 1962, the only change being an appreciative introductory memoir written by Lawrence C. Wroth, and hand-set in Oxford type by the late Steve Watts.

The book remains the solid cornerstone of any typographic library and will continue to be read, influencing generations of printers yet to come.

December 30

"My Dear Sir: I am very desirous of obtaining one of the duplicate copies of the old *Bay Psalm Book* belonging to the Old South Church Library, having a strong veneration for the old volume. I think I have books in my library, such as would not only be appropriate for the Library of the Old South Church but also valuable for reference and for the use of those who rely upon the library for works suitable to be consulted. Among the books which I happen to think of are the original editions of Winthrop's *New England,* and Belknap's *New England Biography* . . . which I would gladly give in exchange (for) one of the duplicates. . . . Nath. B. Shurtleff."

This letter by the distinguished Bostonian, Nathaniel B. Shurtleff, M. D., was written to Loring Lothrop, a deacon of the Old South Church of Boston, under the date of December 30, 1859. Shurtleff, a well-known bibliophile, was hot on the track of what even then was a rare and admirable addition to any library. The good doctor was successful and thus joined two friends, all of whom spirited from the Old South Church within a relatively short time, copies of the first book to be printed in the English Colonies in America.

It all began when the Reverend Thomas Prince, pastor of the Old South Church, began to collect a "New England library" in 1703, which he bequeathed to the church in

253

1758 with the stipulation that his books "be kept entire" and be maintained as a single collection forever. When he first formed his library, copies of the *Bay Psalm Book* were by no means difficult to locate, so he was able to pick up five of them. In 1820 a part of the Prince collection was given to the Massachusetts Historical Society in spite of the stricture of the original donor, but it was finally brought together again in the Boston Public Library in 1866. By that date, however, it was minus three of the Psalm books.

The removals were accomplished very smoothly by truly proper Bostonians of the highest reputation. Edward A. Crowninshield was the first to make a determined effort to secure a Psalm book by buttering up one of the deacons of the church. Deacon Armstrong, no doubt delighted to do a favor for one of the town's upper crust, agreed with Crowninshield's suggestion that the copies of the book on the church's shelves needed new bindings after two hundred years, and allowed the gentleman to haul one of them off for rebinding. And all that Crowninshield wanted in return was one of the duplicates for his own library. The deacon, possibly feeling a little guilty, made a notation in one of the rebound copies still in the Boston Public Library. It was discovered there by Zoltan Haraszti, the authority on the *Bay Psalm Book* and Director of the Library. The Crowninshield copy went through several ownerships and is now in the Yale University Library.

A short time later Mr. George Livermore, so outstanding a citizen that he was eulogized by Oliver Wendell Holmes and Edward Everett Hale, evidently in the confidence of his friend Crowninshield, was just as successful in the same manner. This copy is now in a private library in Brooklyn.

The *Bay Psalm Book* for which Dr. Shurtleff decently exchanged histories worth eight dollars is probably the finest of all, and is now in the possession of the John Carter Brown Library in Providence, Rhode Island.

December 31

On this closing day of the year 1467 was published the first book to be printed within the confines of the city of Rome. While the monastery town of Subiaco near Rome was the scene of the earliest printing to be produced in Italy two years previously, the press there—operated by Sweynheim and Pannartz—removed to Rome in November 1467. By the end of the 15th century there were thirty-eight printing offices in Rome, all operated by German printers.

The Abbot Turrecremata of Subiaco, the patron of Sweynheim and Pannartz, was awarded the red hat and was transferred to Rome, whereupon he invited Ulrich Han, a German printer from Ingolstadt, to establish a press. The first publication was the new Cardinal's own *Meditationes,* which was also the earliest Italian woodcut book and was printed in a round gothic type.

Meditationes in the 1467 edition is a very rare book. The 19th century bibliophile, Dibdin wrote about the volume, "What a day was that in the bibliographic annals of my humble life when I first beheld the *Turrecremata* of 1467! What neither Maittaire, nor the De Bures, nor Marchand, nor his annotator, the Abbé Merceir de Leger, nor Meerman, nor Heincken, nor Audiffredi, nor Santander, nor Bruner had ever beheld, I have seen and closely examined! The decorations are in outline, rudely conceived and still more rudely executed, probably by Han himself. It was rather whimsical of Han to insert all the decorations on the reverse of the leaves with the exception of that on folio xxx."

Historians have been mystified that Turrecremata should have requested Han to print his book, since he had worked so closely with Sweynheim and Pannartz at Subiaco. Dibdin suggests that it was the Cardinal's insistence upon having woodcut illustrations in the volume which placed its execution beyond the skill of the two German printers.

In 1468 Han issued Cicero's *De Oratore* and *Tusculanae Questiones,* for which he cut a roman type. Although appearing two years before the roman of Nicolas Jenson, the Han type is not considered to be the first purely roman letter. Updike says of it that it was difficult to determine whether it was a roman letter under gothic influence or a gothic letter under roman influence. He believed it to be distinctly inferior to the type of the Subiaco press. Before his death in 1478 or 1479, Han produced sixty books, outstripping all of his rivals in the city of Rome.

Index

The Heritage of the Printer, Volume II, *A Printer's Almanac,* has been designed and set by Typekrafters, Inc., Philadelphia, Pa. The Linotype-composed text is 9 point Times Roman, 2 point leaded. The display typography is Ludlow Mayfair Cursive. The book was printed letterpress by The Winchell Company, Philadelphia, Pa. The paper is 60 lb. Warren's No. 66 Antique Publishers White. Binding, in cloth pyroxylin impregnated Holliston Roxite, with stamping in black and gold, is by National Publishing Company, Philadelphia, Pa. Illustrations are by North American Publishing Co. art staff.